James Bonner and
Paul Ts'o, Editors

THE NUCLEOHISTONES

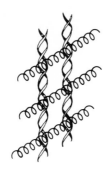

 HOLDEN-DAY, INC.
San Francisco, London, Amsterdam
1964

Library of Congress Catalog Card No. 64-16574

Printed in the United States of America

LIST OF CONTRIBUTORS

ALLFREY, VINCENT   The Rockefeller Institute, New York 21, N. Y.

BILLEN, D.   Department of Biochemistry, Baylor University Medical School, Houston, Texas.

BIRNSTIEL, MAX L.   Division of Biology, California Institute of Technology, Pasadena, Calif.

BLOCH, DAVID P.   Department of Botany, University of Texas, Austin, Texas.

BONNER, JAMES   Division of Biology, California Institute of Technology, Pasadena, Calif.

BRADBURY, E. M.   Department of Mathematics and Physics, Portsmouth College of Technology, Portsmouth, England.

BUSCH, HARRIS   Department of Biochemistry, Baylor University Medical School, Houston, Texas.

BUTLER, J. A. V.   Chester Beatty Research Institute, London, England.

CLEVER, ULRICH   Max-Planck-Institut für Biologie, Tübingen, Germany.

CRANE-ROBINSON, C.   Department of Mathematics and Physics, Portsmouth College of Technology, Portsmouth, England.

CRUFT, H. J. Department of Biochemistry, University of Edinburgh Medical School, Edinburgh, Scotland.

DAVIDSON, NORMAN   Division of Chemistry and Chemical Engineering, California Institute of Technology, Pasadena, Calif.

DOUNCE, ALEXANDER   Department of Biochemistry, University of Rochester School of Medicine and Dentistry, Rochester, N. Y.

DULBECCO, RENATO   The Salk Institute, La Jolla, Calif.

FLAMM, W. GARY   Division of Biology, California Institute of Technology, Pasadena, Calif.

HNILICA, LUBOMIR S.   The University of Texas, M. D. Anderson Hospital, Houston, Texas.

HUANG, RU-CHIH C.   Division of Biology, California Institute of Technology, Pasadena, Calif.

HYDE, BEAL B.   Division of Biology, California Institute of Technology, Pasadena, Calif.

IWAI, KOICHI   Department of Biochemistry, Tokyo University, Tokyo, Japan.

JOHNS, E. W.   Chester Beatty Research Institute, London, England.

LEHMAN, I. R.   Department of Biochemistry, Stanford University, Stanford, Calif.

LUCK, J. MURRAY   Department of Chemistry, Stanford University, Stanford, Calif.

MAVIOGLU, HILMI   Department of Biochemistry, Baylor University Medical School, Houston, Texas.

MIRSKY, ALFRED   The Rockefeller Institute, New York, N. Y.

MURRAY, KENNETH   Department of Chemistry, Stanford University, Stanford, Calif.

NEELIN, J. M.   National Research Council of Canada, Ottawa, Canada.

PHILLIPS, D. M. P.   Chester Beatty Research Institute, London, England.

PRESCOTT, DAVID   Department of Anatomy, University of Colorado Medical School, Denver, Colo.

RICHARDS, BRIAN M.   Biophysics Research Unit, M.R.C., King's College, London, England.

RUDKIN, GEORGE   The Institute for Cancer Research, Fox Chase, Philadelphia, Pa.

SINSHEIMER, ROBERT L.   Division of Biology, California Institute of Technology, Pasadena, Calif.

STEDMAN, EDGAR   Department of Biochemistry, University of Edinburgh, Edinburgh, Scotland.

STEELE, WILLIAM J.   Department of Biochemistry, Baylor University Medical School, Houston, Texas.

SWIFT, HEWSON   Department of Zoology, University of Chicago, Chicago, Ill.

TAYLOR, CHARLES W.   Department of Biochemistry, Baylor University Medical School, Houston, Texas.

TS'O, PAUL O. P.   Department of Radiological Sciences, School of Hygiene and Public Health, The Johns Hopkins University, Baltimore, Md.

VENDRELY, R.   Institut de Recherches Scientifiques sur le Cancer, Villejuif, France.

WEISS, S. B.   Department of Biochemistry, University of Chicago, Chicago, Ill.

ZALOKAR, MARKO   Department of Biology, University of California, San Diego; La Jolla, Calif.

ZEEVAART, J. A. D.   Department of Biology, Hamilton College, Hamilton, Ontario, Canada.

ZUBAY, GEOFFREY   Department of Biology, Brookhaven National Laboatory, Upton, Long Island, N. Y.

ACKNOWLEDGMENTS

We wish to acknowledge our thanks and indebtedness to those who made possible the first World Conference on Histone Biology and Chemistry; to the Office of Naval Research, the National Science Foundation, and Mr. H. Kirke Macomber for their financial support; to Mrs. Elizabeth Hanson and Miss Betty Lodge of the California Institute of Technology for their organizational and administrative assistance; to the 56 conference participants whose contributions made this meeting such a memorable one; to our publishers, Holden-Day, Inc., whose encouragement and editorial assistance have been essential; and finally and most of all to the authors of the chapters contained herein.

James Bonner
Paul O. P. Ts'o

TABLE OF CONTENTS

James Bonner
and   Paul O. P. Ts'o

INTRODUCTION

The giant strides which have been made in the study of the biophysics and biochemistry of the nucleic acids have clearly shown that these molecules are the ones entrusted by nature with the task of storage and transfer of genetic information. Rapid developments in the status of the coding problem give promise that the day is near when we shall have full understanding of the genetic language. What new frontier is there, then, for biologists to explore? One logical possibility is gradually to focus our attention upon the mechanisms which control the transcription of the genetic message, the mechanisms which by the exertion of such control bring about organized biological activity of the cell, and indeed cause the development of a single cell into a multicellular organism. What substances in the cell can be expected to serve in the control of genetic activity, to program the expression of the genetic command?

DNA of higher organisms, unlike that of bacteria, is not free within the nucleus of the cell, but is usually bound in varying degree to the histones, the biology and function of which have remained obscure until recently. Histones, because of their quantity, their exclusive location within the nucleus, and their strong interaction with DNA, might be expected to play a key role in the organization of DNA into the superstructure of the chromosome, and thus to regulate the properties and function of DNA. In order to discover this role and to discuss and think about histones from the standpoint not only of histone chemistry, but also of the interaction of histones with DNA and the place of histones within the framework of molecular biology, a first World Conference on Histone Biology and Chemistry was held from April 29 to May 2, 1963. The present volume is the outcome of that conference.

We trust that this volume will serve as a review of present knowledge of the histones and of their complexes with DNA, the nucleohistones. Even more, we hope that the present volume will serve as a preview of the problems important to the future course of research in nucleohistone biology and chemistry. Even now a variety of questions important to the future study of the nucleohistones are readily identifiable. For example, how many kinds of histones are there, and why are there this many? What

is the distribution of the various kinds of histones among the different
DNA molecules of a single nucleus? How and why is this distribution
achieved? Is there a single universal structure for all nucleohistones,
and if so, what, and why? How are histones synthesized and deposited on
the DNA? Because the DNA of nucleohistone replicates in the nucleus
prior to cell division, what happens to the histone during this process?
Because the presence of appropriate histone so clearly represses the
ability of DNA to support RNA synthesis in in vitro systems, how are
nucleohistones related to repression or expression of genetic activity?
In fact, it is this last question which confers upon the nucleohistones a
place of such interest in molecular biology today. Much of the present
volume, therefore, is concerned with the enzymology of the nucleohistones,
and with consideration of the ways in which interaction between histones
and DNA may influence both DNA-dependent RNA synthesis and DNA-
dependent DNA synthesis.

It is a basic tenet of modern biology that the cellular differentiation
of higher organisms results from an orderly and properly programmed
sequential expression and repression of genetic activity. This volume
includes discussion, then, of histones in relation to observable differentiation processes. It is clear that there is still a great gap between our
knowledge of DNA-dependent RNA synthesis in the test tube and the influence of histone upon this process, and for example, the puffing of the
giant chromosomes of flies. Still, the work presented here clearly points
to areas which might profitably be explored. One such area is the implication of steroid hormones in the process of genetic derepression.

Chromosomes, giant aggregates of DNA and protein, have proved
elusive to modern methods of structure analysis, although as the present
volume indicates, we may be getting close to success. We do know, however, that histones staple individual DNA molecules together into chromosomes and are therefore indispensable to the establishment and preservation of chromosome structure. Histones may also play a role in
that coiling and supercoiling of the chromosomes characteristic of the
pre-mitotic stages of the cell. This volume suggests further steps which,
in the light of our new knowledge of the nucleohistones, might be taken
toward the understanding of chromosomal structure and of chromosomal
activities such as coiling.

This volume is presented not as the conclusion to a finished subject,
but rather as an introduction to a field which is just beginning to develop.
It is in this sense that we hope the book may provide not only a summary
of past knowledge, but also a guide to future inquiry. During the past
decade we have witnessed the efforts and the successes of research on the
structures and activities of a variety of cellular organelles, such as the
mitochondria and the ribosomes, as well as of a variety of cytoplasmic
molecules, for example, the soluble enzymes and the transfer RNA's.
The structure and activity of the nucleus remains as a formidable challenge
to the molecular biologist, both because it is complex and fragile and
because well-defined nuclei exist only in the cells of higher organisms.
Such nuclei are not found in bacteria, which were the experimental material

chosen by the molecular biologist in the past. The time is now ripe for us to take up the challenge of the nucleus. Investigations of nucleohistones are now and will continue to be an important step toward the completion of a molecular interpretation of cell theory and cellular function.

I. HISTORY

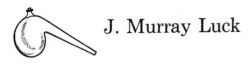 J. Murray Luck

HISTONE CHEMISTRY: THE PIONEERS

I would like to call to mind a few of the early students of the cell nucleus. One could start with Miescher, but to establish a pedagogic lineage I shall go back somewhat earlier, to Hoppe-Seyler, who 100 years ago was the uncrowned king of biochemistry [1]. Ernst Felix Immanuel Hoppe was born on December 26, 1825, the tenth child of pastor and superintendent Ernst Hoppe. Both of his parents died when he was a child, and he grew up in the home of Dr. Seyler, the husband of his oldest sister. Years later, in 1864, the relationship was formalized; he was legally adopted by the Seylers and thereafter used the name Hoppe-Seyler.

He had his early schooling, through gymnasium, in an orphanage in Halle. The educational standards were high, the rules were strict, and the environment was Spartan in all respects. Life therein exercised a decisive influence in shaping the future of the young man. Perhaps he even deserves the credit for discovering the value of the long walk. He and his friend Jahn, the great father of gymnastics, used to walk many miles together — Jahn warming up for the exercise by walking from Freiburg in Thüringen to Halle, a mere 30 kilometers. With all of this came a deep attachment to the outdoors. He had a great love for the mountains and was an expert mountain climber. With a pharmacist in Halle, he used to go on plant collecting expeditions and is credited with discovering in the Riesen mountains a new species of fern.

In later years he went regularly to the Bodensee on his vacations and was a very competent sailor. His last scientific publication reported on the distribution of absorbed gases in the water of the Bodensee and its relation to the plant and animal life of the lake. This followed earlier work with C. Duncan on the respiration of fish at different depths in the lake. His love of plants and his friendship with the Halle pharmacist led him, while still a boy, to carry out chemical experiments on plants and later to study the composition of plant ash. His love of the mountains developed his interest in geology, and he published several papers in this field.

When he finished gymnasium in 1846, he was admitted as a medical student in Halle. There he studied for two semesters and was properly initiated in chemical research by Steinberg, the Professor of Pharmaceutical Chemistry. He would probably have remained in Halle were it not for a hiking trip in the Riesen mountains in the fall of 1847. There he happened to meet Ernst Heinrich and Edward Weber, with whom he soon developed a close friendship, and who persuaded him to continue his studies in Leipzig. This he did, often visiting the Webers, three of whom — brothers — were professors in the University. All of them, but especially E. H. Weber, Professor of Physiology and Anatomy, profoundly influenced the young Hoppe.

Hoppe remained for five semesters in Leipzig. He then went to Berlin, where he finished his medical studies, published his dissertation with E. H. Weber on the composition of chondrin, and in 1851 received his certification as a physician. After a year of migratory study, mountaineering, and travel in Prague, northern Italy, and Vienna he took his state examinations in obstetrics and practiced medicine for a year or two. After another two years of service in the University, he accepted appointment as Prosector in Virchow's new Institute of Pathology. Here he directed the work of the chemical laboratory and gave a series of lectures on chemistry and physiological chemistry for doctors. His students and research associates grew rapidly in number and, thanks to Virchow's influence and his great interest in Hoppe, a second assistant was appointed. Hoppe was promoted to Professor Extraordinarius in 1860 and one year later moved to Tübingen, where in a short time he became Professor Ordinarius. It is evident that he was a stimulating teacher and, in association with Strecker and later with Fittig, was highly regarded for his lectures, carefully prepared experiments, and demonstrations in inorganic, organic, and physiological chemistry and toxicology. The physical facilities for his work were very poor, but this did not dampen his enthusiasm.

In 1872, Hoppe-Seyler was invited to the chair of physiological chemistry in the newly founded University of Strasbourg. He accepted with characteristic enthusiasm and for eleven years occupied quarters in the medical school building. The facilities were not completely suitable, and about 1883 a new building was erected, according to his design, for instruction and research in physiological chemistry. This was the first of its kind in Germany and can well be regarded as a landmark in development of the science as an expanding discipline in its own right. Here he gave lectures and conducted practical courses in physiological chemistry, toxicology, forensic chemistry, metabolism and nutrition, and hygiene. He attracted a great many students, notably Miescher and Kossel. His great textbook on physiological and pathological chemistry, which first appeared in 1858, ran into many editions and was translated into many languages. Every analytical method and every experiment described in this book and in its many revised editions were developed or checked by Hoppe-Seyler personally — a laudable practice that our many writers of present-day laboratory manuals might well emulate. Hoppe-Seyler's name is also indelibly associated with the Zeitschrift für Physiologische Chemie, which he founded in 1877, and with the 150 papers or more on a great diversity of topics that he published during his lifetime.

In his seventieth year, while vacationing on the Bodensee, as he had done for 20 years or more, he was suddenly seized by a heart attack and died on August 10, 1895.

One of his memorable students was Friedrich Miescher [2], whose research in Hoppe-Seyler's laboratory constitutes a fitting introduction to this Conference. Johann Friedrich Miescher was born in Basel on August 13, 1844. His father (1811-1887) was Professor of Pathology and Physiology in Basel from 1837 to 1844, and Professor of General Pathology and Pathological Anatomy from 1850 to 1871. In the interim he held a professorship in Bern, the Heimatkanton of the Miescher family. An uncle on his mother's side was the well-known anatomist Wilhelm His, Professor of Anatomy and Physiology in Basel from 1857 to 1872 — a man whose influence on Johann Friedrich Miescher, was perhaps more decisive than that of Hoppe-Seyler or Carl Ludwig.

The young Miescher almost entered the study of theology, but, fortunately for science, studied medicine instead. He pursued his studies in Basel and Göttingen and qualified in 1868. His father advised him to go into practice, perhaps as an ear specialist — a newly developing field in which he probably had a certain amount of interest, but he was much more interested in scientific research and theoretical studies. So we find him in 1868 in Tübingen with a modest background in inorganic chemistry and organic chemistry, gained from Strecker and Wöhler. Somewhere along the way he became interested in the chemistry of the cell nucleus. His uncle, Wilhelm His, was eager that Miescher should study biochemistry as a tool for a better understanding of histology. Apparently Miescher selected the nucleus for study because it was the least known of the cell constituents, and this was the problem he brought for study to the laboratory of Hoppe-Seyler. At the time he was the only pupil of Hoppe-Seyler.

One suspects that the professor was not particularly enthusiastic about the proposed investigation, but he does not appear to have discouraged Miescher. However, it is not clear why Miescher did not soon abandon the project. As his starting material, he used pus cells obtained from the bandages of clinic patients with suppurating wounds. The difficulties attributable to the stench from the bandages and clumping and slime formation of the cell suspensions would have discouraged any but the most determined. He succeeded in isolating nuclei from which, with alkaline extraction and acid precipitation, he obtained two fractions, "die ich einstweilen ohne weiteres Präjudiz als lösliches und unlösliches Nuclein bezeichnen will" [3]. His soluble nuclein would now be recognized as a crude preparation of DNA. What first excited the curiosity of Miescher and later of many others was the high phosphorous content, coupled with a subsequent finding that such nuclein seemed to be characteristic of all nuclei he examined. The work was ready for publication in the fall of 1869, but Hoppe-Seyler, to whom the manuscript was sent, was frankly skeptical. He withheld publication, with Miescher's full approval, until 1871, when he had himself repeated every essential portion of Miescher's research. Apparently, Miescher, always dubious about the accuracy and the quality of his own investigations, deeply appreciated Hoppe-Seyler's caution.

Late in 1869, Miescher went to Leipzig to study physiology under the great and dramatic Carl Ludwig. He remained almost a year and pursued some research on pain conduction in bone marrow — a problem Ludwig was eager to have studied. The work was published, although Miescher considered it to be quite remote from the main stream of his scientific interests. In 1871 he returned to Basel and in 1872 assumed the Professorship of Physiology hitherto held by his uncle His, now appointed to a chair in Leipzig.

In Basel, eager to continue his studies on cell nuclei, he turned with enthusiasm to salmon spermatozoa. At that time salmon were abundant in the upper Rhine, and Miescher found the spermatozoa excellent material for his work. He again isolated DNA and with it a nitrogen-rich base, as he thought quite simple in structure ($C_9H_{21}N_5O_3$), which he called Protamine. From the unripe testis, he isolated a protein but was unable to find any protamine. It was Kossel, however, who a few years later showed that Miescher's protamine was a protein and that his basic protein from the unripe testis apparently belonged to the class of proteins to which Kossel had given the name histone[1] [4].

Miescher's studies were largely chemical. His uncle His interested

---

[1]In 1896 Schmiedeberg, a close friend of Miescher, published a commentary on Miescher's studies of salmon milt (Schmiedeberg, O., Arch. exptl. Path.u.Pharmakol. 37, 100-155, 1896). In doing so, he worked up the very considerable body of data which Miescher and his assistant Gmelin collected in the closing years of Miescher's life. The interpretation was probably clear to Miescher before his death in August, 1895: Salmon protamine was a tyrosine-free protein (positive biuret, negative Millon's reaction) with 89% of its total nitrogen present as a basic amino acid having the empirical formula of arginine (described by Hedin in 1895 as a constituent of protein hydrolysates). In contrast, the acid-extractable substance from the nuclei of the unripe salmon testis and from carp spermatozoa was clearly recognized by Miescher as a protein and was so described in his paper of 1874.

Schmiedeberg referred to this protein as Kernalbuminose and, though it was phosphorus free, suggested that it served during the maturation process in the salmon as the precursor of both nucleic acid and protamine (". . . das bei der Spermabildung das Eiweiss sich zunächst in zwei Hälften spaltet, und dass aus der einen das Protamin, aus der anderen die Nucleinsäure hervorgeht"). The phosphorus required for the nucleic acid was believed to originate in lecithin, which was abundantly present in the sperm. And since tyrosine and leucine were present in Kernalbuminose but absent from protamine,". . . werden diese also wahrscheinlich bei der Umwandelung der Albuminose in Protamine abgespalten." Whether this primitive theory of protamine and nucleic acid genesis arose with Miescher or Schmiedeberg cannot be determined.

him in the fascinating problems concerned with the spawning migrations of the salmon — the loss of fat, the atrophy and "liquidation" of muscle, the failure of the fish to eat while making the long ascent up the fresh waters of the Rhine and, coincident with the process of liquidation (as Miescher described the events), an increase in the weight of ovaries or testes to 25% of the total body weight. His pursued histological and morphological studies on the tissues of the migrating fish, while Miescher carried out the chemical research. This, as Needham has pointed out, was one of the most fruitful collaborative studies in the history of chemical embryology. It exposed a wealth of problems stemming from the apparent partial liquidation of some organs and the migration of their components to the developing ovary or testis.

His papers were few, for his life was short and he had very little technical assistance (one quarter of a Diener), and in keeping with his very deep convictions and intense motivation, he was determined to do almost everything with his own hands. It is not generally known, for example, that Miescher was probably the first protein chemist to recognize the amphoteric properties of proteins. In a letter to Wilhelm His in May, 1876, he wrote [5]: "The thought always occurs to me that the proteins are really both strong acids and strong bases, which possess a neutral reaction only because of an inner neutralization. If one mixes sodium chloride with protein there must occur protein chloride, sodium proteinate, and protein-proteinate. Different proteins have different affinities, and even the insoluble proteins are not unreactive."

And as Verzár has pointed out [2], Miescher's scientific curiosity also led him into studies of respiration, the spleen, and high altitude physiology. He was the first to prove that respiration is chemically regulated and that carbon dioxide is the stimulating agent.

Miescher sensed that oxygen lack, or tissue hypoxia, was behind the liquidation processes observed in the spawning migrations of the salmon. The cause of the oxygen depletion was not hard to explain; the great skeletal muscles of the fish were almost empty of blood. But where had the blood gone? To answer this question Miescher made his important observation on spleen function [6]. In May or June, when the ovary or testis approaches maturation, the spleen increases in size 15- to 20-fold, and after spawning, returns to a mere 1/2,000 or less of the body weight— its so-called normal size. The enlarged spleen is filled with blood unusually rich in red cells. Why the splenic reservoir fills with blood from the muscles was not clear to Miescher, although today emptying of blood from the musculature is most commonly associated with a lack of sex hormones.

Another aspect of Miescher's interest in respiration was the problem of adaptation to high altitudes. With the help of several colleagues, it was possible to confirm the finding of Viault in 1890 that the number of circulating red cells increases with altitude. Miescher extended the work to experimental animals, as well as man, and was able to show that the stimulus to red cell formation observed at an altitude of 850 meters was noticeably enhanced at 985 and 1,050 meters. Although it was tempting to associate this enhanced red cell formation simply with the reduced partial pressure of oxygen in the inspired air, Miescher was aware of the difficulties in so simple an explanation.

Miescher was seriously ill during the later phases of these studies, and he was obliged to follow the work from his sick bed. His tragic death occurred in the spring of 1894, in his fiftieth year, when he contracted tuberculosis. He went to a sanitarium in Davos, but the disease was severe, progressive, and unresponsive to high-altitude therapy. Though he observed the progress of the disease objectively, he did not give up hope until, in the summer of 1895, he was asked by the university to retire from his professorship. He died on August 26.

A little must be said about Miescher's personal characteristics. He was an introvert and, perhaps because of this, very critical of his own research. This inner insecurity was reflected in his work in some ways; he was never quite certain that his findings were accurate, that the evidence was sufficient, that he had proved his point. To be doubly sure, he did most of his elementary analyses—carbon, hydrogen, nitrogen, and phosphorus—himself. He was myopic and hard of hearing, physical defects that could easily accentuate his introvert tendencies. Like his father, he was very musical, and there were those who regarded his musical talents to be as highly developed as his scientific.

It was in his laboratory, however, where he really lived. Until a new laboratory, the Vesalianum, was constructed, he had only two rooms and part of a public corridor for his work. He also lacked apparatus and time. It is said that when plates were missing from the laboratory, he would draw on his household supply of Sevres porcelain, which his wife would then resolutely seek to retrieve.

The preparation of his lectures was always a very difficult task for him and required an unusual amount of time and effort. He was not an accomplished lecturer like his colleague Bunge, whose well-rounded and explicitly definitive lectures were a pleasure to medical students. But to the few who had imagination and a real sense of scientific curiosity, Miescher's lectures had a great appeal.

Such demands on him left little time for contemplation and active research. When nucleic acid was being prepared, he came to the laboratory at five in the morning and worked in an unheated room late into the night. He wrote to his uncle, "No solution may stand more than five minutes, no precipitate more than an hour, before being placed in absolute alcohol." He was well aware that degradation might otherwise ensue. To him there was a tremendous sense of urgency in all that he did, and he gave the highest priority to his laboratory work. It was even said that on the day of his wedding, someone had to look for him in the laboratory to make sure that he arrived at the church at the appointed time.

Miescher was, unquestionably, one of the great physiologists and biochemists of his time. He antedated Kossel as the real founder of research on the chemistry of the nucleus. The studies that Miescher initiated made a great impression on Hoppe-Seyler, who suggested to Albrecht Kossel that he continue the work.

Albrecht Karl Ludwig Martin Leonhard Kossel [7] was born in Rostock on September 16, 1853. His father, Albrecht Kossel, was the Prussian Consul. He went to the gymnasium in Rostock and entered the newly founded University of Strasbourg in 1872 to study medicine. One of his teachers was Hoppe-Seyler, who engaged Kossel in 1877 as an assistant. Six years later, Kossel was called to Berlin to succeed Baumann as director of the Physiology Institute. He was appointed Professor Ordinarius in 1887. In 1895, he became Director of the Physiology Institute at Marburg. In 1901, he moved to Heidelberg, where he remained until his death on July 5, 1927. In 1910, he received the Nobel prize in medicine in recognition of his work on the chemistry of the cell nucleus. On the invitation of Johns Hopkins University, he visited the United States in 1911 and lectured in many American cities.

The fundamental investigations of Friedrich Miescher formed the starting point for Kossel's studies. His first paper, "On the Chemistry of the Cell Nucleus," initiated an impressive series of publications, which ended 50 years later with "Developmental History of the Basic Proteins," published posthumously [8]. One week before his death, he completed the manuscript of his monograph on the protamines and histones. During his very productive years, he discovered many histones, rediscovered the protamines, and laid a solid foundation for the future in his structural studies on the nucleic acids. The nucleic acid bases, as well as the basic amino acids of the histones and protamines, were among his principal interests. When silver salts were almost impossible to obtain during the troubled years of monetary inflation, he turned to the Badische Anilinfabrik for a supply of aromatic nitrocompounds as possible amino acid precipitants. Out of this approach came the introduction of flavianic acid (dinitronaphtholsulfonic acid) as the ideal arginine precipitant; also a virtual abandonment of his silver-baryta procedure for precipitating the hexone bases.

Kossel's school developed the theory that protamines are made up of two molecules of basic amino acids (principally arginine) to one of monoamino acids. He was never able to determine, as he had hoped to do, whether the basic amino acids were sequentially segregated from a similar clustering of the neutral amino acids or whether a two-to-one recurring sequence was to be found in the protamines. On the basis of rather scanty evidence, he favored the former. He was convinced that protamines and histones were developmentally related; both arose, in his opinion, by the metabolic shedding of monoamino residues, from muscle protein as it wasted away during the spawning migrations of the salmon and other fish. He was confident that the unripe testis contained histone in the cell nucleus, and this protein, by a progressive simplification during the ripening process, became the protamine of the mature spermatozoa. Whether this theory would hold together in the face of what we now know, or think we know, about protein synthesis is another matter.

Another of Kossel's theories, hardly acceptable today, is that histones are actually complexes of protamines with other proteins. "If one adds a solution of protamine to a solution of albumen or protein the liquid remains clear. The subsequent addition of a little ammonia produces a precipitate and this possesses all the characteristics of histone." And then the generalization, "A protamine is a base and binds protein only in alkaline solution to form a basic protein, histone" [9] .

Kossel had many students who engaged in research on histones and protamines with his direction and encouragement. The names of Lilienfeld (who first prepared thymus histone), Huiskamp, A. P. Mathews, Dakin, and Kutscher, for example, are known to most of us. Also well known among the early investigators is Ivar Christian Bang [10] , who, from 1904 until his death in December, 1918, was Professor Ordinarius of medical and physiological chemistry in the University of Lund. Bang was not a member of the Kossel school and, indeed, engaged in several skirmishes with Kossel in the pages of Hoppe-Seyler's Zeitschrift. He is probably best known for his contributions to clinical chemistry, especially for the development of several analytical methods and for the application of new concepts and techniques to blood and urine analysis. Bang's papers on histone and nucleohistone suggest meticulous attention to details in the preparation of products and in testing their properties. He stated, rather surprisingly, that Lilienfeld's method (1894) for preparing thymus nucleohistone was so well known (by 1900) that the substance was in commercial production [11] . But the method, Bang insisted, did not even give a nucleohistone. It yielded, so Bang claimed, a nucleoprotein that was histone free. Actually, the papers by Lilienfield, Huiskamp, Bang, Malengreau, and others from 1894 to about 1904 repeatedly mention nucleoprotein, nucleohistone, histone, parahistone, nuclein, leukonuclein, nucleoalbuminate, nucleoalbumose, plastin, etc. To straighten out the terminology, in the light of what we now know, is a fascinating little exercise. Incidentally, the word nucleohistone was coined by Lilienfeld in 1892 and was applied to the material that was extractable with distilled water from leukocytes or minced thymus and precipitable from the aqueous extracts with acetic acid [12] .

In this description of the early histone chemists, I have done scant justice to Kossel's associates and to his contemporaries. Beyond seeking refuge in what are known as the exigencies of space and time, I can only plead that I have been quite unsuccessful in finding any biographical information on such interesting investigators as Carnoy, Huiskamp, Lilienfeld, Malengreau, and Plosz.

Acknowledgments

I am much indebted to the following for assistance in procuring biographical information or in checking parts of the manuscript: Professor Hugo Aebi, University of Bern; Professor Bengt Bergström, University of Lund; Professor David Bonner, University of California at La Jolla; Dr. Hermann Chinn, American Embassy, Bonn; Dr. Olaf Hougen, American Embassy, Stockholm; Dr. D. C. Martin, The Royal Society, London; The Medical Center, University of Cincinnati; Professor Ernst Miescher, University of Basel; Professor Peter Miescher, New York University; Mr. Grant Miner, Los Altos, California; Dr. Stanford Moore, the Rockefeller Institute, New York; Professor Alexander von Muralt, University of Bern; Mr. Allen Murray, Kirkby in Ashfield, England; Professor Ian Roddie, Queen's University, Belfast; Professor Hans Schaefer, University of Heidelberg; Professor P. E. Verkade, The Hague; Professor H. H. Weber, the Max-Planck Institute, Heidelberg.

REFERENCES

1. The biographical information on Hoppe-Seyler was drawn almost entirely from "Zur Erinnerung an Felix Hoppe-Seyler," by E. Baumann and A. Kossel (Z. Physiol. Chem., 21, i, 1895/96).

2. For the information concerning Miescher, the principal sources were: Friedrich Miescher, 1844-1895, zum hundertsten Geburtstag, by V. Suter, F. Verzár und S. Edlbacher (Basel: Benno Schwabe & Co., Basel); "Professor Friedrich Miescher," by A. Jaquet, Verhandl. Naturforsch. Ges. Basel, 11, 399, 1897; and Die Histochemischen und Physiologischen Arbeiten von Friedrich Miescher (2 vols., Leipzig: F.C.W. Vogel, 1897). Also helpful was the article "Friedrich Miescher, 1844-95. Founder of Nuclear Chemistry," by Jesse P. Greenstein, Sci. Monthly 47, 523, 1943. For additional information, I am greatly indebted to Professor Ernst Miescher of the Physics Institute, University of Basel, and to Professor Peter Miescher of the Department of Medicine, New York University.

3. Miescher, F. Med.-Chem. Untersuch. (Hoppe-Seyler), pt. 4, pp. 441-460, 1871.

4. Kossel, A. Z. Physiol. Chem. 8, 511, 1884.

5. From letter XV in Die Histochemischen und Physiologischen Arbeiten von Friedrich Miescher, vol. 1, and from a personal communication from Professor Peter Miescher.

6. Miescher, F. Arch. Anat. Physiol., Anat. Abt., pp. 193-218, 1881.

7.   The data on Kossel were drawn from "Albrecht Kossel zum Gedächtnis" (S. Edlbacher, Z. Physiol. Chem., 177, 1-14, 1928) and "Albrecht Kossel, Leben und Werk," by K. Felix (Naturwissenschaften, 42, 473, 1955).

8.   Kossel, A., and Schenck, E. G. Z. Physiol. Chem., 173, 278, 1928.

9.   Kossel, A. Deut. Med. Wochschr. 20, 146, 1894.

10.   Two sources were used for the information on Bang: "Nachruf Ivar Christian Bang," by O. Hammarsten (Ergeb. Physiol., 18, xi, 1920) and D. D. Van Slyke's opening address before the International Congress of Clinical Chemistry in Stockholm (August, 1957): "Ivar Christian Bang" (Scandinav. J. Clin. Lab. Invest., 10, Supp. 31, 18, 1957).

11.   Bang, I. Z. Physiol. Chem., 30, 508, 1900.

12.   Lilienfeld, L. Verhandl. Physiol. Gesell. Berlin, April 8, July 22, 1892; Z. Physiol. Chem., 18, 473, 1894.

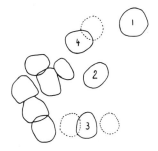

II. HISTONE CHEMISTRY

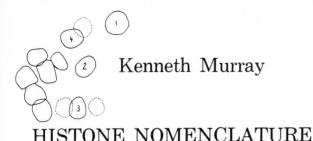

Kenneth Murray

HISTONE NOMENCLATURE

The definition of histones and the distinction between histones and protamines have been considered carefully by Cruft, Mauritzen, and Stedman [1] and also, in a very recent review, by Phillips [2]. The comments and suggestions offered here result from discussions with many investigators in the general field of histone chemistry. It is not claimed that these views are held unanimously by those involved in the discussions, but certainly there is wide agreement with, and acceptance of, the following proposals for definition and nomenclature of histones, at least as an interim attempt to ease a state of increasing confusion.

Histones are basic proteins that at some time are associated with DNA. This definition deliberately does not distinguish between histones and protamines. Such a distinction is arbitrary and, although there are profound differences between histones and protamines, their continued distinction is not readily justified when considered in the context of recent progress in the fractionation of these proteins. Histones and protamines may be considered as homologous proteins [3]. Their distinction is comparable with the distinction between two histone fractions having widely different properties, so it appears equally reasonable to consider histones and protamines collectively. If this is done, only one name is necessary and "basic nuclear protein" may be preferable to either histone or protamine. However, since the names histone and protamine are well established and widely used, perhaps they should persist. It is generally believed that histones (and protamines) contain neither tryptophan nor cysteine. With modern analytical methods, the presence of traces of cysteine has been observed, usually in unfractionated histone preparations [2], and additional examples may well be found in the future. The presence of small quantities of cysteine or tryptophan may indicate the contamination of histone preparations with other proteins, or these amino acids may be true constituents of a histone fraction. These possibilities may often be difficult to distinguish, and for this reason reference to the absence of tryptophan and cysteine has been omitted from the definition of histone.

One additional point should be made. There has been abundant use (largely misuse) of the term impure histone. Histones, and therefore

15

pure histones, have been defined in the preceding paragraph. Impure histones are histones that contain nonhistone material. Histone preparations have been fractionated to varying degrees, and the different fractions, though certainly not homogeneous, are pure histones if they contain no nonhistone material. The difference between impure histones and heterogeneous histone preparations is real, and it is therefore important to avoid confusion of these terms.

In his survey of recent developments of histone chemistry, Butler referred to the problem of nomenclature of histone fractions [4]. Histones were divided by Stedman and Stedman [5] into main and subsidiary categories, and various subcomponents were described in terms of their electrophoretic mobilities as α, β, and γ histones [6], after the manner used for the nomenclature of other proteins. The terms lysine-rich and arginine-rich came into widespread use for the description of histone fractions when relatively few components were recognized and have persisted even though the description arginine-rich is ambiguous, since it depends on the method of presentation of amino acid analyses. The status of histone nomenclature was considered recently by Phillips [2], who described the various histone fractions as very lysine-rich, slightly or moderately lysine-rich, or arginine-rich, according to the molar ratio of lysine to arginine (greater than 4, 4:1, less than 1, respectively), and proper emphasis was placed on the distinction between the arginine-rich histones so described and histones that had previously been termed arginine-rich, but which on the basis of their molar ratio of lysine to arginine would now be slightly lysine-rich histones. In addition to its bulkiness, this descriptive system has two disadvantages. One is that this type of description may imply that the property employed for the description is perhaps the most important feature of a particular histone fraction, whereas this may or may not be so. Thus, although their relative lysine and arginine contents permit a convenient description of different histone fractions (say, very lysine-rich and slightly lysine-rich histones), are these quantities more important than size or relative contents of other amino acids, for example, proline or the aromatic amino acids? This question cannot yet be answered with any degree of confidence, and it is therefore important to avoid the possibility of a misplacement of emphasis, either directly or by inference. The second and more serious disadvantage of what may be termed the descriptive nomenclature is that an arbitrary grouping of histone fractions results, and several quite different histone fractions become similarly named. The multiplicity of histone fractions is now well recognized and makes the limited, descriptive type of nomenclature obsolete.

The molar ratios of lysine to arginine (or arginine to lysine) for various histone fractions furnish a continuous range of values (Table 1). Therefore, the continued use of a nomenclature involving arbitrary division into groups is both undesirable and illogical. It is improbable that a homogeneous histone fraction has been obtained; indeed the true complexity of histones from a given source is not known. This adds to the difficulty of nomenclature of histone fractions, and any system will be

TABLE 1

Histone Fraction	Molar arg: lys	Molar lys: arg	Reference
A	0.09	11.2	9
A	0.06	15.7	10
α_1	0.0	∞	11
α_2	0.16	6.2	11
fla	0.11	9.0	7
E2	0.18	5.7	8
Ia	0.12	8.4	12
Ib	0.10	10.0	12
I. Asc.	0.07	15.5	12
I desc.	0.05	20.3	12
α_3	0.24	4.4	11
C	0.25	4.0	9
0.85γ	0.31	3.2	11
IIb$_2$	0.42	2.4	12
Ix	0.44	2.2	12
B	0.58	1.7	9
Iaa	0.59	1.7	12
IIb	0.59	1.7	12
II	0.66	1.5	12
E1	0.73	1.4	8
1.65γ	0.75	1.3	11
f2	0.75	1.3	7
IIb$_1$	0.77	1.3	12
B	0.84	1.2	10
E3	0.91	1.1	8
B (direct)	0.92	1.1	10
β	1.35	0.74	11

TABLE 1 (Cont'd)

Histone Fraction	Molar arg: lys	Molar lys: arg	Reference
IIaa	1.11	0.91	12
III	1.37	0.73	12
IV	1.42	0.70	12
f3	1.28	0.78	7
EtOH (direct)	1.27	0.79	7
EtOH (direct)	1.56	0.64	7
EtOH (direct)	1.63	0.61	7

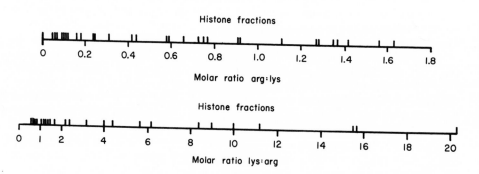

Fig. 1.—The distribution on linear scales of the arg:lys and lys:arg values of the histone fractions listed in Table 1.

necessarily incomplete. While it is essential that each histone fraction should be described in the fullest possible terms, it is also important that an attempt be made to adopt a simple, short nomenclature. A very convenient system which is concise but informative describes fractions in terms of the actual molar ratio of their principal basic amino acids, instead of grouping fractions under descriptive headings on this basis. There are two possibilities — the lysine-to-arginine ratio — which has been quoted in some recent publications [2, 7, 8], or the arginine-to-lysine ratio. Table 1 lists both ratios; these have been taken or calculated from the published data on several calf thymus histone fractions. They have also been represented on linear scales that well illustrate the range of values and thus of fractions implicated, and as histone fractions are resolved, it is probable that fractions having other intermediate values will be found. Careful consideration of these data suggests that the molar ratio of arginine to lysine has a slight but definite advantage over the molar ratio of lysine to arginine. This accrues from the smaller range of values involved, the lower magnitude of the values, and the improbability of confusion with other numbering systems because most values are below unity.

With this proposed system of nomenclature, the various fractions are described as, for example, arg:lys 0.1 histone. This is not necessarily a replacement of terms such as histone fraction A, histone fraction α_2, histone fraction I, etc., for in many cases these will still be required to name fractions having similar molar ratios of arginine to lysine (arg: lys value) but differing in other respects. Indeed, it cannot be over-emphasized that the use of arg:lys values is intended only as a convenient shorthand for the initial description of histone fractions and is not a definitive term. Fractions having similar arg:lys values must be equated in no other sense unless all other intrinsic properties have been shown to be similar. Although the use of arg:lys values will, it is hoped, prove to be more profitable than the descriptive nomenclature, it will still be of the utmost importance to describe histone fractions as fully as possible. Their complete amino acid composition, their chromatographic properties, and their behavior on zone electrophoresis should constitute a minimal description; information pertaining to size and terminal amino acids is desirable.

Comment

As readers of this volume will readily perceive, the nomenclature used for the various histones by different laboratories varies considerably. The virtues of a generally accepted and common histone nomenclature are obvious.

REFERENCES

1.   Cruft, H. J., Mauritzen, C. M., and Stedman, E. Phil. Trans. Roy. Soc. London, Ser. B., 241, 134, 1957.

2.   Phillips, D. M. P. Prog. Biophys. Biophys. Chem., 12, 211, 1962.

3.   Stedman, E., and Stedman. E. Cold Spring Harbor Symp. Quant. Biol., 12, 224, 1947.

4.   Butler, J. A. V. this volume, p. 36.

5.   Stedman, E. and Stedman, E. Phil. Trans. Roy. Soc. London, Ser. B, 235, 565, 1951.

6.   Cruft, H. J., Mauritzen, C. M., and Stedman, E. Nature, 174, 580, 1954.

7.   Johns, E. W., Phillips, D. M. P., Simson, P., and Butler, J. A. V. Biochem. J., 77, 631, 1960.

8.   Johns, E. W., Phillips, D. M. P., Simson, P., and Butler, J. A. V. Biochem. J., 80, 189, 1961.

9.   Crampton, C. F., Moore, S., and Stein, W. H. J. Biol. Chem., 215, 787, 1955.

10. Crampton, C. F., Stein, W. H., and Moore, S. J. Biol. Chem., 225, 363, 1957.

11. Cruft, H. J., Hindley, J., Mauritzen, C. M., and Stedman, E. Nature, 180, 1107, 1957.

12. Rasmussen, P. S., Murray, K., and Luck, J. M. Biochemistry, 1, 79, 1962.

Kenneth Murray

THE HETEROGENEITY OF HISTONES

This discussion will be concerned primarily with heterogeneity of histones extracted from one source, calf thymus, rather than with heterogeneity of histones as indicated from studies of different species, organs, or cell types. The separation of a histone preparation into more than one fraction immediately poses two questions. First, are some of the fractions artifacts produced by degradation of the material from its native state? Second, is a given fraction homogeneous or not? These two questions, particularly the second, have been of special interest to us in Dr. Luck's laboratory in recent years. Although much work of a somewhat parallel nature has been, and is being, done in other laboratories [1], these considerations will be largely restricted to the work with which I am most familiar.

When histone preparation A, obtained by extraction of saline-washed thymus nuclei with sulfuric acid at pH 1.5, was fractionated by ion-exchange chromatography on Amberlite IRC-50, several components were obtained, and the pattern was quite reproducible. If guanidinium chloride solution was used to develop the chromatogram, the separation of histone fractions was as shown in Figure 1. This fractionation was quite different from that obtained when barium acetate solution was used to develop the chromatogram [2, 3], because two principal components, fractions A and B were then obtained. This difference emphasizes the question whether the various histone fractions were native nucleoprotein components. The authenticity of histone fractions Ia and Ib (obtained by the use of guanidinium chloride solution) was particularly suspect, since the work by Crampton, Stein, and Moore [3] showed that degradation during histone extraction led to a division of their histone fraction A into two chromatographically overlapping components. This change appeared to occur at the expense of fraction B and was accompanied by an alteration in amino acid composition of the fractions. A particularly noteworthy change was the introduction of small quantities of histidine and methionine into histone fraction A, which previously had been devoid of these amino acids. That a similar degradation of, for example, histone fraction IIb (Fig. 1) cannot be invoked to explain the presence of fractions Ia and Ib (and the occur-

21

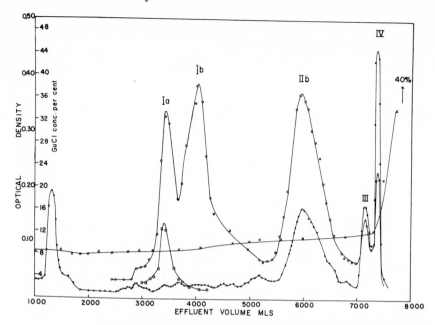

Fig. 1.—Chromatographic fractionation of calf thymus histone preparation A on Amberlite IRC-50 (column; 55 x 7.5 cm diameter) with a gradient concentration of guanidinium chloride (GuCl); 1 g of the histone preparation was used. Protein concentration of the effluent fractions was determined by (a) optical density at 277 mμ (●—●); (b) optical density at 400 mμ of the turbid solutions resulting when 0.5 ml of the effluent sample was mixed with 1.1 M trichloracetic acid in a total volume of 3.0 ml (O—O); (c) optical density at 400 mμ of the turbid solution similarly produced in 0.8 M trichloracetic acid (□—□). Concentration of guanidinium chloride in the effluent is indicated by X—X.

rence therein of small quantities of histidine and methionine) became apparent when histone preparation A was fractionated on Amberlite IRC-50 with the barium acetate elution system to yield a histone fraction I (equivalent to the histone fraction A of Crampton, Moore, and Stein) as a single peak (Fig. 2). This fraction contained neither histidine nor methionine, but was similar in other respects to histone fractions Ia and Ib. Thus it is reasonable to conclude that histone fractions Ia and Ib were not produced artificially and that their separation is a feature of the resolving power of the chromatographic development system. The presence of histidine and methionine in histone fractions Ia and Ib was attributed to contamination of these fractions with the attendant minor chromatographic fractions Iaa, and Ic (not found when barium acetate solution was used to develop the chromatogram; in this case, these fractions may well have been eluted in combination with histone fraction II, or fraction B in the terminology of Crampton, Moore, and Stein). The histone fraction II

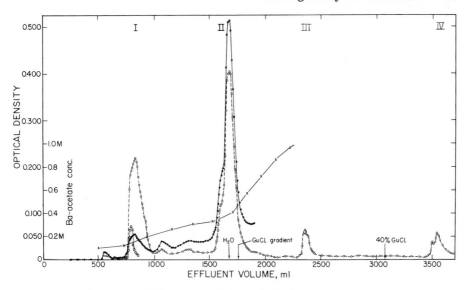

Fig. 2.—Chromatography of histone preparation A (400 mg) on Amberlite IRC-50 (column; 55 x 4.5 cm diameter) with a gradient concentration of barium acetate, followed at 1,760 ml by a gradient concentration of guanidinium chloride. The symbols ●, ○, and □ have the same significance as in Figure 1. Concentration of barium acetate in the effluent, as determined by refractometry, is indicated by X—X.

obtained with the barium acetate elution system appeared to be very similar to fraction IIb obtained with the guanidinium chloride solution. No further fractions were eluted from the resin column with barium acetate solution, but the subsequent use of guanidinium chloride solution removed small quantities of additional fractions. The amino acid composition of each histone fraction is given in Table 1.

The preparations of histone used for the separations illustrated in Figures 1 and 2 were made as follows. Calf thymus glands obtained as soon as possible after the slaughter of the animal had been either frozen on solid carbon dioxide or transported to the laboratory in melting ice and immediately homogenized in ethylene glycol and centrifuged. The sediment was washed twice more in this manner and then four times with physiological saline that was 0.01 M in sodium citrate. Finally, the washed residue was extracted with sulfuric acid at pH 1.5 and 0.7 successively, to yield preparations A and B, respectively, and centrifuged; histone sulfate was recovered from the supernatant solution by precipitation with ethanol. All of these operations were carried out below 4 C.

Two other types of preparation were made in an attempt to establish that there was no appreciable degradation of histone during these operations. In the first of these (preparation C), frozen thymus gland was ground to a powder with solid carbon dioxide. This powder was then gradually added to a boiling solution (105 C) of 3 M guanidinium chloride.

TABLE 1

Amino Acid Composition of Some Chromatographic Fractions of Calf Thymus Histone

Amino Acid	Chromatographic Fraction												
	I asc*§	I desc*§	II*§	Iaa*	Ia*	Ib*	IIaa†	IIa†	IIb*	IIb$_1$*	IIb$_2$*	III‡	IV‡
Lysine	27.9	28.4	12.8	13.8	25.3	26.2	10.2	9.6	13.5	11.5	15.9	9.3	8.9
ε-N-Methyl lysine	0	0	0.4	0	0	0	0.5	0.3	0	0	0	0.7	0.8
Histidine	0	0	2.7	2.2	0.4	0.2	1.9	1.9	2.8	2.8	2.4	1.6	1.6
Arginine	1.8	1.4	8.3	8.2	3.0	2.6	11.2	11.6	7.9	8.8	6.7	12.8	12.7
Aspartic acid	2.0	1.8	5.4	4.5	2.5	2.5	4.9	4.8	5.6	6.1	4.9	4.4	4.5
Threonine	6.0	5.8	5.3	6.2	5.8	5.4	7.1	6.8	5.2	4.5	6.2	7.3	7.3
Serine	6.2	6.7	6.7	6.6	6.4	6.5	5.0	4.6	7.8	5.6	10.0	4.1	4.1
Glutamic acid	3.5	3.4	8.9	8.9	4.5	4.3	9.1	9.6	8.7	9.2	8.2	9.8	10.5
Proline	9.2	9.4	4.6	5.5	8.6	9.1	3.4	3.7	4.7	4.5	4.8	3.8	4.2
Glycine	6.6	7.0	8.5	8.8	6.7	7.3	10.0	9.8	8.2	10.0	6.0	8.7	7.8
Alanine	25.1	25.9	11.9	14.7	24.0	24.2	10.2	11.2	11.5	12.1	10.4	11.7	12.2
Cystine	0	0	0	0	0	0	0	0	0	0	0	0	0
Valine	5.3	4.6	6.0	5.0	4.9	4.0	6.8	6.5	6.7	6.4	7.2	5.8	5.6
Methionine	0	0	0.8	0.6	0.1	0.1	1.2	1.2	0.8	0.2	1.6	1.2	1.2
Isoleucine	1.0	0.9	4.8	3.8	1.3	1.2	5.4	5.4	4.5	4.6	5.0	5.4	5.4
Leucine	4.8	4.2	8.7	8.2	5.3	5.0	8.0	8.7	8.6	10.2	5.0	8.6	8.9
Tyrosine	0.5	0.3	3.0	1.6	0.7	0.7	2.9	2.8	3.0	2.3	4.4	2.4	2.3
Phenylalanine	0.5	0.5	1.3	1.6	0.6	0.6	2.2	2.3	1.3	1.2	1.6	2.5	2.7

*Histone preparation A.
†Histone preparation B.
‡Histone preparation C.
§Eluent solution, barium acetate; all others, guanidinium chloride.

After boiling for 10 minutes, the solution was strained through cheesecloth into distilled water to dilute the guanidinium chloride to a molarity of 0.14. The precipitated nucleohistone was then thoroughly washed with saline, and histone was extracted as before. The purpose here was to inactivate degradative enzymes by thermal denaturation, and guanidinium chloride was used in the hope that its known denaturing effect at this concentration on proteins [4] would also minimize enzymatic action during the brief period before the added thymus gland reached the temperature of the solution.

The third procedure (preparation D) consisted simply of immediate extraction of whole thymus gland with dilute sulfuric acid at 2 C, and here it was hoped that the combination of very rapid extraction, low temperature, and low pH would minimize degradation. Each histone preparation was then fractionated by ion-exchange chromatography on Amberlite IRC-50 with guanidinium chloride solution. Comparable patterns were obtained from all three preparations (Fig. 3). In these experiments, the separation of histone fractions Ia and Ib was less pronounced than that illustrated in Figure 1; this difference is simply a function of the gradient of the eluent concentration, and the more gradual increase, as shown in Figure 1, is that now in routine use.

Corresponding fractions from the three preparations were compared as to their amino acid composition (Fig. 4 and Table 1), behavior on zone electrophoresis in starch gel (see Rasmussen, Murray, and Luck[5] for illustrations of starch-gel electrophoresis experiments discussed here), and (fractions I and Ia) fingerprints of tryptic digests. In these experiments, there was no discernible difference between corresponding fractions obtained by the various procedures. For the preparation of histone from calf thymus it has been shown that although there may often be little difference between products obtained by the two methods, acid extraction is preferable to procedures involving extraction at high salt concentrations [6]. On the basis of these experiments, it was concluded that the histone fractions indicated by Figures 1-3 are probably authentic components of native nucleoprotein.

The question of heterogeneity of the various fractions can now be considered. It was shown by Neelin and his collaborators that zone electrophoresis in starch gels affords a higher degree of resolution of histone components than any of the other methods described for protein fractionation ([7] and later publications). Each chromatographic fraction of histone was therefore examined by this method when multiple components were revealed in each chromatographic fraction. Similar observations have been described by others [8, 9]. However, the well-known tendency to aggregation that histones possess requires that a chemical examination of the individual zones indicated on starch gels be made before these findings can constitute a firm indication of heterogeneity. Clearly the simplest example to choose initially for this purpose was histone fraction IIb. Recovery of histone from starch gels by direct extraction proved very unsatisfactory and for this reason, a continuous elution method of preparative starch-gel electrophoresis was developed [10]. This method afforded separation of the two principal components (IIb_1, the faster

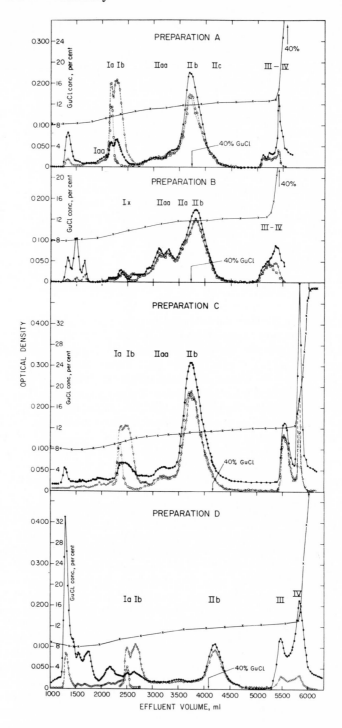

moving zone, and IIb₂, the slower moving zone) of histone fraction IIb, and the amino acid composition of these two components differed markedly (Table 1) so that, in this case at least, the two bands observed on the starch gel represented different proteins (not necessarily homogeneous) rather than different degrees of aggregation of a given polypeptide. In more complex fractions, e.g., fraction III, such separations were rendered very difficult by the relatively low resolving power of the preparative

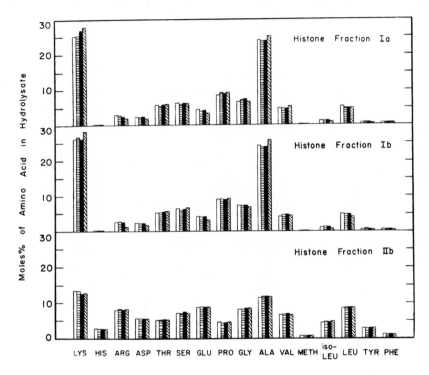

Fig. 4.—Comparison of the amino acid composition of corresponding chromatographic histone fractions from different preparations. Blank bars, fractions from preparation A; horizontally striped bars, fractions from preparation C; solid bars, fractions from preparation D (all three obtained by elution with guanidinium chloride solution); diagonally striped bars, fractions from preparation A (obtained by elution with barium acetate solution).

◄— Fig. 3.—Chromatographic fractionation of calf thymus histone preparations on Amberlite IRC-50 (column; 55 x 7.5 cm diameter) with a gradient concentration of guanidinium chloride (GuCl). The quantity of histone samples applied to the column was: preparation A, 700 mg; preparation B, 570 mg; preparation C, 790 mg; preparation D, soluble part of 750 mg. The symbols ●, ○, and □ have the same significance as in Figure 1, except that 0.1 ml of effluent sample was used for the turbidity measurements.

method and by the very limited capacity of the starch gel. However, it proved possible by this means to separate the faster moving components (collectively) of histone fraction III from the remainder. The material so separated differed in amino acid composition from the original histone fraction III. This indication that the multiplicity of bands observed on starch gels of histone fraction III was due at least partly to heterogeneity of the material was supported by the fact that heat treatment or exposure to 4 M urea of solutions of histone fractions III or IV before electrophoresis had no apparent effect on the bands subsequently observed on the starch gels. Furthermore, preparations of histone fractions III and IV obtained by ethanol precipitation exhibited the same behavior on zone electrophoresis as did corresponding freeze-dried preparations.

After it is established that some of the multiple zones indicated on zone electrophoresis of chromatographic fractions of histones are a true indication of heterogeneity of the fraction, the examination of an apparently homogeneous fraction or subfraction follows. This must be effected through a detailed chemical analysis, which begins with total amino acid analysis and is extended by end-group determinations, but more decisively by a careful and detailed analysis of the peptides furnished by partial hydrolysis.

If the approximate molecular weight range of a particular protein preparation is known, obviously the amino acid composition may often give a useful indication of possible heterogeneity. Thus, it was pointed out by Moore [11] that the amino acid composition of the histone fraction A of Crampton, Stein, and Moore was not consistent with an observed molecular weight of 10,000. Similarly, a molecular weight of over 20,000 is required if histone fraction Ia contains one residue of tyrosine and phenylalanine, whereas the observed molecular weight was about half this value [12]. Histone fraction Ia cannot, therefore, be homogeneous although on zone electrophoresis of this fraction in starch gel, one predominating, diffuse band and several faster-moving, faint bands were observed, the latter obviously being due to components constituting a very small proportion of the total histone fraction. In fact, when histone fraction Ia was reabsorbed on Amberlite IRC-50 and eluted with 0.2 N sulfuric acid, a preparation was obtained (fraction Ia_s) that resembled the original fraction Ia in amino acid composition (except that it now contained neither histidine nor methionine) and in the peptides furnished on digestion with trypsin, but which no longer exhibited the faint bands on zone electrophoresis in starch gel [5]. Similar conclusions regarding heterogeneity apply in the case of histone fraction Ib, although here a larger number of minor components was revealed by zone electrophoresis in starch gels.

It is not possible to draw such confident conclusions regarding heterogeneity from amino acid analyses in relation to size of the other histone fractions. It is, however, of interest to note that an unusual amino acid was found in hydrolysates of histone fractions IIaa, IIa, III, and IV, and the very small quantity in which the amino acid occurred (0.3-0.8 moles per 100 moles) supported the indications from zone electrophoresis that these fractions were heterogeneous. By means of rigorous chromatographic comparison with hydrolysates of flagellin from Salmonella typhimurium (shown by Ambler and Rees [13] to contain ε-N-methyl lysine) and from the mass spectrum of its ethyl ester, this amino acid was shown to be ε-N-methyl lysine [14, 15]. Determinations of N-terminal groups of the various histone fractions also indicate that the fractions are not homogeneous [16-18].

Careful quantitative studies of the peptides derived by partial hydrolysis of given histone fractions offer the most promising approach for further inquiry into the heterogeneity of the fraction. In this connection, the specificity of trypsin for the cleavage of arginine and lysine residues makes this enzyme particularly suitable for the degradation of histone fractions, since many basic peptides must result. Analysis of these peptides (their number, the relative quantities in which they are found, and their amino acid composition) will then afford an estimate of the minimum number of polypeptides contained in a particular histone fraction. A detailed examination of this type has been started by D.C. Lamb on histone fraction Ia, which was selected because it has a lower molecular weight and is perhaps a less complex mixture than the other chromatographic fractions. Preliminary studies have also been made of tryptic digests of other chromatographic fractions of histone. Such structural studies of histone fractions are of added interest in connection with the interaction of histones with DNA and with biological properties and function.

The patterns of tryptic peptides obtained from histone fractions Ia, IIa, and IV by the fingerprinting procedure [19] are shown in Figure 5. Each pattern is very complex, which suggests that these histone fractions may well be heterogeneous. The presence on a fingerprint of 51 peptides from histone to fraction Ia suggests that the fraction is not homogeneous because consideration of the size and amino acid composition of this fraction indicated the presence of 29 trypsin-sensitive bonds. However a detailed analysis of the peptides is required before this question can be answered with certainty because some of the peptides may have arisen from incomplete action of the trypsin at certain centers or from the action of contaminant enzymes in the trypsin preparation.

Separation of the peptides from histone fraction Ia by preparative paper chromatography and electrophoresis was begun, and three different methods were used, in each of which two sheets of Whatman No. 3MM paper were sewed together (end to end) to facilitate the electrophoretic separation. These methods were reasonably satisfactory only for the few peptides that were fairly well isolated on the fingerprints (Fig. 5). In all other cases, particularly in the area where many peptides were found in close proximity to each other, it was impossible to obtain an adequate separation for meaningful amino acid analyses on the individual peptides. Amino acid analyses showed that the peptides so obtained were obviously mixtures (often quite complex), and examination of areas of the paper between peptides always furnished additional mixtures of peptides.

Thus fractionation of the tryptic digest by ion-exchange chromatography was essential, and 26 components were obtained from histone fraction Ia (Fig. 6). Of these, only 15 were homogeneous when examined

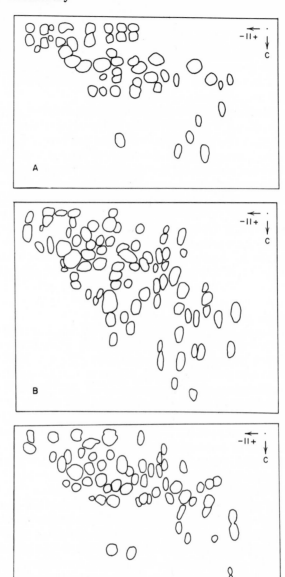

Fig. 5.—Tracings of fingerprints of tryptic digests of histone fractions: A, histone fraction Ia; B, histone fraction IIa; C, histone fraction IV. The histone fractions (1.5-2 mg) were digested with trypsin for 24 hours at 27 C in 0.2 M ammonium bicarbonate, pH 8.7. Chromatographic development was effected with a mixture of butan-2-ol, formic acid, and water (7:1:2) and ionophoresis was done in pyridine acetate buffer solution, pH 3.7.

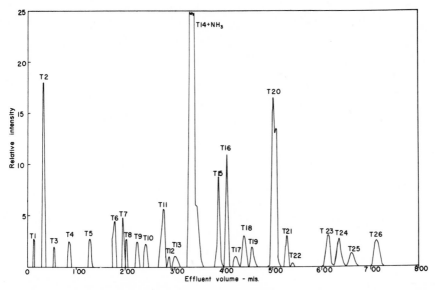

Fig. 6.—Chromatographic fractionation on Dowex 50 ion-exchange resin of the tryptic peptides from histone fraction Ia. The separation was done on an automatic amino acid analyzer with pyridine acetate buffer solutions of increasing concentration [28].

by the fingerprinting method (the first peak, for example, comprised 10 peptides) and the remainder were fractionated further by paper chromatography or ionophoresis, or, where necessary, both. In this manner, 68 peptides have been obtained. Most of these have been analyzed, and sequence studies are proceeding. Some results of particular interest may be mentioned briefly. The various peptides were not obtained in equimolar proportions, and the analyses so far completed give a much larger complement of amino acid residues than would be obtained if histone fraction Ia contained only one major component. A considerable quantity of free lysine and some free arginine was obtained, and several large peptides (8-10 residues) having only one basic amino acid (lysine) have been found. One peptide having 13 residues (1 lysine residue) and 4 nonbasic tetrapeptides have also been found. These results, which clearly support the evidence from the work of Satake, Rasmussen, and Luck [12] on arginine peptides derived from histone, show that basic amino acid residues cannot be distributed along the polypeptide chain in such a manner as to permit the formation of a nucleohistone in which DNA phosphate residues are bound by basic amino acid residues occurring at regular intervals in the polypeptide chain. This fact was also substantiated by the study of Phillips and Simson [20] on tryptic peptides from arginine-rich histone.

The separation and analyses of the tryptic peptides derived from histone fraction Ia provide definite evidence that this histone fraction is heterogeneous, and perhaps markedly so.

Until the quantitative analyses of all the peptides are complete, it is not possible to estimate the minimum number of polypeptides in the histone fraction, and even with these data, the task may be very difficult. If, for example, 300 amino acid residues are contained in the 70 tryptic peptides it may still prove difficult or impossible to differentiate between the existence of either three or four completely different polypeptide chains that would each produce a unique contribution of tryptic peptides, or the presence of a much larger number of polypeptide chains with many long sequences in common with their neighbors but differing in relatively small, occasional sequences. The second alternative permits the possibility that histone fraction Ia comprises a very large number of distinct polypeptides. These two possibilities may perhaps be distinguished by an extension of structural studies of histone fraction Ia. Preliminary observations of the action of trypsin on histone fraction Ia, in which lysine residues were blocked by trifluoracetylation [21], and of the action of chymotrypsin on this histone fraction further illustrate the heterogeneity of the histone fraction. These investigations are being pursued in more detail by P. X. Callahan.

Parallel studies of tryptic peptides derived from other histone fractions, each of which gives an equally, or more complex, fingerprint than fraction Ia are necessary for a proper appreciation of the degree of heterogeneity of these proteins. Fingerprints of histone fractions IIa and IV are included in Figure 5, and the observed numbers of peptides are 80 and 60 for the respective fractions, whereas the number expected from considerations of size and amino acid composition [5, 12] is about 40-45. This information supports other indications (e.g., zone electrophoresis in starch gels) of heterogeneity obtained for histone fractions IIa and IV, but again it must be emphasized that detailed, quantitative analyses of all the peptides are required to verify this conclusion. Experience with histone fraction Ia suggests that the actual number of peptides in the tryptic digests of histone fractions IIa and IV may well prove very large when the peptides are separated by the complementary methods of ion-exchange chromatography, paper chromatography, and ionophoresis.

There is, however, one possibility that may ease the tedious and time-consuming fractionation and analysis of tryptic peptides, at least from the aspect of heterogeneity studies. This approach involves in vivo labeling of histone with a particular amino acid, but for this method to be useful, it is essential to choose an amino acid that occurs in very small quantity in the histone fraction under examination. For example, for histone fractions I, phenylalanine or tyrosine would be selected or for histone fraction IIb, methionine might be more useful. Attention is focused initially on radioactive peptides, thus greatly reducing the number of peptides to be analyzed. For very complex histone fractions, such as fraction III or IV, it should prove possible to exploit the presence of ε-N-methyl lysine. Recently, it has been shown that methionine can be a methyl donor for this amino acid because radioactive ε-N-methyl lysine was obtained from histone extracted from animals previously injected with methyl-labeled methionine [15]. It is not yet known whether lysine residues are methylated before or after incorporation into the polypeptide chain; this question is under investigation, but an unequivocal answer may prove elusive. In Salmonella typhimurium, which appears to be the only other natural source of this amino acid, there is genetic evidence that lysine residues are methylated after incorporation into the polypeptide chain [22]. Thus the search for ϵ-N-methyl lysine-containing peptides in the mixture of peptides resulting from tryptic digestion of an appropriate histone fraction could be greatly reduced by analyzing only radioactive peptides. The number of ϵ-N-methyl lysine-containing peptides may then give a useful indication of heterogeneity of the particular histone fraction under examination. In histone fraction III, the preliminary preparative starch-gel electrophoresis experiments, to which reference has already been made, suggest that several such peptides may be found. There is one reservation to interpreting the presence of several ϵ-N-methyl lysine-containing peptides as an indication of heterogeneity. Should it be proved that lysine residues are methylated after polypeptide synthesis and that the methylation is not essential for the function of the histone, then differing degrees of methylation of a given polypeptide would lead to an apparent heterogeneity which would be a false representation of the native histone.

Analyses of tryptic peptides derived from given histone fractions following in vivo labeling should also prove very valuable in the search for species and tissue specificities of histones.

It is now well established that histones from most, if not all, sources are quite complex, and a continued study of the extent of this heterogeneity is of great importance to our understanding of the nucleoprotein system as a whole. The recognition of this diversity of histone fractions raises an important question concerning their nomenclature. Many, if not all, of us share the view that the "lysine-rich" and "arginine-rich" terminology, which has been and still is in wide usage, is obsolete. The question of replacing this with a more useful system is urgent, and is discussed in the preceding article.

Of the histone fractions so far studied, none is homogeneous, and most may well be quite complex mixtures. The question of how many different histones are to be found in a given preparation cannot be answered, but the number may be very large. It does not appear at all unreasonable that this should be so. As Bloch [23] has stated, it is not possible for DNA to be covered with a continuously varying histone population, but if it is established that the primary function of histones (or of some histones) is that of a genetic regulator, as suggested by Stedman and Stedman [24], then it would not be at all surprising to find a very large number of different histones, each having a different specificity or function. Should these functions include, for example, the control of various ribonucleotide and deoxyribonucleotide polymerase systems, the possibility of which is shown by recent studies [25, 26, 27] then again a large number of different histones would not be unreasonable.

In connection with the control of polymerases by histones, it is probably more significant that some histone fractions do not repress polymerase activity than that others do, for the latter might be expected from the interaction of any polycation with a nucleic acid. Recent progress in various aspects of histone biochemistry has aroused widespread interest in these proteins and brought the study of them to a very interesting phase. The function of at least some histone components may soon be understood, but the heterogeneity of the histones will complicate greatly elucidating the function of other components. Meanwhile, by virtue of their complexity and their association with DNA, histones remain attractive as possible or potential controllers of many biological processes.

Acknowledgments

Others who participated in these studies are Drs. J. M. Luck, P. S. Rasmussen, D. C. Lamb, and P. X. Callahan. The studies were supported by Grant C-484 from the National Institutes of Health, United States Public Health Service.

Comment

It has been found by others also (independently) that the histone fraction A of Crampton, Stein, and Moore [3] is heterogeneous, and at least two components have been resolved by chromatography on carboxymethyl-cellulose. These subfractions are believed to be native nucleoprotein components. Since the number of peptides derived by digestion of histone fraction Ia with trypsin increased with increasing time of digestion, it was suggested that some of these peptides may arise from cleavages by contaminant enzymes. Only when the quantitative analyses of peptides are complete can the data be used for precise discussion of the degree of heterogeneity of the parent histone fraction.

REFERENCES

1.   Phillips, D. M. P., Prog. Biophys. Biophys. Chem., 12, 211, 1962.

2.   Crampton, C. F., Moore, S., and Stein, W. H., J. Biol. Chem., 215, 787, 1955.

3.   Crampton, C. F., Stein, W. H., and Moore, S., J. Biol. Chem., 225, 363, 1957.

4.   Kolthoff, I. M., Anastasi, A., and Tan, B. H., J. Am. Chem. Soc., 81, 2047, 1959.

5. Rasmussen, P. S., Murray, K., and Luck, J. M., Biochemistry, 1, 79, 1962.

6. Butler, J. A. V., Davison, P. F., James, D. W. F., and Shooter, K. V., Biochim. Biophys. Acta, 13, 224, 1954.

7. Neelin, J. M. and Connell, G. E., Biochim. Biophys. Acta, 31, 539, 1959.

8. Johns, E. W., Phillips, D. M. P., Simson, P., and Butler, J. A. V., Biochem. J., 80, 189, 1961.

9. Neelin, J. M., and Butler, G. C., Can. J. Biochem. Physiol., 39, 485, 1961.

10. Murray, K., Anal. Biochem., 3, 415, 1962.

11. Moore, S., Solvay Institute, 11th Chemistry Conference, Nucleoproteins (New York: Interscience Publishers, Inc., 1959), p. 77.

12. Satake, K., Rasmussen, P. S., and Luck, J. M., J. Biol. Chem., 235, 2801, 1960.

13. Ambler, R. C., and Rees, M. W., Nature, 184, 56, 1959.

14. Murray, K., and Luck, J. M., Fed. Proc., 21, 410, 1962.

15. Murray, K., Biochemistry, 3, in press, 1964.

16. Luck, J. M., Rasmussen, P. S., Satake, K., and Tsvetikov, A. N., J. Biol. Chem., 233, 1407, 1958.

17. Phillips, D. M. P., and Johns, E. W., Biochem. J., 72, 538, 1959.

18. Johns, E. W., Phillips, D. M. P., Simson, P., and Butler, J. A. V., Biochem. J., 77, 631, 1960.

19. Ingram, V. M., Nature, 178, 792, 1956.

20. Phillips, D. M. P., and Simson, P., Biochem. J., 82, 236, 1962.

21. Goldberger, R. F., and Anfinsen, C. B., Biochemistry, 1, 401, 1962.

22. Stocker, B. A. D., McDonough, M. W., and Ambler, R. C., Nature, 189, 556, 1961.

23. Bloch, D. P., Proc. Natl. Acad. Sci. U. S. A., 48, 324, 1962.

24. Stedman, E., and Stedman, E., Phil. Trans. Roy. Soc. London, Ser. B, 235, 565, 1951.

25. Huang, R. C., and Bonner, J., Proc. Natl. Acad. Sci. U. S. A., 48, 1216, 1962.

26. Bonner, J., Huang, R. C., and Murray, K., Fed. Proc., 22, 353, 1963.

27. Allfrey, V. G., Littau, V. C., and Mirsky, A. E., Proc. Natl. Acad. Sci. U. S. A., 49, 414, 1963.

28. Guidotti, G., Hill, R. J., and Konigsberg, W., J. Biol. Chem., 237, 2184, 1962.

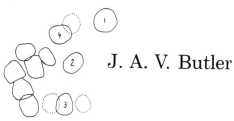

J. A. V. Butler

FRACTIONATION AND CHARACTERISTICS OF HISTONES

Histones are basic proteins associated with DNA in the somatic cells of animal and plant tissues. It has long been suspected that they are concerned with the mechanism of replication of DNA or with the expression of its genic function as suggested originally by Stedman and Stedman [1] . To obtain further knowledge of this, it is necessary to know the number of distinct kinds of histone in any one tissue, their distinguishing characteristics, and the differences between different tissues and different species. The first requisite, then, is satisfactory methods of separating naturally occurring mixtures of histones into their components. Whether the components so obtained are homogeneous chemical individuals or still contain a variety of similar molecules is open to discussion. But this kind of information is necessary as a preliminary to the solution of other problems, such as the way in which the different histones are distributed in the chromatin, e.g., is the same complement of histones present in all the chromosomes, and are different segments of DNA with different functions or compositions combined with different histones? The present stage of cell and chromosome fractionation is probably too elementary to provide a solution of these questions. I propose to outline information obtained in our laboratories by essentially chemical methods that has a bearing on them.

The histones are usually extracted in a more or less contaminated state from cell nuclei or from the isolated chromotin-like material (deoxyribonucleoprotein) by acids. Calf thymus tissue, which contains a relatively small amount of cytoplasm, has long been a favorite source because it gives histone practically uncontaminated with other proteins. With other tissues, unless great care is taken, it is difficult to avoid contamination of the extracted histone with other acidic proteins that are also soluble in dilute acids. In these cases, the proportion of diacidic amino acids in the whole of the protein extracted by acids is often greater than in the whole histone of calf thymus. This contamination can be reduced by careful washing of the nuclei to remove adherent acidic proteins, and a whole histone can then be obtained with a composition approaching that of calf thymus histones.

TABLE 1

Total composition of histones prepared in different ways*

Tissue	Crocker Tumor		Mammary Tumor			Rat Liver		Calf Thymus
Method of isolating nuclei[†]	1	2	1	2	4	2	3	
Dibasic amino acids, %	24.2	24.7	23.3	24.9	24.7	24.4	25.1	26.8
Diacidic amino acids, %	17.8	16.3	17.9	15.6	14.9	15.7	14.6	14.2

*From Laurence, Simson, and Butler [2].
†1, NaCl + 0.5 mM HCl; 2, sucrose + 2mM $CaCl_2$; 3, sucrose + EDTA;
4, NaCl + 0.01 M sodium citrate.

Table 1 gives some analyses of histones extracted from nuclei from different sources and prepared in different ways.

The complete removal of acidic proteins after separation of the histone is difficult because they tend to form complexes which are not easily broken up. However, part of the acidic proteins present can be removed by adding the histone to a slightly alkaline carboxymethylcellulose column, which retains the histones but not the free acidic proteins [3].

It is obvious that the question of the specificity of histones from different sources cannot easily be separated from the question of their possible contamination with other proteins. However, so far as they have been investigated in our laboratories [2, 4], different tissues give histones which are remarkably similar in over-all composition and in their starch-gel patterns. The differences noted could easily be due to residual contamination. At the same time, it has not been definitely demonstrated that there are no real minor differences. It should be noted that a constant over-all composition of histones from different sources implies that the various components are present in similar proportions. However, more accurate analyses than have yet been made would be necessary for a critical evaluation of this.

A wide variety of methods has been used in attempts to fractionate the whole histone into components. In our laboratories, a method of elution from carboxymethylcellulose columns [5, 6] gave three main fractions, which we designated F1 (lysine rich, lys:arg, >1.4); F2 (moderately lysine rich, lys:arg, 1.0-1.4); F3 (arginine rich, lys:arg, <1). Each of these fractions was complex on starch-gel electrophoresis, and methods have been found for the further fractionation of F1 and F2. Recent work on the fractionation of F1 is described by E. W. Johns in another article in this book.

It has also been possible to obtain the main fractions in quantity by extraction fractionation processes starting from the nucleoprotein and, in some cases, from the whole tissue. Figure 1, which is a modification of a process previously described [6] , gives the main fractions from a single sample of the tissue. It is not certain to what extent these processes can be used for the fractionation of tissues other than calf thymus. The chromatographic fractionation on carboxymethylcellulose is certainly impeded by acidic impurity.

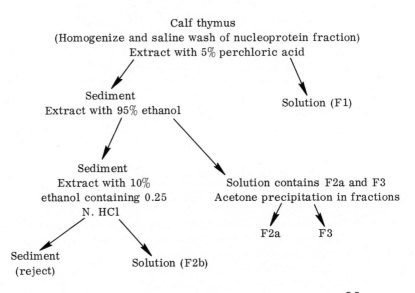

Fig. 1.—Fractionation of calf thymus histones. (Modified from [6].)

Table 2 shows the analyses of the principal fractions from calf thymus so far obtained in our laboratories (except the fractions of F1 to be discussed by E. W. Johns). Table 3 summarizes their distinctive characteristics. F2a is known to be composite, containing at least two fractions which have been partially separated by acetone fractionation (E.W.Johns) and by chromatography (D.M.P.Phillips). They differ in glycine and proline contents. F2b also contains two bands in the electrophoretic gel pattern. The number of electrophoretic bands obtained with F3 depends on the conditions. In strong urea, four bands have been seen; but after dialysis in aqueous solution, aggregation occurs and only two slower bands are normally found. This can be reversed in 4 M urea [7] .

The principal N-terminal groups originally found by Phillips [8] were proline and alanine; proline was associated mainly with F2 and alanine with F3. A more recent assessment of the position, based on a table by Phillips [9] , is given in Tables 4 and 5.

TABLE 2

Composition of main histone fractions from calf thymus

	F1	F2a	F2b	F3
Aspartic } A	2.7	6.4	6.1	4.2
Glutamic } A	7.0	9.0	8.2	12.0
Glycine	5.6	11.9	6.7	6.1
Alanine	22.9	10.3	10.9	13.7
Valine	4.3	6.5	6.7	5.7
Leucine	6.4	14.9	10.7	13.6
Phenylalanine	1.3	1.7	2.1	2.4
Tyrosine	–	3.0	3.2	1.3
Serine	5.5	3.2	8.6	4.2
Threonine	4.2	5.7	6.6	6.9
Proline	7.6	3.2	4.6	4.7
Histidine } B	0.7	1.9	2.5	2.2
Lysine } B	29.7	11.4	14.8	9.0
Arginine } B	2.1	10.9	8.2	14.0
B:A	3.4	1.6	1.8	1.6
Lys:arg	10.4	1.05	1.8	0.63
Principal N-terminal groups (% of all)				
Alanine	35	54	12	95
Proline	50	12	82	3
Glycine	6	11	1	0.5
Serine	3	2	2	–
Threonine	1	1	–	0.5
Lysine	2	11	2	0.5
All others	3	9	1	0.5
Wt. containing 1 mole of N-terminal amino acid	30,000	112,000	15,000	18,000

TABLE 3

Distinctive characteristics of histone fractions

	Lys:Arg	N-Terminal Groups	Other Distinctive Features
F3	0.65	alanine	easily aggregates
F2a	1.05	mainly acetyl	glycine high
F2b	1.8	mainly proline	serine high
F1 (a1)*	23	mainly acetyl	alanine high
F1 (a2)*	14	partly acetyl; glycine	alanine high
F1 (b)*	104	threonine, alanine and serine	alanine and proline high

*Further information about F1 is given by E. W. Johns in another article in this book.

TABLE 4

N-terminal amino acids of histones*

Fraction	Wt. of Histone Containing 1 Mole of All Amino Acids	Chief N-Terminal Amino Acids
F1 (CMC method)	37,000-61,000	proline,alanine,lysine
F1 (HClO$_4$ method)	49,000-68,000	glycine,proline,serine
F2a (acid ethanol)	63,000-149,000	alanine,glycine,proline,lysine
F2b	15,000-17,000	proline,77-82%
F3	16,000-19,000	alanine,95-99%

*From Phillips [10].

TABLE 5

Acetyl Groups in Histones*

Fraction	Wt. of Histone Containing 1 Mole of Acetyl Groups	Wt. of Histone Containing 1 Mole of Acetyl + N-Terminal Amino Acid Groups
F1	15,000-18,000	12,000-14,000
F2a	10,000-14,000	9,000-12,500
F2b	32,000-38,000	10,000-11,000
F3	21,000-28,000	10,000

*From Phillips [10].

Both F1 and F2a yield less terminal amino acid than that correspond-ing to the expected actual molecular weight, and Phillips [10] has found acetyl groups in these fractions in amounts sufficient to account for the deficiency of N-terminal amino acids. Some acetyl groups are also found in the other fractions, but in such cases it is not certain if they are at-tached to the N-terminal amino acids. Table 4 gives a summary of the findings.

As the actual molecular weights of the various fractions are unknown, it is not possible to assess exactly what proportion of the acetyl groups are attached to N-terminal amino acids, but it may be significant that, taking all the acetyl found into account, the weights of histone containing 1 mole of acetyl + N-terminal amino acid are all in the range of 10,000-15,000.

The histone of calf thymus thus consists of a group of well-defined and characteristically different basic proteins. The range of variability with-in each fraction has not been established. In some fractions the presence of significant amounts of N-terminal groups other than the principal ones might suggest the presence of significant quantities of proteins other than the principal proteins in these fractions. However, it must be remembered that quite small amounts of proteolysis will produce significant amounts of additional end groups and also that the extra end groups may belong to quite short peptide chains and thus represent a much smaller fraction of the total weight of histone than the fraction of end groups.

Histone fractions with characteristics similar to those from calf thymus have been isolated from other mammalian tissues [4]. The ques-tion of contamination is again very difficult, since acidic proteins extracted from many tissues by dilute acid are difficult to remove and also interfere with the fractionation procedures. Laurence, Simson, and Butler [2] stud-ied the best conditions for histone preparation and found that the proportion of acidic proteins present could be reduced by careful preparation of clean nuclei before extraction. Table 6 shows the composition of fractions prepared from two tumors. While the correspondence with the calf thymus

TABLE 6

Composition of some histone fractions

Fraction	Method	Source	Diacidics	Alanine	Arginine	Lysine
F1	CMC chromo-tography	Thymus	8.0	23.6	2.9	25.9
		Mammary tumor	9.1	22.2	2.5	24.0
F2a	EtOH-HCl	Thymus	15.4	10.3	10.9	11.4
		Crocker tumor	16.8	9.6	9.5	11.0
F3	EtOH-HCl	Thymus	16.2	13.7	14.0	9.0
		Crocker tumor	15.2	12.4	10.8	10.8

fractions is reasonably good, the arginine content of F3 from Crocker tumor is abnormally low.

The total amount of histone in the nucleoprotein and the amount of DNA has been compared in a few cases. For this comparison to have any value, it is necessary to be sure that the nucleoprotein is free from nonhistone proteins. This is difficult to achieve in tissues other than calf thymus and similar tissues. However, a correction can be made on the assumption that the excess of acidic proteins present in the nucleo-protein is due to contaminants, of which an average composition is known. On this basis, it was found [2] that the ratio of arg + lys to DNA phosphate is approximately the same in the Crocker tumor as in calf thymus. If these and other measurements suggested that there is not quite enough histone in tissues for stoichiometrical combination of all the basic groups of the histone with the phosphates of the DNA, then some part of DNA must be regarded as uncovered by histone.

The relative amounts of the different histone fractions have not been determined with any precision. Preparative yields are unreliable, as some losses are usually unavoidable. The intensity of staining of the protein in bands obtained by starch-gel electrophoresis cannot be regarded as an accurate measure of the amounts. Records of these bands by meas-urement of the light reflected can be made, but the bands show signs of "trailing" considerably and the trail behind one band overlaps the front of the band behind.

An extensive survey of histones from a wide variety of species has still to be carried out. The protein extracted from wheat germ by diges-tion with dilute acids has, however, been examined [11]. This is very different in composition and in starch-gel electrophoretic pattern from histone from any mammalian source.

Fractions with lys:arg = 3.1 and 1.3 were obtained, but no arginine-rich fraction; moreover, the N-terminal group of both of these fractions was alanine, which in the mammalian cells is the N-terminal of the argi-nine-rich histone. It must be noted that the extract from whole wheat germ may contain proteins derived from other constituents besides the chromosomes, e.g., ribosomes (see below); but it seems certain that normal constituents of histones are missing. An examination has also been made of the bacterium B. megaterium, in which it is possible [12] to isolate a "nuclear fraction" containing DNA and a relatively small pro-portion of the DNA in the cell. Because extraction of this with acid failed to give any basic protein, it must be assumed that no histone was present.

We must now consider whether similar proteins exist in other cell constituents, e.g., associated with the RNA in ribosomes or in other cell particles. Basic proteins have in fact been obtained by extraction of ribosomes with dilute acids. Several analyses of the whole protein of ribosomes showed it to be somewhat basic in character [13]. Butler, Cohn, and Simson [14] obtained a protein that approached the property of histone in basic character by extracting lubrol-treated microsomes of rat liver with acids. Further observations were made by Cohn et al [15]. Table 7 gives partial analyses of some of their preparations. It can be

TABLE 7

Basic and acidic amino acids (as % of all) in HCl extracts of
lubrol or deoxycholate-treated ribosomes*

	Deoxycholate-Treated Microsomes from Rat Liver	Lubrol-Treated Microsomes from Rat Liver	Rabbit Reticulocyte Ribosomes
Arginine	9.5	8.3	8.8
Histidine	1.9	2.3	2.1
Lysine	14.4	13.9	13.3
Total basic (B)	25.8	24.5	24.2
Aspartic	8.5	8.6	-
Glutamine	10.3	9.8	-
Total acidic (A)	18.8	18.4	19.1
B:A	1.37	1.33	1.26

*From Cohn and Simson [15].

seen that the total percentage of basic amino acids is about the same
as in histones, but the percentage of acidics is appreciably higher. A
similar material has been extracted from the ribosomes of rabbit reticulocytes, which contain no nucleus, and therefore nuclear contamination
is excluded. These proteins give a complex starch-gel electrophoretic
pattern; but attempts to fractionate them to obtain a fraction with a lower
content of diacidic amino acids, and therefore resembling histone more
closely, have not been successful. Experiments on the relative degree
of labeling with a radioactive amino acid of the histone in the nucleus and
the basic protein of the ribosomes of rat liver [16] have not indicated
any precursor-product relationship between the two. Both are labeled
approximately linearly from the start, but the rate of labeling of the ribosomal protein is markedly lower. It must be concluded that the two types
of protein have independent origins.

To sum up, the histones of mammalian cells are a group of proteins
each of which possesses distinctive and characteristic features. So far as
has been investigated, the same or a very similar group occurs in the
cells of different tissues and species; however, this probably does not
apply to plant tissues and, so far as has been investigated, the DNA of
bacteria is not associated at all with this type of compound. Proteins
of a somewhat similar nature have been found in cytoplasmic ribosomes,
but no metabolic connection has been discovered between them and the
nuclear histones. The existence of characteristically different components

of the histone complex suggests that they have distinct functions. There does not seem, so far as is known, to be any correlation between the number and amount of distinct histones and the number of chromosomes, which would be the case if each chromosome were labeled with a distinctive histone. It is more probable that the different histones combine with and distinguish different parts of a chromosome; they might, for example, be used to distinguish different types of genes; e.g., those having regulative or operative functions; and they may have distinct functions in the mitotic process. The solution of these problems lies in the future. However, it may be noted that some evidence exists that the composition of the DNA correlates to some extent with the composition of the histone. By extracting denatured nucleoprotein for different times or with increasing concentrations of sodium chloride, a partial fractionation of both DNA and histone occurs [17] . The solution contains DNA with an abnormally high content of adenine and also lysine-rich histones. It does not follow with certainty that the extracted DNA and histone were associated with each other, but this is the simplest conclusion and would indicate that portions of the DNA that are rich in adenine are associated with a particular histone fraction.

REFERENCES

1. Stedman, E., and Stedman, E., Phil. Trans. Roy. Soc. London, Ser. B, 235, 565, 1951.

2. Laurence, D. J., Simson, P., and Butler, J. A. V., Biochem. J., 87, 200, 1963.

3. Johns, W. E., Unpublished observation.

4. Hnilica, L., Johns, E. W., and Butler, J. A. V., Biochem. J., 82, 123, 1962.

5. Phillips, D. M. P., and Johns, E. W., Biochem. J., 72, 538, 1959.

6. Johns, E. W., Phillips, D. M. P., Simson, P., and Butler, J. A. V., Biochem. J., 77, 631, 1960.

7. Johns, E. W., Unpublished observation.

8. Phillips, D. M. P., Biochem. J., 68, 35, 1958.

9. Phillips, D. M. P., Progress in Biophysics and Biophysical Chemistry, 12, 211, 1962.

10. Phillips, D. M. P., Biochem. J., 87, 258, 1963.

11. Johns, W. E., and Butler, J. A. V., Biochem. J., 84, 436, 1962.

12. Butler, J. A. V., and Godson, G. N., Biochem. J., 88, 176, 1963.

13. Crampton, C. F., and Petermann, M. L., J. Biol. Chem., 234, 2642, 1959.

14. Butler, J. A. V., Cohn, P., and Simson, P., Biochin. Biophys. Acta, 38, 366, 1960.

15. Cohn, P., and Simson, P., Biochem. J., 88, 206, 1963.

16. Cohn, P., Unpublished data.

17. Lucy, J. A., and Butler, J. A. V., Bull. Soc. Chim. Belgium, 65, 133, 1956.

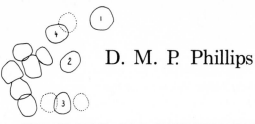

D. M. P. Phillips

STUDIES ON PEPTIDES FROM CALF THYMUS HISTONE

The histones of the nucleus are thought to be attached by salt links to the DNA of the chromosomes. In 2 M NaCl, for instance, histone and DNA separate. Close association is also suggested by the finding of equivalence between the number of phosphate groups on DNA and the number of basic groups in the histones [1, 2]. The phosphate group spacing along the nucleotide chains of DNA can be assumed to be very regular. What then is the spacing of the basic groups of the histones attached to them?

This question has been partly answered by the study of peptides from tryptic digests of four major fractions of calf thymus histones—fractions produced by acid-ethanol and perchloric acid procedures [3, 4] —that account for all the histones of calf thymus. Trypsin has a narrow specificity of proteinase activity, freeing the carboxyl groups of lysyl and arginyl residues in the peptide chain, though such cleavage is inhibited where the next residue is prolyl, aspartyl, or glutamyl. Thus one result of the analysis of tryptic digestion products is to give the spacing between the basic residues in the original protein chain. For example, the demonstration of an ala-arg sequence (where it is not an N-terminal sequence) would imply that the sequence lys-ala-arg or arg-ala-arg occurs in the parent protein, with a spacing of one basic acid between the two basic residues.

On digestion with trypsin, all the histone fractions, except that known as the lysine-rich (lys:arg [molar] = 4-15:1), give a precipitate, a "core," that amounts to 10-27% of the material taken. Some properties of these cores are shown in Table 1. It can be seen that these precipitates are far less basic than the parent histone, and the average spacing between basic residues in them as calculated from the basic amino acid content, is about 6 other residues, compared with a value of 3 for the parent histones before degradation. These precipitates are heterogeneous, as shown by their multiple N-terminal amino acids—chiefly valine, leucine, and glycine in fraction F2a, and valine, alanine, and tyrosine in fraction F3. In both of these cores, one N-terminal sequence is valyl-glycyl. There is insufficient information yet to say where in the parent histones

TABLE 1

Composition of the histone cores*

Fraction:	F2b	F2a	F3
Lys-arg molar ratio	1.7	1	0.8
Aspartic acid + glutamic acid (A)	22	17.9	20.9 moles %
Arginine + histidine + lysine (B)	15.3	13.8	13.4 moles %
B:A	0.7	0.8	0.6
B:A; parent histones	1.8	1.6	1.6
Average basic amino acid spacing	5.5	6	6.5 residues
Average original spacing	3	3	3
Core as proportion of the parent histone	10	27	27 %

*Fraction F1 (lys:arg = 4-15:1) gave no tryptic core.

these cores lie, but in view of the N-terminal amino acids, they do not include, for the most part, the N-terminal of the parent proteins.

Unlike most of the intact histones, the cores produced in the usual 17-hour digestion are soluble at pH 10-12 and insoluble at other pH values. However, the precipitates produced in the first hour or so of digestion (they first appear after a few minutes) are soluble in acid, so that they are apparently slowly digested further in the suspension.

The smaller, soluble peptides from both the arginine-rich fraction F3 (lys:arg = 0.8; alanine N-terminus) and from the fraction F2a (lys:arg = 1; probably acetyl N-terminus) have been examined by electrophoresis and chromatography. Table 2 shows the products identified in fraction F3 [5], from which it can be deduced that the spacing between basic amino acids varies from 0 (juxtaposition) to 4 nonbasic residues, or including the core, from 0 to 7 nonbasic residues. The first 7 products listed are also found in fraction F2a. In F2a, the peptides provisionally identified are shown in Table 3. In this case the spacings between basic amino acids vary from 0 to 8 nonbasic residues.

The lysine-rich histone fraction (lys:arg = 4-15:1) does not give an insoluble core with trypsin. On the other hand, a short acid degradation produced an ultrabasic fragment, which amounted to at least 12% of the protein and had an average of only 1.7 nonbasic residues between each lysyl residue. The average gap for the parent histone is near the usual

TABLE 2

Peptides from histone fraction F3 (lys:arg = 0.8; alanine N-terminus)

	Basic Amino Acid Spacing †
Arg (free)*	0
Lys (free)*	0
Lys-arg*	0,0
Lys-(pro,his)-arg*	0,0,1
Asp-lys*	1
Ala-lys*	1
Ala-arg*	1
Leu-arg	1
Gly-(arg,glu$_2$)-arg	1,2
Gly-(ser,gly,thr)-lys	4

*These peptides were also found in tryptic digests of fraction F2a.
†See the text.

3 nonbasic residues. The pattern of the tryptic peptides from the lysine-rich histone shows that there are several peptides bearing more than 1 lysyl residue, and one third of the peptide N-terminal groups are lysine. This implies that in 9,800 weight (100 residues) there are not less than 7 lysyl-lysyl sequences, equivalent to about 50% of all the lysine residues. This histone fraction does not appear to have much in common with fractions F2a and F3.

In all the calf thymus histones there is thus a marked irregularity in the spacing of the basic amino acid residues. The gaps between them vary from 0 to 6 or 8 other residues, and in this respect the histones do not differ from other proteins such as hemoglobin, lysozyme, myoglobin, ribonuclease, or TMV-protein, which show gaps of 0-22 other residues between the basic amino acids. Since the gel electrophoretic and other analytical studies of the histones from several other sources have shown a close similarity to those obtained from calf thymus [6], it is reasonable to conclude that this irregularity of structure is general among the histones. It is probable that no perfectly pure histone fraction is available. Those used here were certainly mixtures of histones, but since an appreciable proportion of the whole was examined, the over-all conclusion is valid.

TABLE 3

Peptides from histone fraction F2a (lys:arg = 1; acetyl N-terminus)
(other than those in Table 2)*

	Basic Amino Acid Spacing
Gly-lys	1
Gly-gly-lys	2
Glu-gly-lys	2
Gly-(gly,leu)-lys	3
Aspg-(glum,glu)-lys	3
Aspg-(gly,asp)-lys	3
(Gly,aspg or glum,ala)-lys	3
Glu-(gly$_3$ala,ser,thr,val/leu)-lys	8
His-arg	0,0
Arg-arg	0,0
Val-his-arg	1,0
Ser-arg	1
Thr-arg	1
Val-leu-arg	2
Ala-leu-arg	2
Gly-(asp/glu,gly,val,leu,phe,pro)-arg	7

*Aspg = asparaginyl; Glum = glutaminyl; Val/Leu = valine or
leucine; Asp/Glu = aspartic or glutamic acids.

Thus a salt-linkage structure for nucleohistone would be irregular,
with loops of various lengths of nonbasic amino acids, especially in the
cores, bulging out from adjacent phosphate groups. Of especial interest
are the juxtaposed basic amino acids. These studies—covering fraction
F1, about two thirds of fraction F2a and two fifths of F3—show some 18 in-
stances in which juxtaposition must occur, and the studies of Satake,
Rasmussen, and Luck [7] on the arginine peptides from six calf thymus
histone fractions showed the presence of considerable numbers of sequences arg-arg and arg-lys as well as some arg-arg-arg.

Feughelman et al. [8] have reported that it is likely that protamine
fits across the narrow groove of the DNA dyad helix by salt linkage of

the guanidino groups with the phosphate groups. Polyarginine, which approximates protamine, also fits this situation. Juxtaposed arginine residues could bridge the narrow, but not the wide, groove of DNA, and so it is likely that the distances between the side-chain positive groups of the sequences his-arg, lys-lys, and perhaps lys-arg (which occur in the histones) would be too short to bridge even the narrow groove.

The histones may lie in the grooves of the DNA and then, probably, having molecular weights in the range 7,000-18,000, occupy only one or two turns of the dyad helix, depending on the fraction considered. They might also lie irregularly on the surface of the DNA. Either way, they cover only an area of polynucleotide that will ultimately code for 3-7 amino acids (or 6-14, if both strands of the DNA are operative). This assumes a coding ratio of 3, which is the lowest plausible one. Moreover, although there are apparently a minimum of 20 types of histone in a cell, as shown, for example, by starch-gel electrophoretic analysis (at present the most sensitive indicator of heterogeneity [9]), it is clear that a given type of histone must be associated with many different short polynucleotide sequences in the DNA (see also Bloch [10]).

These considerations might suggest that the association of histone and DNA is random and not specific, though the recombination experiments of Crampton [11] suggested a specific attachment, since the product did not dissociate again in the same way as "native" deoxynucleohistone. The results of the partial dissociation of nucleohistone in salt [12-14] also suggested a specific attachment, with the lysine-rich histone showing a preference for the DNA richer in cytosine and guanine.

These somewhat divergent views of the structure of nucleohistone are reconcilable if, for example, the histone and the DNA are synthesized together. There would be no other choice open to a newly synthesized histone molecule but to combine with the particular nucleotide sequence there and then provided.

REFERENCES

1. Vendrely, R., Knobloch-Mazen, A., and Vendrely, C.,The Cell Nucleus (Butterworth Scientific Publications: London, 1960).

2. Vendrely, R., Knobloch-Mazen, A., and Vendrely, C.,Biochem. Pharmacol., 4, 19, 1960.

3. Johns, E. W., Phillips, D. M. P., Simson, P., and Butler, J. A. V., Biochem. J., 77, 631, 1960.

4. Johns, E. W., and Butler, J. A. V., Biochem. J., 82, 15, 1962.

5. Phillips, D. M. P., and Simson, P., Biochem. J., 82, 236, 1962.

6. Hnilica, L., Johns, E. W., and Butler, J. A. V., Biochem. J., 82, 123, 1962.

7. Satake, K., Rasmussen, P. S., and Luck, J. M., J. Biol. Chem., 235, 2801, 1960.

8. Feughelman, M., Langridge, R., Seeds, W. E., Stokes, A. R., Wilson, H. R., Hooper, C. W., Wilkins, M. F. H., Barclay, R. K., and Hamilton, L. D., Nature, 175, 834, 1955.

9. Neelin, J. M., and Neelin, E. M., Can. J. Biochem. Physiol., 38, 355, 1960.

10. Bloch, D. P., Proc. Natl. Acad. Sci. U. S. A., 48, 324, 1962.

11. Crampton, C. F., J. Biol. Chem., 227, 495, 1957.

12. Crampton, C. F., Lipshitz, R., and Chargaff, E., J. Biol. Chem., 206, 499; 211, 125, 1954.

13. Lucy, J. A., and Butler, J. A. V., Biochim. Biophys. Acta, 16, 431, 1955.

14. Lucy, J. A., and Butler, J. A. V., Bull. Soc. Chim. Belges., 65, 133, 1956.

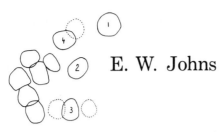

E. W. Johns

STUDIES ON LYSINE-RICH HISTONES

Previous work [1] has shown that lysine-rich histones can be prepared by extracting calf thymus nucleoprotein with 5% (0.75 N) perchloric acid. Starting with 100 g of calf thymus, the yield is about 450 mg, which is 20% of all the histones of calf thymus. The preparation is a good one as judged by amino acid analysis (Table 1) and starch-gel electrophoresis at pH 2. There are, however, some differences between this material and the lysine-rich histone prepared by chromatographic methods. Its content of acidic amino acids is high, and histidine is present. Also, 23% of the N-terminal amino acids is glycine, a minor constituent of the column preparation. The reason for these differences seems to be that the perchloric acid extracts some acidic protein with a glycine N-terminal group that contaminates the lysine-rich histone.

The preparation was therefore fractionated on carboxymethylcellulose at pH 9, with NaCl gradient from 0 to 1.0 M. Figure 1 shows the separation achieved. Peaks 1 and 2 account for 15% of the applied histone, and peak 3, which is obviously still complex, accounts for 85%. Amino acid analyses were carried out on these fractions, and the results are shown in Table 1. The analysis of peak 3 now compares well with the analysis of fraction A of Crampton, Stein, and Moore [2]. The purified fraction contains 6.2% of acidic amino acids and no histidine. Peaks 1 and 2, however, contain over 30% aspartic and glutamic acids and 24-25% basic amino acids. These two fractions are basic and, on electrophoresis at pH 9, migrate toward the cathode. Presumably, many of the acidic amino acids are present as the amides. Another characteristic of these histones is their low threonine content, about half that found in all other histone fractions. It seems unlikely that these are lysine-rich histones contaminated with an acidic protein, because it would require at least a 50% contamination with a protein containing 56% acidic amino acids and 22% basic amino acids to produce these results.

As these histones are of interest, and as there was not sufficient material from the column fractionation to carry out N-terminal amino acid analyses, we have investigated other methods for preparing them. The whole lysine-rich group can be fractionated by dissolving it in 0.01 N

TABLE 1

Amino acid analysis of lysine-rich histones

Amino Acid (moles %)	PCA Extraction	Fraction A, Crampton Stein and Moore [2]	Column Fractions		
			1	2	3
Aspartic	8.9	2.0	11.4	30.9	6.2
Glutamic		3.2	20.1		
Glycine	7.1	6.6	5.6	6.5	7.2
Alanine	22.3	26.0	10.1	8.3	24.3
Valine	4.9	4.8	2.4	2.5	5.4
Leucines	5.6	5.0	5.6	4.2	6.0
Serine	6.3	6.4	5.6	7.6	5.6
Threonine	5.2	5.7	2.9	2.3	5.6
Phenylalanine	1.0	0.5	3.2	3.5	0.9
Tyrosine	0.8	0.5	2.4	3.0	0.9
Proline	9.4	9.0	5.8	7.2	9.2
Histidine	0.3	–	1.3	0.9	–
Lysine	26.3	28.3	19.4	19.0	26.8
Arginine	2.1	1.7	4.2	4.2	1.8

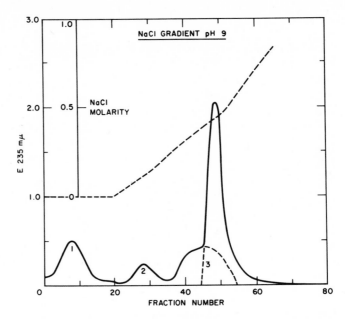

Fig. 1.—Fractionation of lysine-rich histones on carboxymethylcellulose at pH 9.

HCl containing 5% guanidinium chloride and precipitating with acetone. Starting with 650 mg of protein in 200 ml of solution, fractions were obtained at 500 ml, 650 ml, and 1,500 ml of acetone and were designated A, B, and C respectively. Total and N-terminal amino acid analyses are given in Table 2.

A and B are fractions with only 6% acidic amino acids and they amount to about 80% of the whole lysine-rich group together, thus corresponding to the complex peak 3 from the carboxymethylcellulose column. The low yield of N-terminal amino acids is probably due to the acetyl groups that Phillips [3] has demonstrated in the lysine-rich group, amounting to 1 mole per 15,000 g of protein or 66 μmoles per g.

Fraction C, with 20% acidic amino acids, presumably contains the column fractions 1 and 2. It has a much higher yield of N-terminal amino acids, 65% of which are glycine.

Fractions A and B are similar, but differ in the way in which they precipitate with trichloroacetic acid. Fraction A comes down at 16.5% (1.0 M) and fraction B at 13.5% (0.85 M). In this respect, they resemble the two main fractions described by Rasmussen, Murray, and Luck [4]. They do not, however, contain histidine. Both are still complex and give two bands each on starch gel. Attempts have been made to fractionate them further on carboxymethylcellulose and cellulose citrate columns at pH 2, but at these low pH values, about 30% of the applied protein sticks to the column and is very difficult to remove. Similar results have been

TABLE 2

Lysine-rich histones prepared by acetone precipitation

Amino Acid (moles %)	A	B	C
Aspartic			
Glutamic	6.0	6.1	20.0
Glycine	6.7	7.3	7.4
Alanine	26.3	25.5	15.4
Valine	5.4		4.5
Leucine	5.3	10.6	5.6
Serine	5.8	5.6	6.9
Threonine	6.1	6.1	4.0
Phenylalanine	0.5	0.8	1.5
Tyrosine	0.7	0.9	2.0
Proline	9.2	9.4	7.2
Histidine	–	–	0.9
Lysine	26.7	26.1	20.9
Arginine	1.3	1.7	3.8
Main N-terminal group	acetyl	acetyl	glycine (65%)
Wt. (g/mole of N-terminal amino acids)	500,000	500,000	28,000

obtained by Rasmussen, Murray, and Luck [4], using columns of IRC 50, and it seems likely that at these low pH values some form of aggregation is taking place. This was originally suggested by Cruft [5] to explain the fact that the lysine-rich histones are the first to be eluted from Sephadex G-75 with 0.02 N HCl.

Fraction C has only 20% acidic amino acids, compared with 30% for the column fraction 1 and 2. It was therefore applied to a carboxymethyl-cellulose column at pH 9 and eluted with the solvent previously used to elute peak 2. The protein obtained was identical to the column fractions, having 32% acidic amino acids, 24% basic amino acids, and only 2% threonine. On starch gel it gives just one band, and the main N-terminal amino acid is glycine.

TABLE 3

Amino Acid (moles %)	Fractions produced by the acid degradation of lysine-rich histones A and B (see Table 2) and precipitated with TCA				Cruft, Hindley, Mauritzen and Stedman [6] α1
	10%	15%	20%	30%	
Aspartic	7.1	4.8	1.8	1.5	0.3
Glutamic	7.8	6.6	4.3	3.2	0.4
Glycine	7.8	6.6	4.3	3.2	3.7
Alanine	24.5	26.5	30.0	30.9	32.3
Valine	5.8	4.9	4.3	2.9	3.1
Leucines	7.4	3.4		0.5	0.6
Serine	6.6	5.4	3.6	3.6	2.8
Threonine	5.6	6.5	4.8	4.4	4.3
Phenylalanine	0.8	-	0.4	-	-
Tyrosine	0.8	0.3	0.8	0.3	-
Proline	7.3	10.0	12.8	14.6	14.1
Histidine	-	-	-	-	-
Lysine	24.3	30.9	36.9	37.7	38.5
Arginine	1.9	0.7	0.3	0.3	-

Mt. Wt. of TCA fractions based on N-terminal amino acid analyses 3,000-6,000.

It is possible that this histone fraction has some special function in the nucleus, associated as it is with a high content of acidic amino acids. Some preliminary experiments in which calf thymus nucleoprotein is successively extracted with solutions of increasing salt concentration have indicated that this is the first histone to be removed, and therefore it is presumed to be only weakly attached to the DNA.

Another lysine-rich fraction of unusual composition reported to be present in calf thymus histones is the $\alpha 1$ fraction described by Cruft et al. [6]. This protein contains over 80% lysine, alanine, and proline. We have found that a protein of similar composition can be obtained from the supernatant remaining after the precipitation of the other lysine-rich histones with 15% trichloroacetic acid; it can be isolated by increasing the concentration to 20%. However, the yield of this protein is small and extremely variable, and it might be a degradation product. A mixture of fractions A and B was therefore deliberately degraded with 3 N HCl at 100 C for 30 seconds. Fractions A and B were chosen because they have acetyl N-terminal groups, and any degradation is easily followed by the increase in yield of N-terminal amino acids. The partially degraded lysine-rich histone was then separated into four fractions by precipitation with trichloroacetic acid. The analytical results are shown in Table 3, together with the analysis of $\alpha 1$ fraction for comparison.

Although this fraction, with nearly 40% lysine, is a product of acid degradation, it is of interest because it accounts for at least 12% of the original lysine-rich histone, and therefore indicates that there must be an irregular arrangement of basic amino acids in the original sequence because many lysine residues are either next to each other or separated only by one nonbasic residue.

Comment

The analyses of wheat germ histone by Butler confirm the earlier analyses of Stedman in suggesting that the wheat germ histone is less rich than thymus in components containing a large proportion of arginine. Similar observations have been made by Murray on the histone of pea embryo chromatin. Birnstiel and Flamm find that chromatin of pea embryos and of tissue-cultured tobacco cells consists largely of lysine-rich histone. The available data, such as they are, suggest that plant histones may contain a higher proportion of components rich in lysine and poor in arginine than does thymus histone. This suggestion is supported also by the observation that native nucleohistone from plant sources generally has a higher melting point than thymus histone.

The preparation of histone from nuclei is complicated by the presence in the nucleolus of basic proteins of unknown function. These proteins, as studied in the starfish nucleolus by Vincent and in the pea nucleolus by Birnstiel, are poorer in lysine and arginine than are histones (less than 20 moles per 100 moles) and richer in diacidic amino acids (more than 20 moles per 100 moles). This material is a major nucleolar component, and may represent ribosomal structural protein in the process of synthesis.

REFERENCES

1.   Johns, E. W., and Butler, J. A. V., Biochem. J., 82, 15, 1962.

2.   Crampton, C. F., Stein, W. H., and Moore, S., J. Biol. Chem., 225, 363, 1957.

3.   Phillips, D. M. P., Biochem. J., 87, 258, 1963.

4.   Rasmussen, P. S., Murray, K., and Luck, J. M., Biochemistry, 1, 79, 1962.

5.   Cruft, H. J., Biochim. Biophys. Acta, 54, 611, 1961.

6.   Cruft, H. J., Hindley, J., Mauritzen, C. M., and Stedman, E., Nature, 180, 1107, 1957.

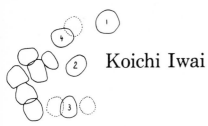

Koichi Iwai

HISTONES OF RICE EMBRYOS
AND OF *CHLORELLA*

Comparative studies on the distribution and properties of histones among various living forms afford a useful approach to elucidate the biological role of histones. Many reports have been published in recent years on the existence of nucleohistones in the somatic cells of higher animals and on the characteristics of these histones. In contrast, little is known about the existence and characteristics of histones in plant cells and unicellular organisms. We have isolated histones from rice embryo and from a unicellular green alga, Chlorella ellipsoidea, and compared these histones with the histone from calf thymus.

Rice embryos were collected from rice bran, washed with water and air dried. Washed cakes of Chlorella cells, cultured in large scale and given to us by the Microalgae Research Institute of Japan, were used after immediate lyophilization.

Two methods of isolation were applied to both of the starting materials. The first method was based on acid extraction of nucleoprotein isolated by a NaCl procedure as presented in Figure 1. The second one, as shown in Figure 2, was based on direct acid extraction of finely ground material.

Each preparation thus obtained was chromatographed on a carboxymethylcellulose column according to the procedure described by Johns et al. [1] for fractionation of calf thymus histone. An elution pattern was obtained by following the ultraviolet absorption at 278 mμ and by applying the Folin colorimetry as modified by Lowry et al. [2].

It is apparent from Figure 3 that the chromatographic pattern of the preparation from rice embryos differs from that of thymus histone by containing no appreciable amount of peak 2, but a new, additional peak 4, which is eluted with 0.1 N HCl. In the preparation from Chlorella cells, all these peaks are present, and peak 1 is predominant. With both plant materials, two methods of isolation caused no change in the number of chromatographic peaks obtained. Quantitatively, however, the amount of peak 1 was always predominant in any preparation isolated by direct acid extraction.

For amino acid analysis of chromatographic fractions, the appropri-

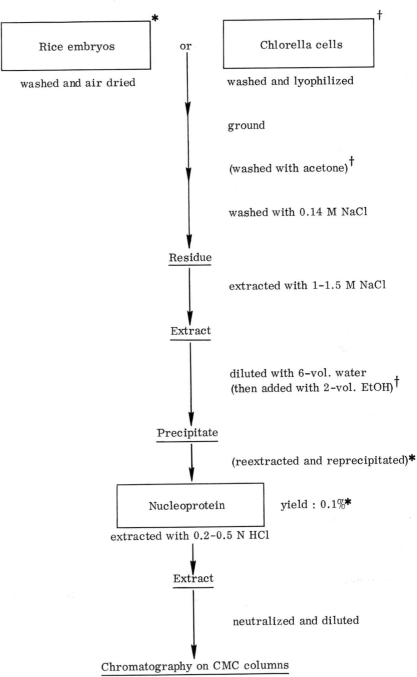

Fig. 1.—Preparation through nucleoprotein. *Treatment applied to rice embryos only. †Treatment applied to Chlorella cells only. Other treatments applied to both.

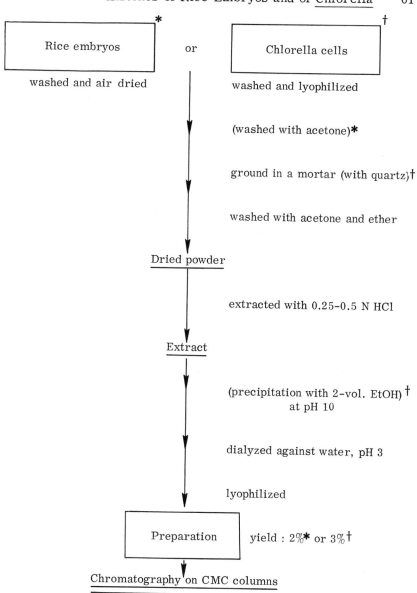

Fig. 2.—Preparation by direct extraction. See Figure 1 for explanation.

ately combined effluents were evaporated to dryness <u>in vacuo</u>. Some fractions were recovered by lyophilization after dialysis. Hydrolyses were effected in evacuated, sealed tubes for 32 hours at 110 C with constant-boiling HCl. Amino acid analyses were carried out with a Beckman Spinco Automatic Amino Acid Analyzer.

Table 1 and Figure 4 show a comparison of the amino acid composition of the fractions obtained from three sources. In the figure, the

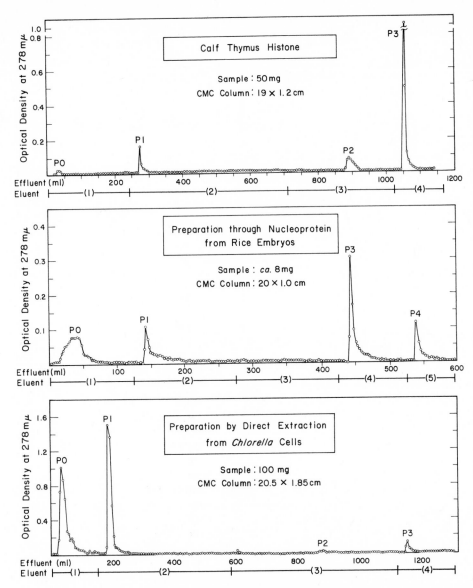

Fig. 3.—Chromatography on carboxymethylcellulose columns. Eluent 1, 0.1 M AcOH–0.03 M NaOH, pH 4.2; eluent 2, 0.17 M AcOH–0.05 M NaOH–0.42 M NaCl, pH 4.2; eluent 3, 0.01 N HCl; eluent 4, 0.02 N HCl; eluent 5, 0.1 N HCl. Flow rate, 0.5-1 ml/min. Effluent fraction, 2.5-5.5 ml/tube.

TABLE 1

The amino acid composition of chromatographic fractions
from three histone preparations (moles %)*

	Calf Thymus			Rice Embryos through Nucleoprotein			Chlorella Cells by Direct Extraction			
	P1	P2	P3	P1	P3	P4	P1	P2	P3	IRC-50
Lys	15.8	11.0	11.9	14.0	7.3	5.4	7.1	7.8	7.5	26.7
His	1.5	2.2	2.8	3.2	2.3	5.4	trace	trace	0.6	1.2
Arg†	7.5	8.9	10.9	8.2	10.9	13.2	3.9	4.1	4.0	4.0
NH₃†	(2.0)	(10.9)	(11.1)	(6.4)	(6.7)	(22.3)	(8.9)	(16.4)	(16.3)	(7.4)
Asp‡	4.2	6.1	5.1	5.1	6.1	6.8	8.5	8.2	9.4	3.9
Thr‡	5.4	5.3	6.2	4.2	4.4	2.9	7.2	8.3	8.2	4.2
Ser‡	6.1	5.3	6.1	5.6	5.8	6.1	8.9	7.7	7.6	4.6
Glu	8.4	10.8	10.0	8.7	13.8	18.2	9.4	10.2	10.1	8.9
Pro	5.9	3.0	3.9	7.1	4.7	4.1	6.7	6.3	7.2	8.7
Gly	10.7	11.2	9.1	9.2	10.1	11.3	7.2	9.6	9.6	6.1
Ala	16.4	12.3	10.7	16.6	10.2	6.7	14.9	13.2	12.8	17.8
Cys/2‡	0	0	0	0	0.2	2.3	2.3	0	-	0.8
Val	5.8	6.8	6.5	4.9	6.4	4.6	7.3	7.5	7.1	5.1
Met	0.3	0.3	1.1	0.9	0.9	1.1	0.8	trace	-	1.0
Ileu	2.8	4.3	5.0	3.8	4.6	2.8	3.9	4.4	4.3	1.7
Leu	8.1	10.2	7.6	6.0	7.0	4.8	6.1	6.9	6.7	3.3
Tyr‡	0.3	1.0	1.4	1.3	2.2	1.9	2.6	2.9	2.0	1.2
Phe	0.9	1.2	1.8	1.3	3.2	2.6	3.2	3.9	3.1	0.9
Yield§	63	488	166	3.3	9.5	1.7	474	22	15	44
mg per	100 g tissue			100 g dry embryos			100 g dry cells			

*Ammonia has been excluded in calculations of the moles % amino acid compositons.

†The values have been corrected by subtracting the amounts of ammonia originated from decomposition of certain amino acids and from reagents used for hydrolysis and amino acid analysis. In some cases, such corrected values were consistent with those of amide ammonia estimated directly.

‡These values have been corrected for decomposition by means of factors derived from analysis data of standard amino acid mixtures which had been "hydro-lyzed" under the same conditions.

§The amount of fractions was calculated by making use of their amino acid compositions.

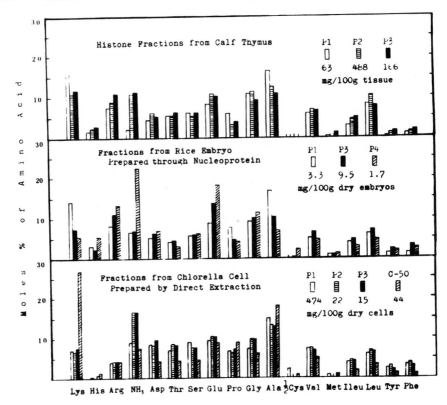

Fig. 4.—Comparison of amino acid composition of corresponding chromatographic fractions from three sources.

composition is expressed as moles per 100 moles of the amino acids recovered. Values for certain amino acids were corrected for decomposition during acid hydrolysis. The values for ammonia were tentatively corrected by subtracting the amounts of ammonia originated from decomposition and the reagents used.

Amino acid composition of fractions obtained from rice embryos, especially those of peaks 1 and 3, is similar to those of respective fractions from calf thymus histone. Peak 1 is rich in lysine and peak 3 in arginine. On the other hand, it may be said that amino acid composition of three chromatographic fractions from Chlorella cells suggests a less basic nature of these fractions. But in separate experiments, the same Chlorella preparations, isolated by direct acid extraction, did give a very basic, lysine-rich fraction when chromatographed on Amberlite IRC-50(XE-64) columns at pH 7.0.

As mentioned earlier, with both plant materials, protein preparations isolated by two different methods gave apparently identical chromatographic fractions. Some difference in amino acid composition was observed in the two fractions, with the fraction isolated by direct acid extraction usually being less basic.

In conclusion, rice embryo contains histone similar to the calf thymus histone in some aspects of heterogeneity on a carboxymethylcellulose column and of amino acid composition. In unicellular <u>Chlorella</u> the lysine-rich histone seems to be present as a predominant <u>fraction.</u>

This work was done in collaboration with T. Tsuchiya and Y. Kobayshi and has already been reported in part [3].

Comment

The mass ratio of isolated histone to DNA in <u>Chlorella</u> cells is 0.25-0.50 in fractions obtained by a direct extraction method (cf. yield of histone fraction IRC-50 or P2+P3 in Table 1). Fraction P1 should be excluded, because it may be contaminated by acidic or a less basic component. (DNA content, 0.1-0.2% of dry weight.) Since, however, the histone fraction was prepared from whole <u>Chlorella</u> cells, it is still uncertain whether all of the basic proteins so extracted was derived from chromatin, or whether a portion may represent ribosomal structural protein. But it might be expected that there would not be a ribosomal contamination in the other preparation, which was obtained through the concentrated NaCl extraction after thorough washing of ground cells by dilute NaCl.

REFERENCES

1.   Johns, E. W., Phillips, D. M. P., Simson, P., and Butler, J. A. V., Biochem. J., <u>77</u>, 631, 1960.

2.   Lowry, O. H., Rosebrough, N. J., Farr, A. L., and Randall, R. J., J. Biol. Chem., <u>193</u>, 265, 1951.

3.   Kobayashi, Y., Iwai, K., and Ando, T., Seikagaku J. Japan. Biochem. Soc., <u>35</u>, 81, 1963.

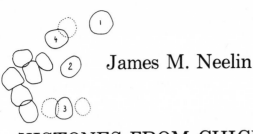

James M. Neelin

HISTONES FROM CHICKEN ERYTHROCYTE NUCLEI

Either histones have presented protein chemists with an unprecedented array of precise and reproducible artifacts, or histones examined by current techniques exhibit an imposing heterogeneity. The latter possibility is the favored working hypothesis, and it is easier to reconcile with theories involving histone in cell differentiation, since multiplicity of histones offers scope for subtle but specific differences between nuclei with different functional capacities.

From initial studies carried out at the University of Toronto, it became apparent that starch-gel electrophoresis revealed a heterogeneity of histones often implied, but not directly evident, by other analytical techniques [1]. Subsequent studies at the National Research Council in Ottawa [2] established that zones resolved in starch gel were authentic components of calf thymus histone, according to the following criteria.

Fractions separated by starch-gel electrophoresis retained their relative mobilities in repeated electrophoresis.

Fractions obtained by independent means, such as cation-exchange chromatography, included groups of zones evident in the starch-gel pattern of the unfractionated histone.

The complex electropherogram was not substantially altered in gels containing concentrated urea, although aggregation at moderate pH was prevented.

Heterogeneity was evident over a wide pH range in a variety of buffers containing urea.

Various preparative methods, including extraction of histone directly from thymus, produced the same zones.

New N-terminal amino acids were not generated by the mild acid extraction of citric acid-washed calf thymus nuclei.

Deliberate deterioration by prolonged storage in solution or use of frozen tissue produced changes readily distinguished from the dozen or more valid zones.

Because these techniques appeared adequately reliable for analysis of calf thymus histone, a search for specificity in the histones of various chicken tissues was initiated [3]. This work will be summarized and augmented with results obtained recently in Dr. J. M. Luck's laboratory at Stanford University.

Chicken spleen and liver nuclei were prepared and washed by repeated blending and centrifugation in 0.010 M citric acid, a method which seemed reliable at the time and worked well with thymus nuclei. Histone was extracted in dilute hydrochloric acid (pH 1.7) and analyzed without prior dialysis or precipitation. Two points about these preparative procedures should be admitted. Some lysine-rich histones presumably are lost during the citric acid washing and may well be in the final saline washes of other methods. While extraction at pH 1.5-1.7 yields a fraction comparable to histone preparation A [4], extraction at a lower pH would probably increase the proportion of certain components in the extract. Nevertheless, the histones mentioned here were prepared in identical fashion from all tissues. Liver and spleen histones did not differ remarkably [3], but the electropherograms of dilute samples and of the mixed histones indicated quantitative differences in relative intensities of intermediate mobility. The fast, diffuse zones, probably resulting from contamination or degradation, varied somewhat with different preparations, especially from liver.

Recently, Dounce and his colleagues have examined the question of proteolysis in nuclear preparations, and they have clearly shown that the "citric acid method" may not be applied safely to tissues other than thymus [5]. Therefore, the same approach was attempted to select safe conditions for isolation of chicken spleen and liver nuclei. While excessive nuclease activity in these tissues interfered with interpretation of the results, proteolysis of added hemoglobin was evidently least between pH 5.0 and 5.5. Histone was extracted with acid from nuclei prepared with homogenization by hand and repeated washings in 0.44 M sucrose, pH 5.5, followed by three washings in isotonic saline. The electropherograms of both spleen and liver histones proved to be as clean as the best obtained by the citric acid method, and superior to that from nuclei in 0.25 M sucrose, 0.003 M $CaCl_2$. Quantitative differences between starch-gel zones of spleen and liver histones were clarified by the absence of gross artifacts.

Histones from two more disparate sources, erythrocytes and testes, were also compared and found obviously dissimilar [3]. Fewer zones were evident in the electropherogram of testis histone, with the absence of the most mobile zones being especially notable.

When erythrocyte histone is compared more closely with that of chicken spleen [3], they differ in two major features. (1) Only traces of zones of intermediate mobilities were perceptible in erythrocyte histone, although these components were readily apparent in spleen histone, in mixed spleen and erythrocyte samples, and in chicken liver, testis, heart and kidney, as well as calf thymus histone. (2) The erythrocyte extract contained two major components of relatively slow mobilities instead of the single zone exhibited by extracts from spleen and other tissues. To clarify the analogy between these zones, the slow component of spleen was isolated by chromatography on the sodium form of Amberlite IRC-50. When mixed with erythrocyte histone, this fraction enhanced the intensity of the more mobile of the two groups of zones in question. At the time of these experiments, no method was available for recovering the slowest erythrocyte histone from the column.

The occurrence of a histone component peculiar to chicken erythrocyte nuclei recalls the observation of the Stedmans more than a decade ago [6] that these nuclei contain a "subsidiary histone" richer in arginine than even the "main histone" from the same source.

On the basis of starch-gel electrophoresis alone, one could not be certain that this component was in fact a histone, and not a form of globin or other cationic protein. To settle this question and to compare the protein to other histones, it was isolated by chromatography on Amberlite IRC-50 (Fig. 1), from which it was the last fraction eluted with a gradient

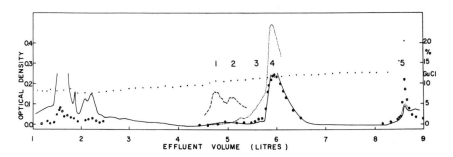

Fig. 1.—Chromatogram of chicken erythrocyte histone on Amberlite IRC-50. Eluent: increasing concentration gradient of guanidinium chloride buffered in 0.1 M sodium phosphate, pH 7. Column size: 55 x 7.5 cm diameter; flow rate: 180-240 ml/hr.; room temperature.   ⊙⊙, ultraviolet absorption at 280 mμ; - - - turbidity (440 mμ) in 1.1 M TCA; .... turbidity (440 mμ) in 0.8 M TCA; _____ fluorometer tracing; . . . . . . percent guanidinium chloride.

of guanidinium chloride in essentially the same position as calf thymus histone fractions III and IV [4]. This zone was nearly homogeneous in starch-gel electrophoresis (Fig. 2) and retained its low mobility in contrast to the heterogeneity and range of mobilities of calf thymus fractions III and IV. In contrast, other chromatographic fractions (for example, peaks 2 and 4, Fig. 1) of erythrocyte histone had electrophoretic properties comparable to their chromatographic analogues (fractions Ib and IIb) from calf thymus [4]. Globin could not be distinguished clearly from histone fractions under these conditions (Fig. 2).

The amino acid composition of erythrocyte histone fraction 5 (Table 1) had little in common with the composition of chicken globin, which was

TABLE 1

Amino acid compositions of globin and histones

(Moles % of total recovered amino acids)

Amino Acid	Calf Thymus Histone			Chicken Erythrocyte	
				Histone	Globin
	Fraction III*	Fraction IV*	β†	Fraction 5	Unfractionated
Lysine	9.3	8.9	9.5	20.0	8.6
ε-N-methyl lysine	0.7	0.8	‡	0	‡
Histidine	1.6	1.6	2.0	1.7	5.6
Arginine	12.8	12.7	11.5	10.2	3.2
Aspartic Acid	4.4	4.5	5.6	2.9	9.2
Threonine	7.3	7.3	5.5	3.9	5.7
Serine	4.1	4.1	5.0	12.1	4.5
Glutamic acid	9.8	10.5	9.2	5.2	8.1
Proline	3.8	4.2	3.3	6.5	4.5
Glycine	8.7	7.8	9.4	5.9	5.2
Alanine	11.7	12.2	12.2	15.1	10.8
Half-cystine	0	0	0	0	2.2
Valine	5.8	5.6	5.8	4.8	7.2
Methionine	1.2	1.2	1.1	0.5	0.9
Isoleucine	5.4	5.4	5.1	3.5	4.2
Leucine	8.6	8.9	10.2	5.5	11.7
Tyrosine	2.4	2.3	2.6	1.8	2.5
Phenylalanine	2.5	2.7	2.2	0.7	5.7

*These analyses are essentially the data reported by Rasmussen, Murray, and Luck [4], but ε-N-methyl lysine values are incorporated (Murray, unpublished).
†These data were reported by Mauritzen and Stedman [7].
‡Not analyzed.

much richer in histidine, phenylalanine, half-cystine, and acidic amino acids. The histone fraction was especially richer in lysine, arginine, and serine, and certainly qualifies for definition as a histone. As predicted by Stedman and Stedman [6], the erythrocyte histone fraction was very basic, containing 32 moles of lysine, histidine, and arginine per 100 moles of total amino acids. Despite its chromatographic position and fairly high

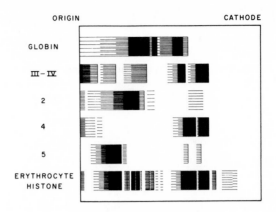

Fig. 2.—Horizontal starch-gel electrophoresis of histone and globin. Gel buffer: sodium acetate, pH 4.8, μ 0.020. Bridge solution: 0.1 M sodium chloride. Electrophoresis: 6 hours at 4 ma/cm^2, ca. 4 V/cm. Samples (top to bottom): chicken globin (unfractionated); calf thymus histone fractions III-IV [4]; chicken erythrocyte histone fractions 2, 4, and 5, respectively (Fig. 1); unfractionated erythrocyte histone (extracted with HCl, pH 1.5).

content of arginine, it could not be described as arginine-rich with an arginine-lysine ratio of 0.5. It differs notably from the β-histone of fowl erythrocytes [7] and from the corresponding chromatographic fractions of calf thymus histone [4] in the absence of ϵ-N-methyl lysine, high content of both lysine and arginine, unusually high serine, and relatively low phenylalanine. The amino acid compositions of other chicken erythrocyte histone fractions from these chromatograms are being examined and compared with their counterparts in calf thymus.

The complex fingerprint of the tryptic peptides of erythrocyte fraction 5 in no way resembles the fingerprint of chicken globin. It also differs significantly from those of all calf thymus histone fractions (Lamb and Murray, unpublished). While coincident peptides are probable in the several dozen spots observed, the fingerprint of the erythrocyte fraction appeared more complex, and more zones migrated rapidly in both chromatographic and electrophoretic dimensions. The fingerprinting of other chicken erythrocyte fractions is being continued.

The evidence is convincing that at least chicken erythrocyte nuclei contain a major histone component not found in other nuclei of the same animal. The correlation with the peculiar properties of erythrocytes, the morphologically simple cytoplasm, small condensed nuclei, mitotic inertia, and dominant synthesis of hemoglobin, all offer opportunity for speculation. Equally challenging is that unusual histones occasionally stand out as exceptions in the ubiquitous occurrence of general histone types. Specificity in other nuclei should perhaps be considered an open question as yet; however, it may be noted that any variation observed appeared most often in the corresponding chromatographic fraction, that is, in protein easily aggregated and generally overlooked in earlier methods of fractionation.

Comment

An additional peculiarity of chicken erythrocyte nuclei is the lack of RNA synthesis, which might be related to unusual histone composition. Dr. L. Hnilica has found a similar chicken erythrocyte component, with lysine, arginine, and serine contents in good agreement with the values indicated in Table 1.

It appears firmly established that the histones of different cell types may be different in composition, at least those of the chicken, in which the histones of erythrocyte nuclei are clearly distinguishable from the histones of liver and spleen.

Acknowledgments

This work received financial support from the National Institutes of Health, the United States Public Health Service (Grant C-484).

REFERENCES

1.   Neelin, J. M., and Connell, G. E., Biochim. Biophys. Acta, 31, 539, 1959.

2.   Neelin, J. M., and Neelin, E. M., Can. J. Biochem. Physiol., 38, 355, 1960.

3.   Neelin, J. M., and Butler, G. C., Can. J. Biochem. Physiol., 39, 485, 1961.

4.   Rasmussen, P. S., Murray, K., and Luck, J. M., Biochemistry, 1, 79, 1962.

5.   Dounce, A. L., and Umaña, R., Biochemistry, 1, 811, 1962.

6.   Stedman, E., and Stedman, E., Nature, 166, 780, 1950.

7.   Mauritzen, C. M., and Stedman, E., Proc. Roy. Soc. (London) Ser. B, 150, 299, 1959.

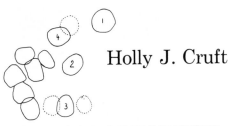

Holly J. Cruft

ELECTROPHORESIS AND GEL FILTRATION OF HISTONES

The results obtained by electrophoresis of histones through starch gels [1, 2] are very different from those obtained by moving-boundary electrophoresis [3]. Differences seem to be greater than can be accounted for by molecular sieving effects alone. The relatively slow mobility of the α (or lysine-rich) histone fraction, in particular, appears to be anomalous. Furthermore, the adverse effects on resolution of increasing pH, the influence of histone concentration on mobility and the sharp leading edge of many bands, suggest some degree of combination between the histones and the starch itself. This is probably emphasized by the use of low ionic strengths, which is customary in starch-gel electrophoresis.

For this reason, a medium free of any dissociable carboxyl groups has been sought to reduce combinations due to ionic interactions. It was also desirable to find, if possible, a medium in which molecular sieving effects could be varied at will. A technique employing polyacrylamide gels for electrophoresis [4] has been investigated for use with histones, and an improved method of polymerization of the gel has been evolved [5]. No special apparatus for this method is required other than that normally used for zone electrophoresis.

THE PREPARATION OF GELS

Chemicals:

    Acrylamide (Kodak, Ltd., London)
    N N' methylene-bisacrylamide (L. Light & Co., England)
    N N N' N' tetra methyl ethylene diamine (L. Light & Co., England)
    Ammonium persulfate (B.D.H., England)

The N N N' N' tetra methyl ethylene diamine is prepared as a 10% (v/v) stock solution in ethanol and is stable as such for at least 6 months.

An aqueous 10% (w/v) solution of ammonium persulfate must be freshly prepared for each polymerization.

Method. Gels containing 10% acrylamide have routinely been used, but any concentration between 3 and 15% may be used. However, the amount of cross-link agent (N N' methylene-bisacrylamide) used should always be 2% of the weight of acrylamide used. The required amounts of acrylamide and N N' methylene bisacrylamide are weighed out and dissolved in the appropriate quantity of the buffer at room temperature, and 1% (v/v) of the catalyst N N N' N' tetramethyl ethylene diamine's stock solution is added and mixed by gentle inversion, followed by 1% (v/v) of the freshly prepared ammonium persulfate solution, mixing again by inversion. The solution is immediately poured into a plastic trough, preferably 0.3 cm deep, and the lid is put on to expel excess liquid and any air bubbles. The gel sets in 15 minutes, but is generally not used for several hours.

Example: For 10% gels, 2 g of acrylamide plus 40 mg of N N' methylene bisacrylamide are dissolved in 20 ml of buffer. To this is added 0.2 ml of N N N' N' tetra methyl ethylene diamine stock solution and 0.2 ml of fresh ammonium persulfate solution. (The two catalyst concentrations need not be altered in preparing gels of a different percentage of acrylamide.)

Gelling is unaffected by buffer ionic strength or pH within the range of 2-11. Nearly any common buffer may be employed, but for histone studies 0.01 M sodium acetate, buffer pH 4.2 is routinely used. Histone solutions in the buffer are applied on filter paper strips inserted into slits cut in the gel, which is then completely covered except for the ends by a thin plastic sheet.

No cooling is used. Runs last about 5 hours at potential gradients of 3 to 4 volts per cm (measured directly on the gels with an electronic voltmeter). After removal from the trough, gels are stained with naphthalene black 10B in water-methanol-acetic acid (5:5:1) and cleared with similar solvent. There is no need to slice gels before staining, as the bands are straight and the gel completely transparent. A gel thickness of 0.3 cm permits rapid staining and destaining. Bands may be photographed by transmitted light or, alternatively, if 1% glycerol is added to the last solvent wash, gels may be dried down, still transparent, onto glass plates.

Acrylamide gels of a concentration higher than 15% become rather brittle and difficult to cut, but resolution is good. Acrylamide concentrations slightly below 5% yield poorer resolution, but aggregates of high molecular weight can migrate through such gels, and this is frequently useful. Acrylamide concentrations greatly below 5% produce gels too weak to be usable.

The addition of lanthanum to the buffer (i.e., 0.01 M sodium acetate and 0.02 M lanthanum acetate) prevents smearing of aggregating β-histone fractions and permits observation of additional bands without affecting other components.

To perform electrophoresis runs at very high pH's, such as pH 12, in determination of the isoelectric point of basic protein, gels should be poured at a lower pH (pH 9) and the required higher pH buffer introduced into the gel by ionophoresis from inner electrode compartments during a preliminary 5-hour run at high potential gradient before insertion of the sample. This method avoids the difficulties encountered in polymerization at high pH and in the accurate measurement of the pH after polymerization, during which pH alterations occur. Electroendosmosis may be neglected in polyacrylamide gels.

ELECTROPHORESIS

All experiments described here were done with ox thymus gland histones prepared by our routine procedures [3, 6]. Thus far, no histone fraction has been obtained that yields a single band on electrophoresis.

<u>Whole (unfractionated) histone</u>. Nine or more bands may be distinguished (Fig. 1), four or more being fast moving bands associated with very lysine-rich α-histones. The heavy band containing the γ-histones is closely followed by four fainter bands, which vary in resolution and intensity with the pH and age of the histone solution. The first pair appear to be α-histones of high molecular weight, while the second pair is associated with β-histone and its aggregates.

α-<u>Histone fractions</u>. The α-histone product from ethanol fractionation is also shown in Fig. 1. The four fast-moving bands are prominent, but two slower bands are also apparent. As loading is increased, other bands become apparent. Preparations have been obtained by preparative electrophoresis that contain only the fast-moving bands, which seem to correspond to our α_1 and α_2 histone fractions.

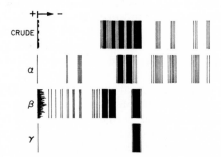

ELECTROPHORESIS of HISTONES in 10 %
POLYACRYLAMIDE GELS

Fig. 1.—Diagram of results obtained by electrophoresis of different histone fractions through polyacrylamide gels. The four fastest bands are a turquoise blue color; the remainder, grey-blue. Run for 5 hours at 4 volts per cm. Sodium and lanthanum acetate buffer.

β-Histone fractions. These fractions are remarkably complex. Three major bands are apparent and have their counterparts in the pattern yielded by crude histone. In the presence of lanthanum ions, nine very sharp, faint bands are found near the origin, which itself shows irregular staining due to the presence of large aggregates of β-histone trying to penetrate the gel. These fine bands, which have not been detectable before, are believed to be intermediates produced in the aggregation of β-histone. Similar bands are found with β-histones from other tissues.

γ-Histone fractions. Preparations of γ-histones generally yield a single broad band, as indicated in Fig. 1. This may, however, be resolved into two components by electrophoresis for a longer distance.

The above results show that unfractionated histone contains many components, but it is not yet clear which of them may represent combinations of histones that occur individually as other bands. More study with different buffer systems will be necessary before this can be decided. The present method of electrophoresis shows the complexity of the α-histones and a complexity in the β-histone fractions that is not seen on starch-gel electrophoresis.

The complexity of bands produced by histones in polyacrylamide has also been noted in a recent paper by McAllister, Wan and Irvin [7].

To interpret the patterns produced on gel electrophoresis, some knowledge of molecular or particle weights is essential. At low ionic strengths such information cannot be obtained by ultracentrifugation because of the large but ill-defined charge effects associated with histones. Some data is available, however, from experiments with molecular sieving materials at low ionic strengths. A preliminary report on the use of Sephadex for this purpose [8] has recently been extended by P. S. Muecke working in our laboratory [9].

SEPHADEX G-75 RESULTS

Figure 2 shows the results obtained with medium-grade G-75 Sephadex suspended and poured in 0.02 N HCl (pH 1.7). Columns were 150 or 125 cm long and 3 cm in diameter. Crude ox thymus histone samples (100 or 200 mg) were dissolved in 0.02 N HCl to give 6% solutions and applied to the column. Experiments were conducted at room temperature at a flow rate of 10 ml per hour.

The effluent was analyzed by quantitative ninhydrin color and by ultraviolet absorption at 276 mμ. The material in the various peaks was recovered, when practicable, by acetone precipitation and identified by starch-gel electrophoresis.

Peak 1 emerges in the effluent at a volume that is 25% of the packed column volume (void volume for the column should be about 23% of the packed volume). Thus this peak, which is of the highest particle weight, hardly enters the Sephadex granules. Nevertheless, starch-gel electro-

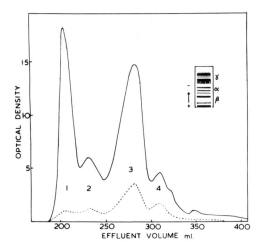

Fig. 2.—Filtration diagram of calf thymus histone on Sephadex G-75 in 0.02N hydrochloric acid. Solid line, ninhydrin color. Dotted line, ultraviolet absorption. Fraction volume 4.5 ml. Inset, starch-gel electrophoresis pattern of the unfraction-ated histone.

phoresis clearly shows that the material is α-histone (plus a little material at the origin). The high ratio of ninhydrin color value to the ultraviolet absorption confirms that it is mainly α-histone.

Peak 2 contains the fast-moving β, arginine-rich histone. The position and size of this peak were found to be rather variable.

Peak 3, which is markedly asymmetric, contains the γ-histones.

Peak 4, which is composite, contains some of the fastest-migrating γ-histone material that is capable of aggregating, as is β-histone.

The total recovery of histone based on ninhydrin color was 96%.

The most interesting point in connection with gel filtration is the fact of the emergence of the α-histone fraction first. This indicates that its molecular weight is more than 40,000. We have no explanation for this behavior at the moment, although it may fit with the slowness with which the α-histone fraction moves in starch-gel electrophoresis, and the more slowly-moving bands that it yields in polyacrylamide gels.

The effects of ionic strength, pH, and grade of Sephadex have been systematically investigated. Use of 0.05 N HCl (pH 1.3) for the medium rather than 0.02 N HCl causes peak 2 to move into the trailing edge of peak 1. Recovery remains about 100%.

Further increase in HCl concentration to 0.2 N (pH 0.85) simplifies the pattern to two major peaks, the first of which is heterogeneous and contains α- and β-histones, but is poor in γ-histones. The second peak contains only γ-histones. Total recovery is 90%. Clearly, even in 0.2 N HCl much β- and α-histone association or aggregation has occurred, with little alteration in the γ-histones.

In view of the effect of ionic strength on the aggregation of β-histone, it seemed logical to increase greatly the ionic strength with NaCl while leaving the pH at 1.7, i.e., in 0.02 N HCl. This results in a first peak that contains β and some γ components, presumably associated, closely followed and overlapped by the α-histone peak. The third peak contained only γ-histones. It is particularly interesting that the high ionic strength (1 M NaCl) does not lead to a breakdown of the α-histone peak to one of lower particle weight.

Similar results are obtained by allowing aggregation to proceed by raising the pH rather than the ionic strength. The use of an 0.1 M sodium acetate buffer pH 5.3 results in a peak 1 containing principally β-histone, indicating less association of the γ-histones. Some of these are present in the second and third peaks. It may be significant that the order of separation here is the reverse of the order of separation on starch-gel electrophoresis. This implies that, under these conditions, the decreasing order of particle size or weight is β, α, γ.

The results with gel electrophoresis and molecular sieving well illustrate the difficulties involved in determining the number and quantities of histone components. That several different types of association are possible is clear, but the behavior of the products produced and their stability during, for example, chromatographic procedures, are not. Until more is understood about the conditions for their dissociation, many of the questions concerning the number and size of the fundamental histone units will probably remain unanswerable.

Comment

Proteins cannot be easily recovered from polyacrylamide gels. Diffusion of protein from strips of gel is slow and is virtually useless even if the gel is first broken into fragments. Freezing of the gel does not cause them to become spongy on thawing as is the case with starch gels.

One method that we have employed for the isolation of the major protein components is as follows: A normal separation is carried out by electrophoresis across the middle of a 15 x 15 cm square slab of gel from a filter paper strip 5 cm long. A 1 cm wide strip is cut from the gel to form a trough along one side of the migration path. The strip containing the ends of the histone bands is then stained in the normal way to show the position of the bands at the edge of the trough (allowing for gel contraction on staining).

Celluloid strips 1.5 cm long are inserted across the trough at points between bands and the sections thus formed are filled with a CM-cellulose slurry in 0.01 M buffer, pH 7.

The whole gel and trough is covered with a plastic sheet and coupled up to the electrodes in such a configuration that electrophoresis is at right angles to the first direction of migration. The histone bands are thus caused to migrate into the CM-cellulose traps. The proteins can then be displaced from the respective portions of ion exchange cellulose by acid and recovered in a micro centrifuge tube.

Quantitative recoveries have not been obtained so far and uniform packing of the sections with slurry up to the celluloid spacers is critical if loss of histone past the traps is to be avoided.

Although this method is feasible for very small amounts of histone, it does not appear to be suitable for adaption to large scale preparation in its present form.

REFERENCES

1.   Neelin, J. M., and Neelin, E. M., Can. J. Biochem. Physiol., 38, 355, 1960.

2.   Johns, E. W., Phillips, D. M. P., Simson, P., and Butler, J. A. V., Biochem. J., 80, 189, 1961.

3.   Cruft, H. J., Mauritzen, C. M., and Stedman, E., Phil. Trans. Roy. Soc. London, Ser. B, 241, 93, 1957.

4.   Raymond, S., and Wang, Y., Analyt. Biochem., 1, 391, 1960.

5.   Cruft, H. J., Biochem. J., 84, 47P, 1962.

6.   Cruft, H. J., Mauritzen, C. M., and Stedman, E., Proc. Roy. Soc., London, Ser. B, 149, 21, 36, 1958.

7.   McAllister, H. C., Jr., Wan, Y. C., and Irvin, J. L., Analyt. Biochem., 5, 321, 1963.

8.   Cruft, H. J., Biochim. Biophys. Acta, 54, 611, 1961.

9.   Muecke, P. S., Ph.D. Thesis, University of Edinburgh, 1962.

Harris Busch
and Hilmi Mavioglu

PEPTIDES OF HISTONE FRACTION 2A

RP2-L. A few years ago, studies were made in our laboratory of the distribution of the isotope of L-lysine-U-C^{14} in the chromatograms of histones from a number of tissues. These histones were obtained by acid extraction of whole nuclei, and the chromatography was carried out on carboxymethylcellulose with 1 M and 8 M formic acid as the eluting agents [1]. Radioactive peak 2, called RP2-L because it was labeled with C^{14} lysine, was initially found only in the Walker tumor, and not in the nontumor tissues studied. Subsequently, this peak has been found in a number of tumors, both in our laboratory and in others, and, to our knowledge, there are no published reports of its appearance in nontumor tissues.

To determine the components of this peak, mass chromatography was carried out on extracts of Walker tumor tissue [2]. Starch-gel electrophoresis of this fraction at about pH 2.3 revealed that RP2-L consisted of a mixture of proteins in which the F1 fraction, or the very lysine-rich fraction, was a very minor component, and the faster bands coded as 2a and 2b were the major components. RP3-L, or the later-emerging radioactive band of the tumor, consisted of a mixture of components, but these components are the more slowly moving ones.

Subfractions of RP2-L. To isolate and purify the components of RP2-L, a series of fractionations was carried out [3]. The fractions were purified by the technique of Johns et al. [4-6], and the fractions obtained from the tumor seemed to be more highly purified than those obtained from other tissues.

Fraction 2a was the fastest moving of the bands obtained on gels, and the 2b fraction moved more slowly. Since proline is the N-terminal amino acid of the 2b fraction, which apparently contains only one protein, this protein has been referred to as the N-proline histone.

Amino acid analysis of fraction 2a. The amino acid analyses of these fractions are presented in Table 1. The 2a fraction has about 10% alanine, about 12% glycine, and 12% arginine. It has no special features except that it is the most rapidly running of the bands in the gel electrophoresis. The slightly lysine-rich 2a fraction is similar in arginine content to the so-called arginine-rich fraction; it is also similar in alanine and lysine

TABLE 1

Amino acid composition of some histone fractions of the Walker tumor*

	2a	2b	3
Alanine	10.4	10.4	11.5
Arginine	11.7	7.1	10.2
Aspartic acid	5.3	5.0	6.8
Glutamic acid	8.5	9.0	14.6
Glycine	12.5	6.9	5.7
Histidine	2.4	2.3	1.9
Isoleucine	4.8	5.1	4.1
Leucine	9.9	6.0	10.6
Lysine	9.9	14.3	9.1
Methionine	0.4	0.7	1.4
Phenylalanine	1.6	1.8	2.6
Proline	3.1	4.6	3.7
Serine	3.2	9.5	4.9
Threonine	5.6	6.4	5.6
Tyrosine	2.8	3.1	1.9
Valine	7.2	6.9	5.1

*From Hnilica and Busch [3].

contents, so that 2a has little but its electrophoretic mobility to distinguish it.

The amino terminals are relatively small in amount, but the 2a fraction is like the F3 (arginine-rich fraction) in having alanine as an amino terminal [4-6].

Although this fraction was purified by chromatography on carboxymethylcellulose [4-6], the 2a fraction was not completely pure. Three components were found on ultracentrifugation, two appearing very quickly and another appearing as a shoulder later on in the course of ultracentrifugation. Some progress is being made in the isolation of a single ultracentrifugal peak.

Peptides of fraction 2a. Peptides from fraction 2a were purified by fingerprinting, as described by Phillips and Simson [7]. Various amino acids have been found in the peptides, and the elementary composition of

TABLE 2

Amino acid code

Alanine	1
Arginine	2
Aspartic acid	3
Glutamic acid	4
Glycine	5
Histidine	6
Isoleucine	7
Leucine	8
Lysine	9
Methionine	10
Phenylalanine	11
Proline	12
Serine	13
Threonine	14
Tyrosine	15
Tryptophan	16
Valine	17
Cystine	18
Hydroxyproline	19
Glutamine	20
Asparagine	21

some has been determined. A coding system for these peptides has been developed, which we hope will at least make it possible to distinguish some of these amino acid compositions numerically (Table 2).

For a peptide such as the seventh (Table 3) for calf thymus and the Walker tumor, such a representation shows that amino acid no. 2, arginine, is present in the Walker tumor peptide and is missing from the calf thymus peptide. In the case of amino acid no. 9, lysine, two occur in the calf thymus seventh peptide, and only one in the corresponding peptide from Walker tumor.

TABLE 3

Codes for elementary amino acid composition for
peptide 7 of histone fraction 2a

Walker tumor	$1 - 2 - 4 - 5_2 - 9 - 13 - 14$
Calf thymus	$1 - 4 - 5_2 - 9_2 - 13 - 14$

TABLE 4

Differences in elementary amino acid composition
of peptides of fraction 2a

Peptide No.	Tumor	Calf Thymus
2	asp	----
3	arg, gly_2	asp,gly,thr(?)
5	ser_2(?)	ser
6	ala_2	ala,arg
7	lys,arg	lys_2
9	ala,arg,gly_2	ala_2,arg_2,gly

Table 4 is a composite of data on the differences in the elementary amino acid compositions of peptides of fraction 2a. Significant differences were found in the peptides of the Walker tumor and calf thymus, although the spots appear in very similar positions on the fingerprint.

It should be recognized that these data are preliminary and that further purification of the peptides is necessary before a final elementary amino acid analysis can be recorded. It should also be noted that the ultimate objective of these experiments is to provide a linear sequence of amino acids for the main component of fraction 2a.

Acknowledgments

This work was supported by grants from the Jane Coffin Childs Fund, the American Cancer Society, and the U. S. Public Health Service.

REFERENCES

1.   Davis, J. R., and Busch, H., Cancer Res., 19, 1157, 1959.

2.   Busch, H., Hnilica, L. S., Chien, S. C., Davis, J. R., and Taylor, C., Cancer Res., 22, 637, 1962.

3.   Hnilica, L. S., and Busch, H., J. Biol. Chem., 238, 918, 1963.

4.   Johns, E. W., and Butler, J. A. V., Biochem. J., 82, 15, 1962.

5.   Johns, E. W., Phillips, D. M. P., Simson, P., and Butler, J. A. V., Biochem. J., 77, 631, 1960.

6.   Johns, E. W., Phillips, D. M. P., Simson, P., and Butler, J. A. V., Biochem. J., 80, 189, 1961.

7.   Phillips, D. M. P., and Simson, P., Biochem. J., 82, 236, 1962.

Lubomir S. Hnilica, Charles W. Taylor, and Harris Busch

PEPTIDES OF HISTONE FRACTION 2B

The question whether there is tissue or species specificity of histones has long been a subject of interest. In the present preliminary study, the peptides of histone fraction 2b from calf thymus and Walker tumor were examined for their identity or difference. Fraction 2b was isolated by recently developed chemical and chromatographic techniques that have permitted isolation of purer fractions than were previously available [1-6].

The 2b fraction is a slightly lysine-rich fraction that was obtained from crude nucleoprotein preparations or from saline-washed nuclei by extraction with ethanol-HCl and with 0.25 N HCl [1]. This fraction was extracted along with the very lysine-rich fraction 1. The latter was separated quantitatively on carboxymethylcellulose columns, with potassium acetate buffer pH 4.2 containing 0.3 M KCl as eluent [6]. The 2b fraction was then eluted with 0.01 N HCl.

Purity of the 2b fraction. In starch-gel electrophoresis, the 2b fraction moved as the second fastest major band [3, 6]. In all preparations, a faster moving edge was observed, representing trace contamination by a histone fraction that moved slightly faster in starch gel. Amino acid analyses of the 2b fractions from calf thymus, rat thymus, rat spleen, and Walker tumor have shown that the 2b fractions have an excess of lysine (16%) over arginine (7%) and are quite rich in serine (10%), with a leucine to isoleucine ratio of 1:1. This ratio in other histone fractions is close to 2:1. The chief N-terminal amino acid of the 2b fractions from different tissues is proline (average, 80-90%) [7].

In the analytical ultracentrifuge, the 2b fraction was homogeneous* in potassium acetate buffer pH 4.2 and in veronal-acetate buffer pH 5.0, both 0.2 M. The molecular weight calculated from S_{w20} (1.12×10^{-13} second) and D_{w20} (3.02×10^{-7} cm^2/second) was 22,000. The molecular weight calculated from the yield of N-terminal proline was 23,000-25,000, which is slightly more than twice the minimal molecular weight calculated from amino acid composition.

---

*The authors appreciate the initial studies on this point made by Dr. H. Mavioglu.

Because of the relative homogeneity of fraction 2b as indicated by the N-terminal amino acid analysis, electrophoresis in starch gel, sedimentation in the ultracentrifuge, and fingerprinting [7], further studies were made on its substructure.

Fingerprinting of the peptides. All the fingerprints showed 25 major ninhydrin-positive spots after the 2b fractions from calf thymus, rat thymus, rat spleen, and Walker tumor were digested by trypsin and then analyzed by a combination of paper electrophoresis and chromatography, introduced by Ingram [8] as fingerprinting. The distribution of the spots and their qualitative content of arginine, histidine, and tyrosine were essentially the same for all the tissues studied [7].

Aliquots containing 5 mg of the digested sample were applied to Whatman 3 MM paper, and the electrophoresis was carried out in pyridine-acetate buffer pH 3.7 (1250 volts, 100 milliamps, 2 hours). The sheets were dried and chromatographed in n-butanol, secondary-butanol, acetic acid, water, iso-amyl alcohol, and ethylacetate (1:1:1:1:0.5:0.5), in descending arrangement, for 16 hours. The pattern obtained after staining with ninhydrin is shown in Figure 1. The peptides were localized by heating the sheets at 100 C for 15 minutes and by inspecting them in ultraviolet light [9, 10]. The main and most discrete spots, nos. 1-5,

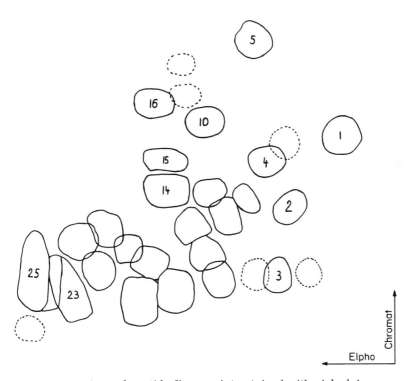

Fig. 1.—Tracings of peptide fingerprints stained with ninhydrin.

10, 14-16, and 23-25 (Fig. 1), were cut out, sewed together, and eluted with 10% acetic acid by descending chromatography. The eluates were evaporated to dryness, hydrolyzed with constant-boiling HCl in evacuated and sealed tubes, and analyzed for amino acid composition.

Amino acid composition of the peptides. The amino acid composition of the peptides and the suggested elementary amino acid analysis are shown in Table 1. The amino acid composition of the corresponding peptides from calf thymus and from Walker tumor were very similar. The difference in leucine content of peptide no. 5 is probably significant. In peptide no. 10, numerical differences were found for the content of alanine and tyrosine, but the lower value for tyrosine found in Walker tumor may have been caused by destruction of tyrosine during hydrolysis. Other differences were found, but a greater number of analyses of more purified fractions are required before a definitive conclusion can be reached.

Chromatography of peptides on Dowex-50. To eliminate the possibility that peptides obtained from paper were not contaminated or partial-

TABLE 1

Some peptides of fraction 2b

No.	Source of Peptide	Formula
1	Calf thymus	(glu, gly, ser_3, tyr, val) lys
	Walker tumor	(glu, gly?, ser_3, tyr, val) lys
2	Calf thymus	(asp, glu, gly, his, ile, pro, ser_2, thr, val) lys
	Walker tumor	(asp, glu, gly, his, ile, pro, ser_2, thr, val) lys
3	Calf thymus	(asp, gly) lys
	Walker tumor	(asp, gly) lys
4	Calf thymus	(ala, glu, ile, thr, val) arg
	Walker tumor	(ala, glu_2, ile, thr, val) arg
5	Calf thymus	(ala, glu, gly, leu_3, pro) lys
	Walker tumor	(ala, glu, gly, leu_4, pro) lys
10	Calf thymus	(ala, leu, tyr) his
	Walker tumor	(ala, leu) his
14	Calf thymus	(ala, thr, val) lys
	Walker tumor	(ala, thr, val) lys
15	Calf thymus	(tyr, val) lys
	Walker tumor	(tyr, val) lys
16	Calf thymus	(leu, val) lys
	Walker tumor	(leu, val) lys

ly destroyed during processing of the chromatograms, chromatography of tryptic digests was initiated on Dowex-50 columns. The histones of fraction 2b from calf thymus and from Walker tumor were digested by trypsin (2 mg of trypsin per 100 mg of protein in ammonium bicarbonate buffer pH 8.6), and 300 mg portions of the digests chromatographed with an automatic amino acid analyzer (Spinco). A representative elution pattern obtained for calf thymus fraction 2b digest is shown in Figure 2. Approximately 40 ninhydrin-positive peaks can be observed. Some of the peaks were very low and might represent hydrolytic products of the contaminating protein. A similar elution pattern was obtained for the digests from Walker tumor (Fig. 3), but peak no. 5 was missing.

Peptides purified by column chromatography. The central part of each peak was hydrolyzed with constant-boiling HCl in evacuated, sealed tubes and analyzed for amino acid content. The first two peaks, in both calf thymus and Walker tumor, contained all the amino acids present in

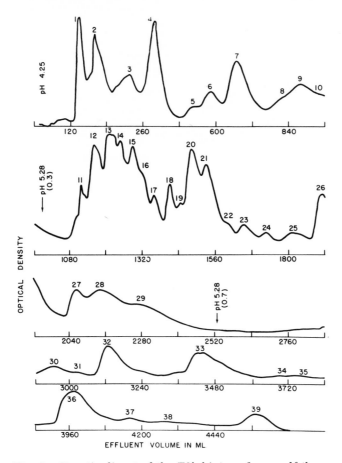

Fig. 2.—Tryptic digest of the F2b histone from calf thymus.

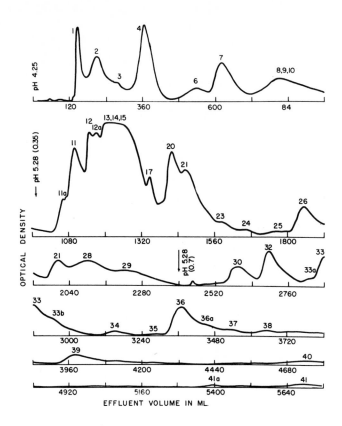

Fig. 3.—Tryptic digest of the F2b histone from Walker tumor.

fraction 2b, with a very low yield of basic amino acids, suggesting that these peptides are either acidic or very large. (They may represent the indigestible core observed by Phillips and Simson [11] in some histone fractions.) The elementary amino acid composition of some of the recovered peptides is shown in Table 2. The peptides contained from 3 to 7 or more residues per molecule. As can be concluded from the lysine and arginine content, several peptides must contain more than 1 basic residue per molecule.

Peptides recovered from Walker tumor fraction 2b digest were similar to those obtained from calf thymus, but only peptide no. 29 was identical in amino acid composition. Differences were found between calf thymus and Walker tumor F2b (Table 2). Approximately 20% of the digest was insoluble in citrate buffer pH 2.2.

TABLE 2

Amino acid composition of some of the peptides recovered from
Dowex 50-X4 columns

No.	Source of Peptide	Amino Acids
4	Calf thymus	ala, arg, asp, glu, gly, iso, lys, val
	Walker tumor	ala, arg?, asp, glu, gly, lys, thr, val
6	Calf thymus	ala_2, lys_2, pro, ser
	Walker tumor	ala_2, lys_2, pro_2, ser
17	Calf thymus	ala, asp, leu, lys_4
	Walker tumor	ala, lys_3, ser_2, thr, tyr
20	Calf thymus	leu_2, lys_3, val_3
	Walker tumor	ala, gly?, leu_2, lys_3, ser?, val_2
21	Calf thymus	ala, arg_2, gly, leu_2, lys_2, val
	Walker tumor	ala, arg, gly, leu, lys_2, ser_2, val
26	Calf thymus	arg_5, leu, lys
	Walker tumor	ala, arg_3, leu, lys, thr
27	Calf thymus	ala_3, arg, his, leu_2, tyr
	Walker tumor	ala_2, arg, his_3, leu, tyr
28	Calf thymus	ala_3, arg, his, leu_2, tyr_2
	Walker tumor	ala_2, arg, his_2, leu_2, tyr
29	Calf thymus	lys, phe, val
	Walker tumor	lys, phe, val
30	Calf thymus	ala_2, arg_2, glu, gly_2, leu, lys
	Walker tumor	ala, arg, gly?, leu_2, lys_2, thr
32	Calf thymus	ala, arg, leu_2, lys_2, ser
	Walker tumor	ala_2, lys_3, gly, thr, val

Discussion

Many differences were noted in the amino acid composition of peptides obtained by column chromatography from hydrolysates of fraction
2b of the Walker tumor and of calf thymus. This result differs from the
findings obtained from analyses of peptides after fingerprinting. A possible explanation of this difference is that the peaks obtained by column
chromatography are still heterogeneous, so that the mixtures of peptides
obtained include those from the minor protein contaminants.

The N-terminal amino acid analysis recently performed on some of
the calf thymus peptides obtained by chromatography shows that there is

overlapping of some peptides (Table 3). Because the amounts of peptides were small, it was necessary to pool the contents of the whole peak for N-terminal analysis. It is obvious that this sample is much more contaminated than the sample used for amino acid analysis. When pools of peaks 4, 6, 7, 8, 21, 25, 26, and 32 were analyzed, only peaks 6 and 25 gave consistent results, with a high order of homogeneity (assuming they do not contain several peptides with the same N-terminal group). All other peaks analyzed showed the presence of two or three N-terminal amino acids.

It is evident that more extensive studies of the homogeneity and sequence in isolated tryptic peptides combined with studies on chymotryptic digests are necessary.

TABLE 3

N-terminal amino acids of some calf thymus F2b peptides recovered from Dowex-50 columns

	Peak No.							
	4	6	7	18	21	25	26	32
Alanine	17.9			58.4	27.9			
Glycine					15.2			
Leucines	20.8		30.1		12.8	81.6	31.6	37.0
Lysine	16.8			22.3		15.1	47.2	63.0
Serine	23.1	77.4	50.2		36.2			

Summary

Tryptic peptides of F2b histone fractions from calf thymus and Walker tumor were analyzed by combined paper electrophoresis and paper chromatography (fingerprinting) and by chromatography on Dowex-50 columns. Some peptides were analyzed, and the amino acid composition showed some differences between corresponding peptides from calf thymus and from Walker tumor. N-terminal amino acid analyses of peptides recovered from some peaks revealed heterogeneity of the peptide fractions, suggesting that at least a part of the differences in amino acid composition may be caused by changes in proportions of different peptides composing the peak.

Acknowledgments

These studies were supported in part by grants from the National Science Foundation, the Jane Coffin Childs Fund, the United States Public Health Service, and the American Cancer Society.

REFERENCES

1. Johns, E. W., Phillips, D. M. P., Simson, P., and Butler, J. A. V., Biochem. J., $\underline{77}$, 631, 1960.

2. Johns, E. W., Phillips, D. M. P., Simson, P., and Butler, J. A. V., Biochem. J., $\underline{80}$, 189, 1961.

3. Johns, E. W., and Butler, J. A. V., Biochem.J., $\underline{82}$, 15, 1962.

4. Hnilica, L. S., Johns, E. W., and Butler, J. A. V., Biochem. J., $\underline{82}$, 123, 1962.

5. Rasmussen, P. H. S., Murray, K., and Luck, J. M., Biochemistry, $\underline{1}$, 79, 1962.

6. Hnilica, L. S., and Busch, H., J. Biol. Chem., $\underline{238}$, 918, 1963.

7. Hnilica, L. S., Taylor, C. W., and Busch, H., Exptl. Cell Res., Suppl. $\underline{9}$, 367, 1963.

8. Ingram, V. M., Biochim. Biophys. Acta, $\underline{28}$, 236, 1962.

9. Phillips, D. M. P., Nature, $\underline{161}$, 53, 1948.

10. Sanger, F., and Tuppy, H., Biochem. J., $\underline{49}$, 463, 1951.

11. Phillips, D. M. P., and Simson, P., Biochem. J., $\underline{82}$, 236, 1962.

III. THE STRUCTURE OF NUCLEOHISTONES

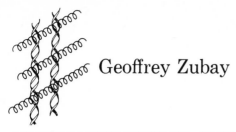 Geoffrey Zubay

NUCLEOHISTONE STRUCTURE
AND FUNCTION

NUCLEOHISTONE STRUCTURE

While the RNA and total protein contents of chromosomes vary greatly
[1], DNA, in the chromosomes of most higher organisms, is complexed
with an approximately equal weight of histone [2]. For this reason there
is some justification for regarding the nucleohistone complex as the building block of the chromosome. Most of the work discussed here is concerned with the structure of nucleohistone extracted from thymus gland
and easily obtained with little contamination from enzymes and nonbasic
or "residual" proteins.

The separation of DNA and histone in aqueous solution requires exposure to high ionic strength or acid, indicating the primarily electrostatic
nature of the bonding between them. In the absence of salt, nucleohistone
behaves as a gel in water, swells progressively on dilution with more
water, and may, when stirred at a concentration below 0.1% nucleohistone, be dispersed into molecules with a sedimentation constant of about
50 s [3]. Reconcentrating the solution phase leads to a return of the gel
state, and either state may be maintained indefinitely; this fact suggests
that the transition is not caused by enzymatic degradation. Since native
DNA does not form such cross-linked gels, it seems likely that gel formation is encouraged by histone bridges formed between DNA molecules, as
indicated in Figure 1.

Optical dispersion and infrared studies indicate that about two thirds
of the histone is in the α-helix form [3, 4]. The surface of the DNA molecule has two helical grooves with a pitch angle of about 30°. The small
groove is about 12 Å across, and the larger about 18 Å. An α-helix would
conveniently fit into the large groove running parallel to it (Fig. 2). In
dilute solution, where there are single nucleohistone molecules, it has
been proposed that most of the histone is bound as an interrupted α-helix
wound around the large groove of the DNA [3]. The formation of a bridged
network between nucleohistone molecules probably requires some alteration of this structure.

The similarities in the X-ray diffraction patterns obtained from DNA
and nucleohistone demonstrate that the double-helix configuration is mostly
preserved in the nucleoprotein [5]. Thus a stretched fiber of nucleohis-

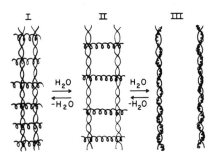

Fig. 1.—Diagram of the reversible transitions of nucleohistone from gel (I), to expanded gel (II), to solution (III). In the gel state, the DNA molecules are held together by histone bridges.

tone (Fig. 3) shows: (1) a 3.4 Å diffraction spot on the meridian, arising from the regular translation of base pairs along the helix axis; (2) the layer line pattern arising from the helically arranged sugar phosphate backbone of the double helix; and (3) the strong first-order equatorial reflection in the region between 22 and 35 Å (exact dimension depends on the degree of hydration), which is a measure of distance between the centers of adjacent double helices.

The nucleohistone diffraction pattern also has characteristics that clearly distinguish it from that of DNA: (1) The absence, or poor development, of spots on the layer lines, indicating a lack of regularity in the packing of the nucleohistone molecules. Since DNA packs regularly, histone must interfere with regular packing; this suggests that it is bound more or less uniformly along the length of the DNA. (2) A strong 60 Å equatorial reflection in stretched fibers at 98% relative humidity, believed to result from small amounts of lipid impurity. This subject has been discussed elsewhere [5]. (3) The frequent occurrence of spacings between 55 and 125 Å under some conditions, the significance of which is undetermined. (4) A fairly sharp 35 Å ring with poor meridional orientation. The degree of sharpness of this diffraction ring is indicative of a structure that has 10-20 repeats in regions where it occurs. It appears in nucleohistone diffraction patterns whether the material is preserved intact during preparation, dispersed as single nucleohistone molecules in water, or dissociated into DNA and histone in strong salt. The 35 Å spacing does not appear in diffraction patterns from DNA or histone alone (however, see Zubay and Wilkins [6]). It seems to be a characteristic of the 3-dimensional nucleohistone complex and has led us to suggest that it arises from regularly spaced histone bridges between DNA molecules [5]. Although most features of the nucleohistone diffraction pattern are sensitive to hydration, the spacing at 35 Å is not. It is at 37 Å on dehydrated nucleohistone, around 35 Å at intermediate humidities, and at 38 Å above 98% relative humidity. The alleged nucleohistone bridges alone do

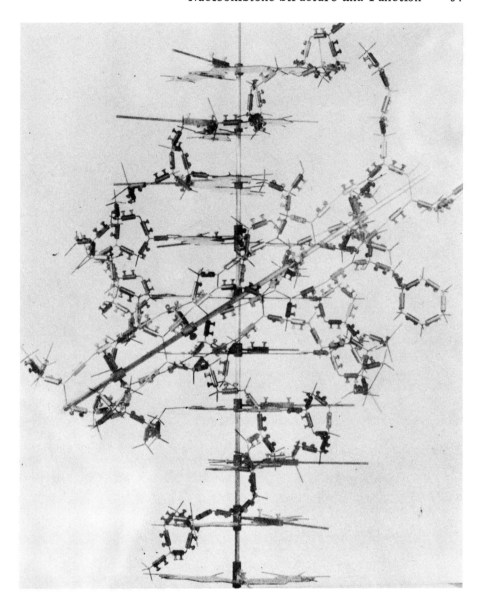

Fig. 2.—A wire model (constructed by the author in the laboratory of Dr. M. H. F. Wilkins, King's College, London) showing (1) the large groove of a DNA double helix, with the helix axis oriented vertically; (2) a segment of protein α-helix, with the helix axis oriented parallel to the groove (i.e., at an angle of 60° to the DNA axis).

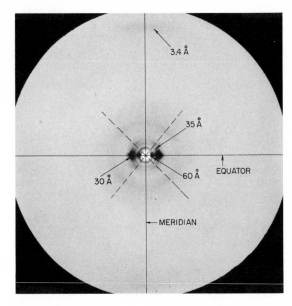

Fig. 3.—The best-oriented X-ray diffraction pattern from a fiber of nucleo-histone; relative humidity 98%. Most important features are indicated. Broken lines pass through the spots on the first, second, and third layer lines, which give rise to the crosslike pattern characteristic of double-helix diffraction patterns.

not appear to determine the exact separation of the DNA molecules, which, unlike the separation of the bridges themselves, is sensitive to hydration. In fact, the bridges may be entirely broken, as when the nucleohistone gel is dispersed into a solution of molecules. The meridional orientation of the 35 Å spacing is always much poorer than the orientation of the DNA diffraction components; this is probably a key to its significance.

The structure of nucleohistone has also been studied by electron microscopy, and some preliminary results have been published [7]. Stretched fibers of wet nucleohistone were fixed and embedded in araldite plastic, and longitudinal sections showed an appreciable fraction well oriented into anastomosing bundles of variable diameter (50-200 Å). The bundles themselves often showed considerable internal structure in the form of a meshwork or plaits. The long fibers in the direction of stretch-ing must be formed primarily by the DNA components, and the frequently occurring bridges between them are probably made mostly of histone. These assignments are based on: (1) The fact that DNA molecules are very long and heavy—about 8×10^6, whereas histone molecules weigh about 10^4; (2) the use of relatively specific staining—at neutrality, heavy metal cations, such as the uranyl and the indium, stain the DNA component much more than the histone, while heavy metal anions, such as phospho-tungstate or permanganate, preferentially stain the histone; and (3) information from X-ray diffraction that the DNA component is oriented in the direction of stretching. Very similar bridged structures are clearly visible in published electron micrographs of interphase nuclei (e.g., Davies and Spencer [8]), although the authors have failed to comment on them. X-ray diffraction diagrams have also been obtained from fixed specimens of oriented nucleohistone embedded in araldite [7] that closely resemble those from untreated fibers of nucleohistone in the fully hydrated state, showing, for instance, the characteristic 37 Å diffraction ring. These observations suggest that the preparative procedures for electron microscopy are preserving a good deal of the original organization of the oriented fibers. The preservation of the meridional orientation of the 37 Å spacing is in itself a technical achievement. In plastic-embedded material the nucleohistone orientation is fixed. It has not been possible to maintain tension and thereby preserve the orientation in untreated wet nucleohistone long enough to get an X-ray diffraction pattern. The result is that untreated wet nucleohistone shows no orientation.

Histone is heterogeneous, and it seems unlikely that the different fractions perform identical functions, but the results suggest a model for that part which produces the histone bridges. This model is consistent with all physicochemical observations and involves minimum modification of the structure believed to exist in solution. Figure 4 depicts histone bridging DNA molecules, with its long axis parallel to the large groove of the DNA of adjacent nucleohistone molecules. The regular spacing of these bridges measured by X-ray diffraction (35-38 Å) is approximately equal to the pitch of the DNA. In the electron microscope, bridges along the DNA axis should be 37-43 Å $\left(= \dfrac{37\ \text{Å}}{\sin 60°} \right)$ apart—about 37 Å if the electron density is concentrated at one point and about 43 Å if the bridges are long and have a uniform electron density. Observations to date show them at 40-70 Å; further work may determine the spacings more precisely. If the histone making the bridges is to be bound regularly in the large groove,

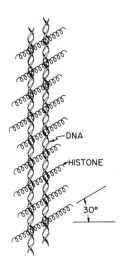

Fig. 4.—A model of oriented nucleohistone in the gel state. Histone bridges formed between DNA molecules lie parallel to the large groove of the DNA, with their long axis at an angle of 60° to the long axis of the DNA. Separation of the DNA molecules is sensitive to the amount of water present, but the spacing of the histone bridges is not. How many DNA molecules may be held together by the same histone bridges is unknown.

the pitch of the DNA must increase from its normal 34 Å to between 37 and 43 Å. This would result in a less tightly coiled double helix with 11 to 13 nucleotides per turn instead of the usual 10.

Little or no orientation of the α-helix component of the histone is indicated by infrared dichroism and X-ray diffraction studies on nucleohistone in which the DNA component is well oriented. This shows that the polypeptide chains of the histone are not well oriented parallel or perpendicular to the length of the DNA molecules; a factor consistent with the proposed model [6]. The poor orientation of the 35-38 Å spacing relative to the DNA would be explained by the fact that in a rotation fiber diffraction pattern, in which the DNA component is highly oriented, one would expect a strong diffraction arc extending about 30° on each side of the meridian. That the disorientation of the 35-38 Å spacing is somewhat greater than this suggests that forced orientation by stretching disrupts some of the histone bridges.

The proposed model results in a sheetlike structure, with the bridges in the plane of the sheet. If the plane of the sheet is oriented parallel to the X-ray beam, the meridional orientation of the 35 Å spacing relative to the DNA should be greatly improved. (Sheet specimens approximately 10 μ thick were made by allowing an aqueous solution of histone to evaporate on a glass slide. The plane of the molecular sheets should tend to lie parallel to the plane of the glass slide. The film was removed and mounted parallel to the incident X-ray beam.) The approximate X-ray diffraction pattern is illustrated in Figure 5, and is similar to that given by an ordinary stretched fiber of nucleohistone, except that the meridional orientation of the 35 Å spacing relative to the DNA component is far superior.

CHROMOSOME STRUCTURE

Although extracted nucleohistone certainly differs from the intact chromosome, it is interesting to explore the possibility of a structural relation between them. It is clear that DNA in unstretched nucleohistone in vivo and in vitro is not well oriented [9-14]. The evidence suggests that a combination of histone and DNA causes the DNA molecules to coil and be joined by histone bridges. Discussion of chromosome structure here refers to chromosomes that are capable of undergoing both replication and division and have nucleohistone as a major component. This excludes giant polytenic chromosomes such as those in drosophilia salivary glands, oocyte lampbrush chromosomes (which contain only about 0.2% DNA), and nucleoprotamine sperm. Confusion in the literature seems to result partly from expecting to find the same type of structure in these atypical chromosomes, as in typical chromosomes. Evidence from Taylor, Woods, and Hughes [15] indicates that chromosomes replicate semiconservatively, and Simon [16] has shown that the same is true for the DNA of the chromosome. It is also clear that crossing over occurs between

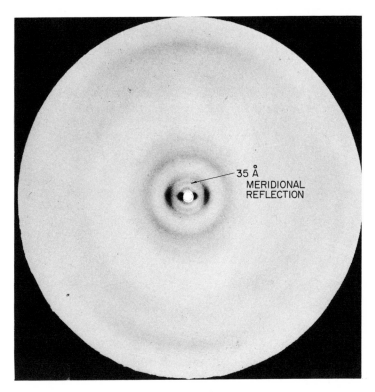

Fig. 5.—An X-ray diffraction pattern from a thin sheet of nucleohistone, with the plane of the film held parallel to the X-ray beam. The pattern is similar to that obtained from a stretched fiber of nucleohistone, except that the meridional orientation of the 35 Å reflection is greatly improved.

sister chromatids [17] and that single locus or point mutations can be produced in both macro- and microorganisms [18, 19].

These several observations favor the idea that the chromosome consists of many double-helix DNA molecules interconnected in one long string. Such a structure would have a contour length of several feet, indicating the extreme amount of coiling necessary in highly condensed mitotic chromosomes. It seems likely that the ordinarily assumed rodlike double helix itself engages in supercoiling. Conceivably, in the supercoiled structure of the mitotic chromosome, the adjacent segments of a DNA double helix are held together by histone bridges (Fig. 6). Before they could become metabolically active, the supercoiled regions would have to be unwound and the bridges broken and possibly reformed during interphase between less highly coiled filaments of DNA. These arguments encourage the belief that histone facilitates the supercoiling of DNA in chromosomes.

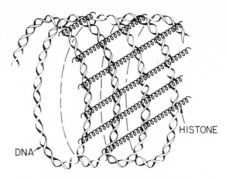

Fig. 6.—Diagram suggesting the function of histone bridges in chromosomes. DNA must form supercoils in mitotic chromosomes. It seems likely that the adjacent coils of the supercoiled DNA are held together by histone bridges. The dimensions of the supercoil are unknown.

REGULATION OF RNA AND PROTEIN SYNTHESIS

The structural importance of histone seems beyond question, but it has also been suggested that histone functions is a gene regulator [20]. Thus it is essential that the fundamental requirements for gene regulation be understood.

A most stimulating theory by Jacob and Monod [21] concerning the regulation of enzyme synthesis suggests that enzyme induction and enzyme repression operate by very similar mechanisms. The basic elements of the control system are a structural gene, a regulator gene, and an operator gene. The structural gene produces a messenger RNA molecule which serves as the template for protein or enzyme synthesis. The regulator gene produces a repressor RNA molecule which can interact with the operator gene. The operator gene is always adjacent to the structural gene it controls; indeed, it may be part of it. When the repressor combines with the operator gene, it prevents the structural gene from making messenger RNA. Metabolites can influence the repressor-operator complex in two ways: In induction, the inducing metabolite is thought to combine with the repressor to prevent its interaction with the operator gene; in repression, the combination of the repressing metabolite and the repressor RNA is believed to facilitate interaction with the operator gene. This theory is summarized in Figure 7. An alternative theory is also suggested, in which control is exerted not at the level of RNA synthesis, but at the level of protein synthesis. Here the controlling elements are basically similar, but the repressor interacts with the RNA product of the operator gene (broken lines in Fig. 7). These two theories are considered mutually exclusive, the former being favored by Jacob and Monod. Although developed primarily to explain enzyme adaptation in bacteria, the regulator-operator concept might also apply to higher organisms, and, with various

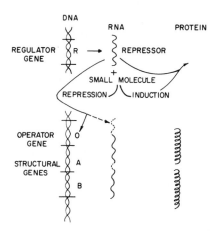

Fig. 7.—Jacob-Monod model for the regulation of protein synthesis.

modifications, account for the regulation of protein synthesis in general [22] . McClintock [23] has demonstrated the existence of regulator-operator-like control systems in maize.

There are certain drawbacks to the Jacob-Monod theory. First, it is difficult, if not impossible, to imagine how small-molecule metabolites can form specific complexes with RNA because the adaptability of a poly-nucleotide chain (in contrast to a protein polypeptide chain) does not seem sufficient to allow the production of binding sites of the required specificity. (However, there is no proof of this statement; it is a tentative conclusion reached after considerable inspection of molecular models.) Second, com-bination of the repressor RNA and the operator gene presumably involves the formation of Watson-Crick-like base pairing between the two polynu-cleotides. One can see how the inducing agent could destroy this by inter-action with repressor RNA, but is is difficult to understand how a repressing metabolite could provide a favorable base pairing situation where one did not previously exist.

The only known specific complexes formed by metabolites and RNA are those of amino acids and transfer RNA. The formation of these com-plexes is catalyzed by enzymes. This suggests a solution to the first ob-jection, and in fact has been proposed by Paigen [24] . In his theory, the repressor RNA produces an enzyme that mediates the formation of a specific repressor RNA and metabolite complex. A simpler hypothesis would be that the regulator locus produces an RNA to serve as a template for the synthesis of a repressor protein, since it is clear that, with the latter, a metabolite could form a specific complex. One could also imagine that in induction the interaction of the metabolite would compete with the operator locus, or, in repression, that the repressing metabolite could interact in a cooperative way, so as to augment the binding of the repressor by the operator gene. These types of specific binding are well known, and the system proposed here (Fig. 8) appears to resolve all major objections to the original Jacob-Monod theory.

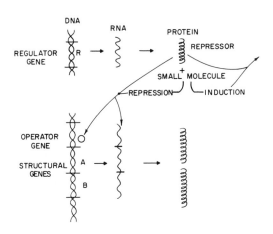

Fig. 8.—General model for the regulation of protein synthesis.

The next question to be considered is the level—gene or messenger RNA—at which the repressor operates. Yanagisawa [25] has suggested it may operate at both levels. The various possibilities were further explored.

The first consideration is the mode of synthesis of RNA. It is quite clear that DNA is involved as primer, and that a single chain of DNA can serve as the template for the synthesis of a complementary chain of RNA. The results of Geidushek, Nakamoto, and Weiss [26], Wood and Berg [27], and Warner et al. [28] indicate that the main difference between single-chain DNA and native double-chain DNA is that the product of the former is a DNA-RNA complex double helix, whereas the product of the latter is RNA fully dissociated from the DNA. This suggests that native DNA serves as a template for RNA synthesis via the following steps: (1) local unwinding of the DNA, (2) synthesis of RNA on one chain of the DNA as template, and (3) release of the RNA from the DNA template by the rewinding of the DNA double helix. These steps, depicted in Figure 9, suggest three sites of action for the hypothetical repressor protein: (1) the DNA chain that serves as the template for RNA synthesis; (2) the DNA chain that serves as the "release factor"; or (3) the messenger RNA product. These possibilities are not mutually exclusive, since the sequences of bases in 2 and 3 should be the same. If the repressor protein specificity resides in its interaction with a specific sequence of bases, it could interact simultaneously with 2 and 3 or singly with 1.

RNA   SYNTHESIS

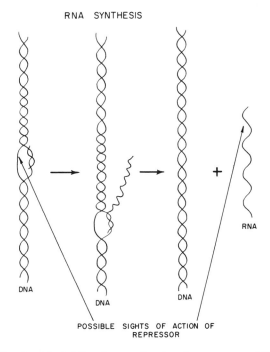

POSSIBLE SIGHTS OF ACTION OF
REPRESSOR

Fig. 9.—Model for the synthesis of messenger RNA.

ROLE OF HISTONE

To support the idea that histones act as gene repressors, it has been shown in vitro [29] that DNA, not nucleohistone, acts as primer for RNA synthesis. These in vitro incorporation studies, unfortunately, require such salt concentration that one would expect aggregation of most nucleohistone. Since gross aggregation in vivo seems unlikely, these observations alone are not strong support for the histone-repressor concept in vivo.

X-ray diffraction studies suggest that in vitro the histone is deposited uniformly along the surface of the DNA [5], and therefore histone would have to be locally removed before the DNA can serve as a template for RNA synthesis. In this sense, histone could be regarded as a repressor. However, according to presently available data, the interaction between histone and DNA is primarily nonspecific and electrostatic. Since histone is heterogeneous, it is not impossible that a small fraction of what is now collectively called histone functions as a class of specific-site repressor proteins.* However, histones are not found in bulk in bacterial systems

---

*Since this paper was presented, Monod, Changeux, and Jacob [31] have also suggested that protein is most likely to act as gene repressor.

[30] in which regulation of protein synthesis is highly developed. For these reasons it seems likely that most histones function solely as structural proteins, which, during mitosis, facilitate chromosome coiling and, during interphase, permit development of differential chromosomal activity.

Acknowledgments

The experimental work described here represents the joint effort of several people: Drs. E. Blout, E. M. Bradbury, P. Doty, A. Elliott, H. E. Huxley, W. C. Price, M. H. F. Wilkins, G. R. Wilkinson, and H. R. Wilson.

The author has profited from recent discussions with Drs. J. A. Bergeron, E. M. Bradbury, A. Cole, G. Donnelly, A. H. Sparrow, and J. H. Taylor. He also wishes to acknowledge the assistance of Mrs. Mac Zubay in the preparation of the manuscript.

This research was carried out at Brookhaven National Laboratory under the auspices of the United States Atomic Energy Commission.

REFERENCES

1.   Mirsky, A. E., and Ris, H., J. Gen. Physiol., 34, 475, 1951.

2.   Cruft, H. J., Mauritzen, C. M., and Stedman, E., Phil. Trans. Roy. Soc. London, Ser. B, 241, 93, 1957.

3.   Zubay, G., and Doty, P., J. Mol. Biol., 1, 1, 1959.

4.   Bradbury, E. M., Price, W. C., Wilkinson, G. R., and Zubay, G., J. Mol. Biol., 4, 50, 1962.

5.   Wilkins, M. H. F., Zubay, G., and Wilson, H. R., J. Mol. Biol., 1, 179, 1959.

6.   Zubay, G., and Wilkins, M. H. F., J. Mol. Biol., 4, 444, 1962.

7.   Huxley, H. E., and Zubay, G., J. Biophys. Biochem. Cytol., 11, 273, 1961.

8.   Davies, H. G., and Spencer, M., J. Cell Biol., 14, 445, 1962.

9.   Caspersson, T., Chromosoma, 4, 605, 1940.

10.   Wilkins, M. H. F., Biochem. Soc. Symp., 14, 13, 1956.

11.   Wilkins, M. H. F., Cold Spring Harbor Symp. Quant. Biol., 21, 75, 1956.

12. Ris, H., Colloq. Ges. Physiol. Chem. Mosbach/Baden, 1958–59.

13. Kaufmann, B. P., and McDonald, M. R., Cold Spring Harbor Symp. Quant. Biol., 22, 223, 1956.

14. De Robertis, E. D. P., Nowinski, W. W., and Saez, F. A., Gen. Cytol., (2d ed., Philadelphia: W. B. Saunders, 1954).

15. Taylor, J. H., Woods, P. S., and Hughes, W. L., Proc. Natl. Acad. Sci. U. S. A., 43, 122, 1957.

16. Simon, E. H., J. Mol. Biol., 3, 101, 1961.

17. Taylor, J. H., Sci. Amer., 198, 36, 1958.

18. Ingram, V. M., Nature, 183, 1797, 1959.

19. Helinski, D. R., and Yanofsky, C., Proc. Natl. Acad. Sci. U. S. A., 48, 173, 1962.

20. Stedman, E., and Stedman, E., Nature, 166, 780, 1950.

21. Jacob, F., and Monod, J., J. Mol. Biol., 3, 318, 1961.

22. Monod, J., and Jacob, F., Cold Spring Harbor Symp. Quant. Biol., 26, 389, 1961.

23. McClintock, B., Am. Naturalist, 95, 265, 1961.

24. Paigen, K., J. Theoret. Biol., 3, 268, 1962.

25. Yanagisawa, K., Biochem. Biophys. Res. Commun., 10, 226, 1963.

26. Geidushek, P., Nakamoto, T., and Weiss, S., Proc. Natl. Acad. Sci. U. S. A., 47, 405, 1961.

27. Wood, W. B., and Berg, P., Proc. Natl. Acad. Sci. U. S. A., 48, 94, 1962.

28. Warner, R. C., Samuels, H. H., Abbott, M. T., and Krakow, J. S., Proc. Natl. Acad. Sci. U. S. A., 49, 533, 1963.

29. Bonner, J., and Huang, R. C., J. Mol. Biol., 6, 169, 1963.

30. Zubay, G., and Watson, M. R., J. Biophys. Biochem. Cytol., 5, 51, 1959.

31. Monod, J., Changeux, J.-P., and Jacob, F., J. Mol. Biol., 6, 306, 1963.

Brian M. Richards

X-RAY DIFFRACTION AND ELECTRON MICROSCOPIC STUDIES OF NUCLEOHISTONES

INTRODUCTION

An important aspect of investigations on cell structure and function is the study of the structure of the component parts of cells in terms of the associations between the macromolecules of which they are composed. The successful determination of the structure of DNA has given great impetus to this approach. In particular, it has led to attempts to correlate the X-ray diffraction patterns and electron microscope images of the cell structure. Chromosomes are among the most interesting of the cell structures that can be studied in this way. This article describes some of the work done at King's College, London, on nucleohistone and cell nuclei, with the general aim of learning something about the structure of chromosomes.

X-RAY DIFFRACTION PATTERNS FROM EXTRACTED NUCLEOHISTONE AND CHANGES WITH DRYING

X-ray diffraction from nucleohistone consists mainly of diffuse rings and poorly oriented arcs. The patterns are much less sharp than those from DNA alone, and a general rule is that the less basic the protein of the nucleoprotein the less sharp the X-ray diffraction pattern. Lysine-rich nucleohistone [1], for example, shows a well-oriented pattern of arcs in which some of the features of the DNA pattern are visible (in particular the 3.4 Å spacing due to the stacking of the nitrogen bases along the DNA double helix) while the best-oriented pictures of wet extracted nucleohistone (Fig. 1) show only a series of rings at 12, 16, 21, 30, and 38 Å and an equatorial arc at 34 Å. If we consider only the reflections that correspond to spacings of 35 Å or larger, we find that the X-ray diffraction pattern of nucleohistone taken at a series of decreasing relative

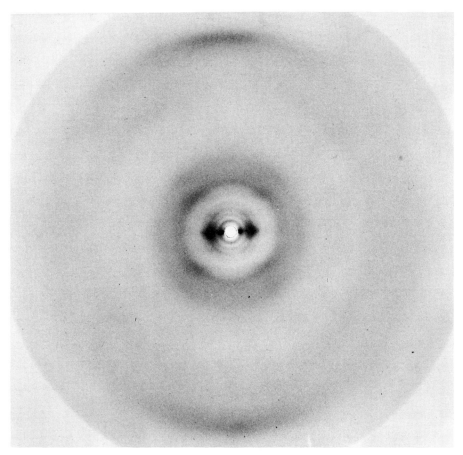

Fig. 1.—Best oriented X-ray diffraction picture of wet nucleohistone. Pattern shows rings at 12, 16, 21, 30, and 38 Å, and equatorial arcs at 34 Å. From Wilkins, Zubay, and Wilson [2].

humidities shows a characteristic series of changes. The changes are summarized in Table 1.

As a nucleohistone preparation dries, the 38 Å ring seen in the wet state is replaced by a 35 Å ring that orients into a meridional arc at lower humidities. When the specimen is almost dry, however, the 35 Å arc disappears and a 37 Å ring of weak intensity is found. As complete dryness is approached, a meridional arc at 75 Å appears and becomes very strong in fully dried specimens. A possible explanation for these observations is seen in Figure 2.

The 38 Å reflection seen in the wet nucleohistone may be from the separation between the parallel DNA double helices. In the wet nucleohistone, the protein lies as a gel between the DNA helices and gives no

TABLE 1

Low-angle spacings in X-ray diffraction patterns from extracted
nucleohistone at various stages of drying

Spacings	Relative Humidity			
	Wet	98% (~30% water in specimen)	75% (~15% water in specimen)	35%
35–38 Å region	38 Å ring	35 Å ring or meridional arc	35 Å meridional arc	37 Å spacing (weak)
75 Å spacing	–	–	75 Å arc	75 Å meridional arc (very strong)

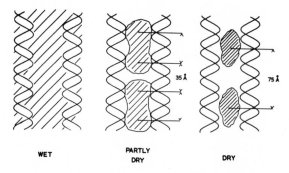

Fig. 2.—Schematic interpretation of changes in relative intensity in X-ray
diffraction patterns of nucleohistone at successive stages of drying.

well-defined X-ray diffraction pattern. If we assume that the histone molecules cross-link adjacent DNA helices at the point of shortest distance
between helices, then the linkages will be separated by about 35 Å, which
is about the length of the helix pitch. During the initial stages of drying,
the histone molecules shrink and may tend to concentrate at the points of
linkage to the DNA; this may be why the relative intensity of the reflection at 35 Å increases. As drying progresses, the relative intensity of
this reflection continues to increase and also becomes better oriented

meridionally, indicating a periodicity along the DNA helix axis. The intense 75 Å reflection in dry nucleoprotein may be due to contraction of
histone molecules—each associated with two pitch lengths of the DNA
helix—to the point where successive histone molecules come to lie as
dense blobs separated by 75 Å along the long axis of the DNA helix.

X-RAY DIFFRACTION PATTERNS FROM ISOLATED
ERYTHROCYTE NUCLEI

Wilkins, Zubay, and Wilson [2] described the X-ray diffraction pattern of isolated chick erythrocyte nuclei mounted in 0.14 M NaCl as showing a ring reflection corresponding to a spacing of 38 Å. More recently,
Spencer (unpublished) found a ring at 39 Å for frog erythrocytes. These
spacings may be the separation between adjacent DNA helices, as is thought
to be the situation in extracted nucleohistone. In addition, Spencer (unpublished), who used a crystal monochromator and a low-angle camera, found
rings at 3.2, 12, and 62 Å. This last reflection might be due to the lipids
of the cell membranes that are not removed by the preparative procedure.
     Unfixed wet preparations of erythrocyte nuclei seem, therefore, to
show the main reflection at 38-39 Å, as in unfixed wet preparations of
nucleohistone. If we are to attempt to correlate the features of the X-ray
diffraction patterns with the electron microscope images we must also
investigate the possible changes in the material wrought by the preparative procedures for electron microscopy. Huxley and Zubay [4] fixed
stretched fibers of extracted nucleohistone in osmium fixative containing
10^{-2} M calcium chloride (similar to the fixative used by Kellenberger,
Ryter, and Sechaud [5], but with no amino acids) and then dehydrated and
embedded the material in Araldite before placing it in the X-ray camera.
In the resulting diffraction pattern they found reflections at 37 Å and 66 Å
in addition to smaller spacings. Therefore they suggested that the X-ray
diffraction pattern from the nucleohistone as prepared for electron microscopy corresponded to the pattern from unfixed, fully hydrated fibers of
nucleohistone.
     The difficulties that can arise in studies of this kind can be illus-
trated by the results of some preliminary experiments we have recently
made to compare the X-ray diffraction pattern from unfixed, wet nuclei
of frog erythrocytes with that after osmium fixation (with or without 0.01 M
calcium chloride), dehydration, and embedding in methacrylate. The diffraction from the small amounts of crystalline material was strong enough
to overshadow the weaker diffraction from the erythrocytes.
     Blood was aspirated directly from the beating heart of a pithed frog
and hemolyzed immediately in a fixing solution in which the osmium tetroxide was replaced with saponin to a final concentration of 0.3%. After

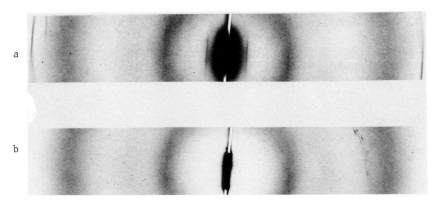

Fig. 3.—(a) Low-angle picture of frog erythrocytes, saponin-haemolyzed, fixed, and embedded in methacrylate polymerized at 48 C. Pattern shows diffuse rings at 12 Å and 4.8 - 5 Å and sharp reflections at 35, 12, 4.2, and 3.8 Å. (b) Methacrylate polymerized at 48 C, showing diffuse rings at 12 Å and 4.8 - 5 Å.

washing, the hemolyzed cells were fixed in osmium tetroxide (plus calcium) dehydrated and embedded in methacrylate and sealed in stainless steel cells with mica windows. Polymerization of the methacrylate was by heating at 48 C overnight. Exposure times were 2-4 days.

Several spacings were observed (Fig. 3). Diffuse rings at near 12 Å and 4.8-5 Å are due to the polymerized methacrylate; the other reflections are from the erythrocytes. Dense scattering at 100 Å upwards at the center of the picture is bordered by less dense scattering corresponding to spacings between 75-100 Å. Sharp reflections at 35, 12, 4.2, and 3.8 Å are much sharper than reflections from unfixed preparations. A preliminary interpretation is that some of these sharp reflections may arise from changes in the saponin-treated lipids of the cell membranes, in much the same way as those described by Dourmashkin, Dougherty, and Harris [6]. These authors described well-defined rings 30 ± 5 Å thick, separated from each other by a distance of at least 10 Å. Work is in progress to establish which, if any, of the X-ray diffraction reflections described here are due to the nucleohistone and which to induced crystallinity in saponin-treated and heat-polymerized specimens.

ELECTRON MICROSCOPY OF ERYTHROCYTE NUCLEI

Erythrocyte nuclei have been studied extensively in the electron microscope by Davies and his collaborators. A very recent observation by Tooze and Davies [7] that, in the nuclei of intact cells, hemoglobin not only surrounds the chromosomes (nuclear pool hemoglobin), but is also within them, is obviously relevant to any attempt to correlate X-ray diffraction patterns with appearances in the electron microscope. This demarcation into pool and chromosome is striking in chick and frog erythrocytes and appears to be a general phenomenon.

The evidence for the presence of hemoglobin was attained in the following way. The same 0.1μ section was photographed first in ultraviolet light to determine the location and amount of hemoglobin, and then in the electron microscope for identification of chromosome and "pool" regions. Figure 4 shows a densitometer trace over a cell and the photographs in ultraviolet light and in the electron microscope. The trace begins (a) with zero absorption in the background, rises sharply (b) for the hemoglobin of the cytoplasm, falls for the chromosome region (c), and rises once more for the central hemoglobin "pool" (d). The important feature of the trace is that appreciable ultraviolet light absorption is found for the chromosome region. Tooze and Davies checked that this was not simply due to inclusion of part of a pool above or below a chromosome body by measuring the absorption of successively thinner sections until they found measurable light absorption in sections about one-tenth the diameter of an average chromosome body. Chromosomal hemoglobin was shown to have an absorption spectrum similar to that of the cytoplasm. Hemoglobin appears, therefore, to be present in close association with the chromosomes of erythrocyte nuclei, and Tooze and Davies have suggested that there may be an electrostatic association—similar to that between DNA and histone—between the negatively charged phosphate groups on the DNA and the hemoglobin, which has a net positive charge. Calculations show that the nuclear hemoglobin, which is 40-50% of the chromosome mass, would satisfy less than about 3% of the total possible charge on the DNA, and would not necessarily interfere with the electrostatic binding between DNA and histone. The possible association between hemoglobin and DNA has led Davies and Tooze to suggest that this interaction may be partly responsible for nuclear structure in erythrocytes and, further, that this may be the mechanism by which the product (hemoglobin) is responsible for "turning off" its own synthesis.

It is clearly important to be aware of this association, because all studies of erythrocyte nuclei by X-ray diffraction have of necessity been done on hemolyzed cells. The appearance in the electron microscope of the nuclear material of erythrocytes is very sensitive to preparative procedures. Davies [8] and Davies and Spencer [3] have shown that two features are especially important. The first is the presence or absence of calcium ions (0.01 M, pH 6.3) in the osmium fixative, and the second is the presence or absence of hemoglobin.

In intact erythrocytes—those that were not hemolyzed before fixing— without calcium ions in the fixative, the chromosome material of the nuclei appears as an open network; if calcium ions are present, it has a very compact uniform appearance. After lead staining, the zero-calcium nuclei show anastomosing threads of variable diameters predominantly in the range 100-200 Å; in plus-calcium nuclei, most threads are about 20-40 Å (Davies, unpublished).

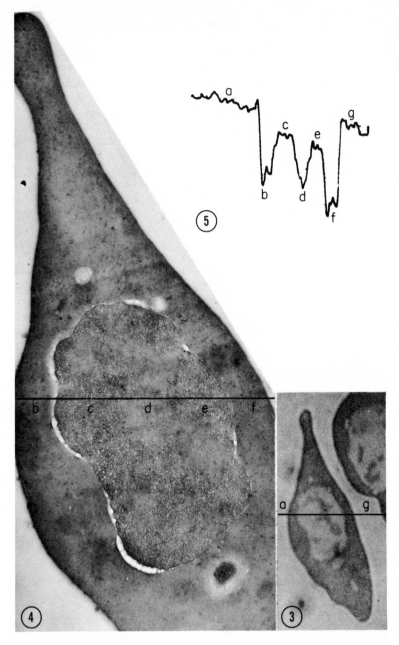

Fig. 4.—Demonstration of hemoglobin within the chromosome regions of frog erythrocyte nuclei. (From Tooze and Davies [7]).

As a better basis for comparison between X-ray data and electron microscope appearance, Davies and Spencer [3] also studied erythrocyte nuclei that had been hemolyzed before fixation. In such cells the presence of calcium ions had a profound effect on the appearance. The zero-calcium nuclei showed an open structure, with thread diameters around 100-200 Å and, occasionally, 20-40 Å. The zero-calcium sections were more condensed than those from corresponding nonhemolyzed cells, possibly because the absence of hemoglobin allowed greater binding of the calcium ions to DNA. The unanswered question is whether the fine threads (20-40 Å) tend to occur as organized units 100-200 Å in diameter that are less apparent because of the close packing in the plus-calcium isolated nuclei.

Summary

1. Correlation of X-ray diffraction patterns and electron microscopic appearance of biological structures containing nucleohistone is very difficult, but is likely to be of considerable importance in relation to chromosome structure. The cells that have been most studied—nucleated erythrocytes—present the special difficulty that hemoglobin seems to be a part of the intact structure, but is normally removed before studies for X-ray diffraction and normally retained in preservation for study in the electron microscope.

2. Low-angle X-ray diffraction data on isolated erythrocyte nuclei show similarities to that from extracted nucleohistone, but the interpretation of the data in terms of molecular structure of nucleohistone and nucleoprotein in nuclei or chromosomes is far from certain.

3. The strong 75 Å reflection in the X-ray diffraction pattern from dry nucleohistone suggests that the electron microscope should perhaps show a similar repeat unit. Thus far, the observed structures in the electron microscope pictures are fibers ranging from 20-40 Å up to structures several hundred Å in diameter. Furthermore, their appearance is highly dependent on the presence or absence of calcium ions in the fixative, and on many other factors, such as the pH of fixing. Much work clearly remains to be done.

Acknowledgments

Several people have been involved in this work. The author wishes particularly to thank for considerable help in the preparation of the manuscript Professor M. H. F. Wilkins, Drs. H. G. Davies, M. Spencer, H. R. Wilson, and more recently, Mr. J. Tooze. Sir John Randall kindly provided the necessary facilities.

REFERENCES

1. Wilkins, M. H. F., Cold Spring Harbor Symp., 21, 75, 1956.

2. Wilkins, M. H. F., Zubay, G., and Wilson, H. R., J. Mol. Biol., 1, 179, 1959.

3. Davies, H. G., and Spencer, M., J. Cell Biol., 14, 445, 1962.

4. Huxley, H. E., and Zubay, G., J. Biophys. Biochem. Cytol., 11, 273, 1961.

5. Kellenberger, E., Ryter, A., and Sechaud, J., J. Biophys. Biochem. Cytol., 4, 671, 1958.

6. Dourmashkin, R. R., Dougherty, R. M., and Harris, R. C. J., Nature, 194, 1116, 1961.

7. Tooze, J., and Davies, H.G., J. Cell Biol., 16, 501, 1963.

8. Davies, H. G., J. Biophys. Biochem. Cytol., 9, 671, 1961.

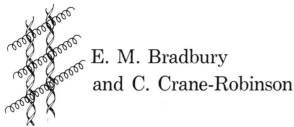
E. M. Bradbury
and C. Crane-Robinson

PHYSICAL STUDIES OF THE MOLECULAR CONFIGURATIONS OF HISTONE AND OF NUCLEOHISTONE

INTRODUCTION

The nuclei of all cells of higher organisms, with the exception of the sperm heads of certain species, contain DNA in combination with the basic protein histone and possibly a small amount of nonbasic protein. This nucleohistone complex is an important constituent of chromosomes and in some cells forms the major part. In recent years, attempts have been made to elucidate the molecular structure of nucleohistone as a first step toward understanding the way in which chromosomes are built up.

X-ray diffraction studies have shown that the structure of DNA is the same whether in isolation or in combination with histone or protamine [1, 2], and these findings have been supported by spectroscopic studies of oriented films of DNA and nucleoprotein with polarized infrared radiation [3, 4]. It has not been possible to determine the conformation of the protein component of nucleohistone from X-ray diffraction data, although similar studies have led to proposals concerning the structure of nucleoprotamine [1]. The uncertainty in the case of nucleohistone results from the diffuse nature of the diffraction patterns so far obtained for both extracted total histone and nucleohistone [2, 5]. Unless the diffuse nature of these patterns is a result of preparative procedures that can be improved by further biochemical studies, X-ray diffraction methods are unlikely to lead to the determination of a unique molecular structure—if such a structure in fact exists.

To decide how much is known about the structure of the nucleohistone complex, it is necessary at this stage to consider the results obtained by other techniques, notably infrared spectroscopy, optical rotatory dispersion, and deuteration, and to discuss these results together with those obtained from X-ray diffraction.

TECHNIQUES

In general, the most important technique employed in structural de-terminations of complex molecules is X-ray diffraction, although it must be stressed that it gives information mainly about those regions of the specimen where the molecules are in an ordered array, i.e., the crystal-line regions, and gives little information regarding the other parts. In-frared spectroscopy, particularly the study of oriented films with polar-ized infrared radiation, is a very useful complementary technique in structural studies and, moreover, gives information concerning the whole specimen and not just the crystalline regions. Although it is not easy to interpret the X-ray diffraction patterns obtained from macromolecules in solution, some very interesting recent results obtained by this technique [6-8] could lead to a re-evaluation of ideas concerning polypeptide con-formations in solution. Infrared spectroscopy is also difficult to apply to aqueous protein solutions because of the intense absorption of H_2O in the regions of main interest, i.e., at 3 and 6 μ. Meaningful results can, how-ever, be obtained by using concentrated solutions in D_2O. For investiga-tions into protein and polypeptide conformations in solution the most use-ful technique is optical rotation and optical rotatory dispersion, particu-larly since measurements may be made in aqueous solution. The deu-teration rates of proteins in solution often provide evidence for intra-chain shielding of peptide hydrogen atoms and indicate whether or not folded structures are present. Both optical rotatory dispersion tech-niques and deuteration can also be applied to solid films though care has to be exercised in interpreting the results.

X-ray Diffraction

Briefly, the X-ray diffraction patterns obtained for fibers of biological macromolecules are compared with the patterns calculated for proposed model structures. A series of model structures are constructed, with acceptable bond angles and bond lengths, until a stereochemically rea-sonable structure is found whose calculated diffraction pattern agrees closely with the observed. The bond angles and bond lengths used in model building are taken from the conformations determined for similar groups in simpler compounds. It is essential to know the chemical struc-ture of the subunits from which the biological polymer is built up before a structural determination can be undertaken. In this way, the structure of the macromolecule in the crystalline regions can be established, pro-vided the X-ray diffraction pattern contains sufficient information that ambiguities do not arise.

Infrared Spectroscopy

The existence of characteristic group frequencies in infrared spectra is well known, and in particular the vibrations of the amide group give rise to a set of characteristic bands. Some of these have been shown to be conformation sensitive, notably the amide I (1,660-1,620 cm^{-1}) and the amide II (1,560-1,520 cm^{-1}) [9, 10]. Studies on polypeptides show that the α-helix is associated with bands at ca. 1,660 cm^{-1} for the amide I and at ca. 1,555 cm^{-1} for the amide II and that the extended β-structure is associated with bands at ca. 1,630 and 1,530 cm^{-1}, respectively. This frequency-conformation correlation has been used extensively in infrared spectroscopic studies of proteins, although it was subsequently pointed out that conformations other than the α-helix can give rise to bands in the 1,650-1,660 cm^{-1} region [11-14]. It is only recently that the detailed reasons underlying this conformation-frequency dependence have been understood. Recent papers have evaluated the effects of interactions between vibrations of amide groups, both along the polypeptide chain and across the hydrogen bonds [15-17]. These interactions are different for the various conformations of polypeptide chains. The essential correctness of these ideas has been verified for the behavior of the amide I band from a study of polypeptides in the extended form and a homologous series of polyamides [18]. This work has led to different, and it is believed more accurate, values for the interaction constants. It is now possible to use frequency-conformation correlations with more confidence; the presence of an amide I band at ca. 1,630 cm^{-1} indicates that the polypeptide is in the extended form, and if this band is accompanied by a higher frequency band at ca. 1,690 cm^{-1} then the arrangement of chains is antiparallel. Both the α-helix and random coil forms are expected to give rise to an amide I band in the 1,650-1,660 cm^{-1} region, as experimentally observed by Elliott. The occurrence of a band in this region is not sufficient to prove the presence of the helical form unless it is supported by additional evidence, e.g., from dichroic studies, optical rotatory dispersion, or deuteration.

If it is possible to obtain oriented films of biological polymers, e.g., proteins, DNA, or nucleoproteins, then the use of polarized infrared radiation can give very important information concerning their conformations. Each group vibration giving rise to a characteristic frequency has associated with it a transition moment, which is the vector representing the maximum change of dipole moment during the vibration and is the direction along which the E-vector of the radiation must lie for maximum absorption. The directions of the transition moments for the various vibrations are obtained from studies on simple model compounds, and it is assumed that the direction does not change greatly when the group becomes part of a polymer chain. In an ordered film of macromolecules the transition moments of the different vibrations lie in preferred directions, and if the spectrum is recorded by polarized infrared radiation with the E-vector parallel and then perpendicular to the direction of orientation, dichroic effects are usually observed. By measuring the dichroic ratios for the various bands associated with the group and knowing the approximate directions of the transition moments for the vibrations involved, the orientation of the group relative to the axis of the molecule can be found. For example, the transition moment associated with the N-H stretching vibration lies within 5° of the N-H bond direction, and in the α-helix the N-H bond lies approximately parallel to the helix axis. This band therefore exhibits high parallel dichroism. For the normal β-structure, in which the N-H bond lies approximately perpendicular to the axis of the polypeptide chain, high perpendicular dichroism is observed. Since a random chain conformation would be expected to show no dichroic effects, the presence of a band at ca. 1,660 cm^{-1} showing parallel dichroism indicates a helical chain. It must be pointed out that the uncertainties in the method with regard to transition-moment directions and the interpretation of dichroism are such that only the approximate orientation of the group is obtained, and it is not possible by this method to distinguish between the different helical structures that have been proposed for polypeptides and proteins.

Optical Rotatory Dispersion

For optically active polypeptides and proteins in helical conformations, Cohen [19] pointed out that there should be a form rotation, which can either reinforce or reduce that caused by the asymmetric centers. This form rotation was observed by several workers [20, 21], and of several attempts to calculate this dispersion, that of Moffitt has proved to be the most useful [22, 23], although it was later shown that the treatment was not theoretically sound [24]. However, the equation proposed by Moffitt has been found to fit the experimental data with reasonable accuracy. The optical rotation as a function of wavelength is represented by a two-term expression:

$$(R_{vac.})_\lambda = a_o \lambda_o^2/(\lambda^2 - \lambda_o^2) + b_o \lambda_o^4/(\lambda^2 - \lambda_o^2)^2,$$

where $(R_{vac.})_\lambda$ is the residue rotation in vacuo at wavelength λ given by

$$(R_{vac.})_\lambda = \frac{[\alpha]_\lambda M}{100} \frac{3}{n^2 + 2} .$$

$[\alpha]_\lambda$ is the specific rotation, M the residue weight and n the refractive index.

The constant a_O is expected to depend on the nature of the side chain and the solvent, whereas λ_O and b_O should be intrinsic properties of the helical skeleton, provided interactions between side-chain chromophores can be neglected. $(R_{vac.})_\lambda$. $(\lambda^2 - \lambda_O^2)$ is plotted against $1/(\lambda^2 - \lambda_O^2)$, λ_O being chosen to give the best fit to a straight line. Determination of λ_O by this method requires accurate results over a wide wavelength range. If such data are not obtainable, the value of $\lambda_O = 2,120$ Å is used. It has been shown experimentally [25] that for poly-γ-benzyl-L-glutamate and poly-L-glutamic acid in a variety of solvents, $\lambda_O = 2,120 \pm 50$ Å and b_O is in the range -580 to -660°. The values of b_O obtained from the rotatory dispersion of proteins have been used to make an estimate of the helical content by taking a value of $b_O = -630°$ as representing 100% helix. The value of 70-80% obtained in this way for the helical content of myoglobin [26] is in close agreement with that determined by Kendrew and his co-workers (77%) from their X-ray diffraction results. An excellent and exhaustive review of the application of optical rotation and optical rotatory dispersion to proteins and polypeptides has recently been published [27].

The optical rotatory dispersion of solid films is more difficult to measure than that of solutions. The films are cast onto strain-free glass [13], great care being taken that no birefringent material whatsoever is present. Caution has to be exercised in interpreting the data as a result of possible side-chain orientation. In solutions, the side-chain chromophores are generally free to rotate and will not contribute to the rotatory dispersion unless they are very close to the polypeptide backbone and thereby restricted. In solid films of polypeptides the side chains are frozen, and if they have an ordered spatial arrangement with respect to the helix axis, the side-chain chromophores can contribute to the dispersion. Thus, whereas for solid films of poly-γ-benzyl-L-glutamate in the α-helical form [28]. the value of b_O is -800°, that observed for poly-β-benzyl-L-aspartate, in which the main side-chain chromophores are closer to the peptide backbone, is -3,560° [29]. In complex proteins such as the histones it is unlikely that runs of identical amino acids occur in sufficient numbers to give spurious results, and thus b_O values obtained from solid films can be used for a rough estimate of helical content.

Deuteration

Measurement of the deuteration rates of peptide hydrogens in proteins and polypeptides can often indicate the presence or absence of a folded structure and sometimes reveals whether more than one such structure is present. In solutions of globular proteins, the presence of a slowly exchanging fraction of hydrogen atoms (first observed by Lenormant and Blout [30]) has been attributed by Linderstrøm-Lang and his co-workers to those involved in intrachain hydrogen bonding. For polypeptides in solution, it has been observed [31] that, whereas the amide hydrogens of poly-γ-benzyl-L-glutamate in the random-coil form exchange very rapidly, in the α-helical form little exchange takes place even after several weeks. There is little doubt that for poly-γ-benzyl-L-glutamate the residual hydrogen is in the amide group, since this is the only labile hydrogen, and the exchange is readily followed by observing the change in intensity of the N-H stretching band. With proteins it is not always certain that the slowly exchanging hydrogens reside in the amide group, since labile hydrogens in the side chains may be present in ionized groups and thus resistant to exchange at certain pH values [32]. A study with NMR of the deuteration rates of ribonuclease [33] has shown that in this case the resistant hydrogens are in the side-chain guanidinium groups. Whether resistant hydrogens occur in the side chains of proteins can readily be checked if the exchange is followed by infrared spectroscopy. The amide II band at 1,520-1,560 cm^{-1} in protein spectra results from a mixed vibration involving the N-H bend and C-N stretch and disappears on complete deuteration of the amide groups. If a residual amide II band is observed in the spectrum of the partly deuterated protein, there can be no doubt that some slowly exchanging amide hydrogens are present. The observation that a protein film is deuterated rapidly is a clear indication of the presence of a random form. If, however, a slowly exchanging fraction of peptide hydrogens is noted, it is impossible to decide on the basis of the deuteration rates alone whether the hydrogens are shielded by intrachain folding or are prevented from exchanging rapidly by the regular packing of the polypeptide chains in crystallites, into which the D$_2$O molecules cannot readily penetrate. A decision between these two possibilities can sometimes be made on the basis of the residual amide II frequency.

HISTONES

All the physical measurements so far made on extracted histones have involved the total material and not any of the fractions known to make up the histone complex. A comprehensive review of the histones has recently been published by D. M. P. Phillips [34].

De Lozé [35] has made an infrared spectroscopic investigation of total histone prepared by three different methods. The presence of an amide I band at 1,655-1,660 cm^{-1} with a pronounced shoulder at 1,625-1,630 cm^{-1} was observed in the spectra of histones prepared by the method of Gregoire and Limozin [36] and by the method of Crampton, Moore, and Stein [37]. The shoulder is at a frequency characteristic of extended β-chains and is enhanced in intensity by the addition of sodium xylene sulfonate. Histone prepared by de Lozé's third method (which involves extracting nucleohistone according to the method of Crampton, Lipshitz, and Chargaff [38]), precipitating out the DNA with 0.1 N HCl and lyophilizing the supernatant containing the histone gave a single amide I band at 1,655-1,660 cm-1. If this material is treated with sodium xylene sulfonate, a shoulder appears at 1,625-1,630 cm^{-1}. A shoulder has also been observed at ca. 1,630 cm-1 in the spectrum of a film of total histone cast from water [39], the shoulder being reduced in intensity if the histone was cast from ethylene chlorhydrin, a solvent known to favor helix forma-tion. It has been remarked [4] that, whereas fresh histone prepared in a manner similar to de Lozé's third method shows no shoulder at 1,630 cm-1 in the spectrum of films cast from water, a shoulder at this fre-quency has been observed in the spectra of aged, freeze-dried specimens.

The X-ray diffraction patterns of extracted total histone [5] give very diffuse rings in the regions of 4.5 and 10.0 Å. The diffraction pat-terns of histone prepared according to Zubay and Wilkins' method I (which is the same as de Lozé's second method) show a sharp meridional arc at 4.7 Å and a sharp equatorial arc at 10 Å. The interpretation of these sharp reflections is that they arise from the interchain spacing and the intersheet spacing, respectively, of extended polypeptide chains in the β-form. Histone prepared by Zubay and Wilkins' method II gave only very faint rings, and the amide I band showed no shoulder at 1,625-1,630 cm-1 [4]. De Lozé has suggested that the use of ethanol as a precipitant in histone preparation causes denaturation of the protein, which then goes into the β-form. This suggestion receives support from the observations of Zubay and Wilkins.

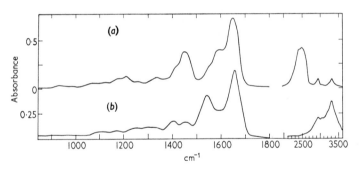

Fig. 1.—Infrared spectra of (a) deuterated histone and (b) histone. (From Bradbury et al. [4].)

The infrared spectra of undenatured histone films show an amide I band in the region 1,650-1,660 cm-1 and an amide II band between 1,535 and 1,545 cm-1 [4, 39-41]. Zubay and Doty and de Lozé used the fre-quency of amide I as an indication that the protein is in the α-helical form; other forms, however, absorb at this frequency, in particular the random coil [11-13, 21, 31], and the observation of such a band is no longer suf-ficient evidence for the presence of α-helices.

The deuteration rates of histone films exposed to D_2O vapor have been measured [4], and a slowly exchanging fraction of amide hydrogens ob-served. The exchange of these residual amide hydrogens, which must arise from the presence of some regular structure in the protein, requires 3 weeks in a film 2 to 3 μ thick. Even this exchange appears to take place because of changes in the histone conformation, because hydrogenation of the fully deuterated protein by exposure to H_2O vapor takes less than an hour and redeuteration is even faster still. The presence of a slowly exchanging fraction in histone can also be seen from the spectrum of a 10% solution of histone in D_2O in which there is a residual amide II band at 1,550 cm-1 [40, 41]. No comment is made, nor, unfortunately, is the time of exposure of the histone to the D_2O given; however, the process of solution should be sufficient to deuterate any random material. The presence of a residual amide II band shows that the resistant hydrogens (if they are of one type only) are in the amide groups and not in the side chain, and its position at 1,550 cm^{-1} indicates a helical form rather than an extended β-structure, since the latter would give a peak at ca. 1,525 cm-1.

Optical rotatory dispersion studies of histone in solution and of solid films also reveal the presence of helical material. In ethylene chlorhydrin solution, the helical content of histone has been quoted as 67% from a de-

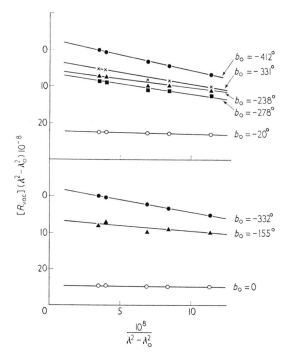

Fig. 2.—Optical rotatory dispersion curves for histone in solid films and in solution. ●, ethylene chlorhydrin solution; o, aqueous solution; ▲, films cast from water; ×, films cast from ethylene chlorhydrin solution of fresh histone; ■, films cast from ethylene chlorhydrin solution of histone 5 days old. (From Elliott, Bradbury, and Zubay [43].)

termination of b_0 [27, 42], and a figure of 65-66% has been given for a similar determination by Elliott, Bradbury, and Zubay [43]. In aqueous solutions a value of 20% has been derived from b_0 determinations [27, 42]. Other investigators [27, 28], however, have shown that for two separate preparations (one fresh and one aged and freeze dried) in 0.5% w/v solution the b_0 values are 0, indicating that the protein is in the form of a solvated random coil. It appears that in dilute water solution most of the histone goes into the random form, and the discrepancy between the above studies may result from slight differences in experimental technique, such as temperature or the length of time before recording the results. The helical content may be a function of concentration, since de Loze's infrared spectra of 10% w/v histone solutions show the presence of a fraction which deuterates slowly. As the specimen ages, it has also been shown [28] that the value of b_0 diminishes, indicating a certain amount of denaturation. Optical rotatory dispersion measurements made on solid films of histone [28], show a contribution from form rotation. For films of fresh histone cast from water, the helical content was estimated at 38%, while for films cast from ethylene chlorhydrin, a value of 53% was obtained. A freeze-dried sample stored for 7 months at 5 C showed a reduced helical content of 24% in films cast from water. Deuteration

TABLE 1*

Preparation	How measured	b_0	λ_0	$\dfrac{b_0}{630}$ x 100%
Z-2-9	Solution in ethylene chlorhydrin	−412°	2121°	65·5%
	Solution in water	−20°		0
	Solution in 8 M urea	−30°		0
	Films cast from ethylene chlorhydrin:			
	(a) Fresh histone	−331°		52·6
	(b) Histone 5 days old	−278°		44
	Films cast from water (fresh histone)	−237°		37·6
Z-1170	Solution in ethylene chlorhydrin	−332°		52·7
	Solution in water	0		0
	Films cast from water	−155°		24·5

*From Elliott, Bradbury, and Zubay [43].

of films cast from the older sample gave the slowly deuterating fraction of hydrogen as 22%, based on the intensity of the residual N-H stretching band [4]. These results possibly indicate that the slowly deuterating fraction is identical with that inferred by optical rotatory dispersion measurements to be in the helical form.

The X-ray diffraction patterns of fresh undenatured histone give two very diffuse rings at 4.5 and 10 Å. Zubay and Wilkins [5] point out the difficulties in interpreting these diffuse patterns and note that while disordered native myoglobin, hemoglobin, and ribonuclease all give similar diffuse patterns [44], their helical contents are known to be very different. Nevertheless, the X-ray data are not inconsistent with the presence of α-helical chains, although they cannot now furnish any more specific information.

Discussion

Infrared and X-ray diffraction studies show that histone readily denatures and that part of it goes into the β-form. De Lozé's suggestion that the use of ethanol as a precipitant partly denatures histone is supported by the X-ray data. The ease with which histone denatures is also shown by the changes in optical rotatory dispersion with time, and it would appear that it is not possible to store extracted histone without irreversible conformational changes.

The X-ray diffraction patterns of fresh undenatured histone are very diffuse and do not furnish positive evidence for the presence of α-helices. However, it is possible to infer from infrared, deuteration, and optical rotation studies that part of the histone is in a folded form and that this is probably the α-helix. Optical rotatory dispersion studies show that about two thirds of the protein is capable of taking up the α-helix in ethylene chlorhydrin, and it is likely that the proline content of 5% prevents further increase in helical content [39]. Although there is somewhat conflicting evidence concerning the amount of histone in the helical form in dilute aqueous solution, it is evident that the greater part of the histone capable of forming helices goes into the random form. It would, however, appear that at high concentrations a certain (undetermined) fraction of the histone slowly deuterates, and is probably in a folded form. The aggregation of histones at higher concentrations may well stabilize the helical component.

NUCLEOHISTONE

The infrared spectrum of nucleohistone in the 3 and 6 μ regions is dominated by the protein bands [4, 40, 41, 45]; the amide I and II frequencies being 1,658 and 1,546 cm^{-1}, respectively. No trace of a shoulder

at 1,625 cm^{-1} characteristic of the β-form has been found in fresh nucleohistone, although de Lozé and Lenormant [45] have shown that the
treatment of nucleohistone with sodium xylene sulfonate results in the
appearance of a strong shoulder at 1,625 cm^{-1}. The amide I frequency
has been used to demonstrate the presence of α-helices [40, 41, 45, 46],
though this evidence is now known to be insufficient. Thin films of nucleohistone have been exposed to D_2O vapor [4], and a slowly exchanging fraction of labile hydrogens was observed that required 3 weeks to
exchange fully. Even this exchange takes place only as a result of changes
in the protein conformation. Penetration of the nucleohistone film by the
D_2O molecules is assumed to take place very readily since the DNA component is observed to undergo complete exchange within a few minutes,
as does a film of isolated DNA [3]. Thus, if the DNA is accessible to
D_2O, the protein component should be also. The fraction of slowly deuterating protein has been estimated to be approximately 58%. The residual amide II band at 1,554 cm^{-1}, which can also be seen in de Lozé's spectrum of nucleohistone in 10% solution, is evidence that the resistant hydrogens are in the amide groups. Its frequency is an indication of the
helical form, since β-forms absorb at ca. 1,530 cm^{-1} and any random
coil material is assumed to have exchanged.

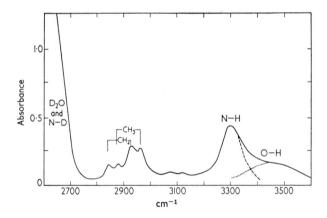

Fig. 3.—Infrared spectrum of partly deuterated nucleohistone in the 3 region.
(From Bradbury et al. [4].)

    Zubay and Doty [39] have measured the specific rotation of nucleo-
histone at 5,460 Å, and by assuming that the specific rotations of the DNA
and protein are additive, have suggested that about half of the histone is
in the helical form. Thus it is assumed that the interaction between the
histone and the DNA does not affect the rotation of either the DNA or the
possible histone conformations. The rotatory dispersion of nucleohistone
gave a curve when plotted in the usual manner. A straight line fitted to
the data by the method of least squares indicated a b_0 value in the region

of -400°, i.e., a helical content of 65%. The authors suggest that these
results indicate that at least half of the histone is in the helical conformation.

It has not been possible to use the X-ray diffraction data to determine
with any certainty the conformation of the protein in nucleohistone. At
high humidities, the diffraction from the histone is not visible [2], and
its disappearance apparently results from the swelling of the protein by
water [5]. In dry nucleohistone fibers, two diffuse rings are found at 4.7
and 9.7 Å which are the regions where diffraction would be expected from
disordered α-helices.

The X-ray diffraction studies of Wilkins and co-workers [2, 47, 48]
have shown that the molecular configuration of DNA is the same in the
nucleohistone complex as in the isolated material. At high humidities
(~98%), although diffuse patterns are obtained, enough characteristic diffraction of the DNA double helix is present to show that the DNA is in
the B configuration. This is also supported by the polarized infrared
studies of Bradbury et al. [4], who show that, in the region of the nucleohistone spectrum free from protein bands (below 1,300 cm^{-1}), the
DNA bands exhibit dichroism and have dichroic ratios of the same sign
and approximately the same magnitude as those observed for oriented
films of isolated DNA. The bands in this region arise from the vibrations
of groups in the phosphate-ester chains of DNA, and the similar dichro-
isms show that the orientation of the phosphate-ester chains are the same
in both cases. Bands arising from vibrations in the DNA bases indicate

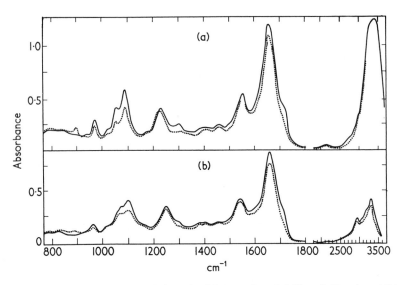

Fig. 4.—Infrared spectrum of nucleohistone (a) at 94% relative humidity and
(b) at 0% relative humidity. Solid line, electric vector perpendicular to direction
of orientation; broken line, electric vector parallel to direction of orientation.
(From Bradbury et al. [4].)

that the latter are approximately perpendicular to the direction of orientation. This fact is also observed by de Lóze on the basis of a polarized infrared study of nucleohistone in the 6 μ region [40]. The presence of a band at 1708 cm^{-1} in the spectrum of DNA at high humidity, which was found to vary with water content, has been used as a conformation-sensitive band to indicate the DNA form present [40, 45]. The results obtained by using this band are, however, in disagreement with the X-ray diffraction studies of Franklin and Gosling [49] for the range of humidities over which the A form of DNA exists and therefore they must be accepted with reservation.

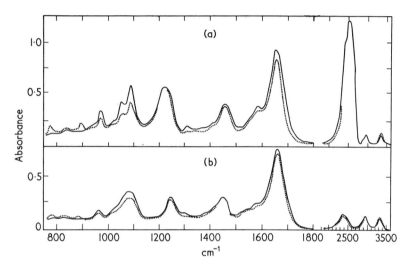

Fig. 5.—Infrared spectrum of partly deuterated nucleohistone (a) at 94% relative humidity and (b) at 0% relative humidity. Notation same as for Figure 4. (From Bradbury et al. [4].)

Although the DNA bands in the polarized infrared spectrum of nucleohistone are highly dichroic, those characteristic of the protein are not [4]. Four amide bands arise from vibrations whose transition moments lie in different directions in the plane of the amide group. There is more than one possible interpretation of the complete absence of dichroism for all the amide bands in the ordered film of nucleohistone where the DNA molecules lie along the direction of orientation. First, there is the obvious one that in spite of the orientation of the DNA molecules, the protein component is completely disordered. However, if it is assumed that a regular structure exists for a reasonable proportion of the nucleohistone (although there is no definite physical evidence to support this assumption yet), then there is only one orientation of the protein with respect to the ordered DNA for which a complete absence of dichroism for all the protein bands would be expected. This is when the axis of a polypeptide helix always makes an angle of 55° to the direction of orientation and has all possible orientations around that direction. The fact that the DNA molecules lie in the direction of orientation and the grooves in the DNA molecule make an angle of approximately 58° to the helix axis suggests that an ordered nucleohistone structure may involve protein lying in the grooves. This has been proposed by Wilkins, Zubay, and Wilson [50], who point out that α-helical structures can fit into the larger of the two grooves and suggest a structure with lengths of α-helical histone wrapped around a single DNA molecule. This structure, however, requires a regular distribution of basic amino acid residues to neutralize the phosphate groups of the DNA and, as Phillips [34] pointed out, this is not compatible with the irregular distribution of basic residues so far observed. It also requires that the helical histone contain a sufficient number of fairly regularly spaced breaks so that the protein can wrap itself around a single DNA molecule. Such breaks might occur either by the inclusion of proline or groupings of non-helix-forming amino acids. These restrictions on the helical component of the histone are removed if we consider structures of nucleohistone that involve more than one DNA molecule bound by single histone chains. Luzzati and Nicolaieff [51] have suggested from the swelling behavior of nucleohistone in water that it consists of several DNA molecules joined together by basic proteins. Furthermore, Wilkins, Zubay, and Wilson [2, 50] have interpreted the presence of a meridional reflection at 37 Å as indicating a system of histone bridges linking DNA molecules. Nucleohistone structures involving groupings of several DNA molecules packed together and joined by α-helical histone chains lying in the larger grooves would not be expected to exhibit dichroism in any of the protein bands, provided that there exists fiber type of orientation—i.e., a random distribution around the direction of orientation. Structures of this type may be compatible with the irregular distribution of basic amino acids, and specific histones involved in a structural role may be found with runs of basic amino acids separated by runs of nonbasic residues. A nucleohistone structure involving DNA molecules joined together by histones in a globular form would also fit the physical evidence so far available.

Summary

The following points concerning nucleohistone structure have been established with reasonable certainty.

1. An appreciable fraction of isolated histone exists in a helical form, and this form is probably the α-helix. Part of the histone in nucleohistone is also likely to be in this conformation, and both deuteration and optical rotation suggest that over half is helical. Further work is necessary before the exact amount present in the helical form can be established.

2. Whereas isolated histone was found to denature readily and in part take up the β-form, there has been no indication of this in nucleohistone from either X-ray or infrared studies. Zubay and Wilkins [5] have suggested that the combination of histone with DNA stabilizes the histone.

3. X-ray diffraction and polarized infrared studies of ordered specimens show that the DNA molecules in nucleohistone at high humidities lie approximately parallel to the direction of orientation and have the same form as isolated DNA at high humidities, i.e., the B-form.

4. A meridional reflection at 37 Å has been attributed by Wilkins, Zubay, and Wilson [2, 50] to a tertiary structure in the nucleohistone, and they suggest that it arises from a system of histone bridges linking DNA molecules.

At present it is not known with certainty whether nucleohistone consists of a single DNA molecule attached to histone or several DNA molecules joined together by the basic protein. The latter seems the more likely, and the X-ray scattering experiments of Luzzati and co-workers may lead to suggestions concerning the number of DNA molecules involved in the nucleohistone unit. The mode of attachment of the protein to the DNA is not understood, and the lack of physical data is such that any proposed structure for nucleohistone must be regarded as speculative.

REFERENCES

1. Feughelman, M., Langridge, R., Seeds, W. E., Stokes, A. R., Wilson, H. R., Hooper, C. W., Wilkins, M. H. F., Barclay, R. K., and Hamilton, L. D., Nature, 175, 834, 1955.

2. Wilkins, M. H. F., Zubay, G., and Wilson, H. R., J. Mol. Biol., 1, 179. 1959.

3. Bradbury, E. M., Price, W. C., and Wilkinson, G. R., J. Mol. Biol., 3, 301, 1961.

4. Bradbury, E. M., Price, W. C., Wilkinson, G. R., and Zubay, G., J. Mol. Biol., 4, 50, 1962.

5. Zubay, G., and Wilkins, M. H. F., J. Mol. Biol., 4, 444, 1962.

6. Luzzati, V., Nicolaieff, A., and Masson, F., J. Mol. Biol., 3, 185, 1961.

7. Luzzati, V., Cesari, M., Spach, G., Masson, F., and Vincent, J. M., J. Mol. Biol., 3, 566, 1961.

8. Luzzati, V., Witz, J., and Nicolaieff, A., J. Mol. Biol., 3, 367, 379, 1961.

9. Ambrose, E. J., and Elliott A., Proc. Roy. Soc. (London), Ser. A, 205, 47, 1951.

10. Bamford, C. H., Elliott, A., and Hanby, W. E., Synthetic Polypeptides (New York: Academic Press, 1956).

132   The Structure of Nucleohistones

11. Elliott, A., and Malcolm, B. R., Trans. Faraday Soc., 52, 528, 1956.

12. Elliott, A., Hanby, W. E., and Malcolm, B. R., Nature, 180, 1340, 1957.

13. Elliott, A., Hanby, W. E., and Malcolm, B. R., Discussions Faraday Soc., No. 25, p. 167, 1958.

14. Beer, M., Sutherland, G. B. B. M., Tanner, K. N., and Wood, D. L., Proc. Roy. Soc. (London), Ser. A, 249, 147, 1958.

15. Miyazawa, T., J. Chem. Phys., 32, 1647, 1960.

16. Miyazawa, T., and Blout, E. R., J. Am. Chem. Soc., 83, 712, 1961.

17. Miyazawa, T., In Stahmann, M., (ed.): Polyamino Acids, Polypeptides and Proteins (Madison: Univ. of Wisconsin Press, 1962).

18. Bradbury, E. M., and Elliott, A., Polymer, 4, 47, 1963.

19. Cohen, C., Nature, 175, 129, 1955.

20. Doty, P., and Yang, J. T., J. Am. Chem. Soc., 78, 498, 1956.

21. Elliott, A., Hanby, W. E., and Malcolm, B. R., Nature, 178, 1170, 1956.

22. Moffitt, W., J. Chem. Phys., 25, 467, 1956.

23. Moffitt, W., Proc. Natl. Acad. Sci., U. S. A., 42, 736, 1956.

24. Moffitt, W., Fitts, D. D., and Kirkwood, J. G., Proc. Natl. Acad. Sci., U. S. A., 43, 723, 1957.

25. Moffitt, W., and Yang, J. T., Proc. Natl. Acad. Sci., U. S. A., 42, 596, 1956.

26. Urnes, P. J., Imahori, K., and Doty, P., Proc. Natl. Acad. Sci., U. S. A., 47, 1635, 1961.

27. Urnes, P. J., and Doty, P., Advances in Protein Chemistry (New York: Academic Press, vol. 16, 1961).

28. Elliott, A., Bradbury, E. M., Downie, A. R., and Hanby, W. E., In Stahmann, M., (ed): Polyamino Acids, Polypeptides and Proteins (Madison: Univ. of Wisconsin Press, 1962).

29. Bradbury, E. M., Brown, L., Downie, A. R., Elliott, A., Hanby, W. E., and McDonald, T. R. R., Nature, 183, 1736, 1959.

30. Lenormant, H., and Blout, E. R., Nature, 172, 770, 1953.

31. Elliott, A., and Hanby, W. E., Nature, 182, 654, 1958.

32. Blout, E. R., In Stahmann, M., (ed.): Polyamino Acids, Polypeptides and Proteins (Madison: Univ. of Wisconsin Press, 1962).

33. Wishnia, A., and Saunders, M., J. Am. Chem. Soc., 84, 4235, 1962.

34. Phillips, D. M. P., Progr. Biophys. Biophys. Chem., 12, 211, 1962.

35. de Lozé, C. T., J. Physiol. (Paris), 48, 506, 1956.

36. Gregoire, E.-J., and Limozin, M., Bull. Soc. Chim. Biol., 36, 15, 1954.

37. Crampton, C. F., Moore, S., and Stein, W. H., J. Biol. Chem., 215, 787, 1955.

38. Crampton, C. F., Lipshitz, R., and Chargaff, E., J. Biol. Chem., 206, 499, 1954.

39. Zubay, G., and Doty, P., J. Mol. Biol., 1, 1, 1959.

40. de Lozé, C. T., Thèses (Paris: Masson et Cie, 1958).

41. de Lozé, C. T., Compt. Rend., 246, 599, 1958.

42. Doty, P., Proc. 4th Intern. Congr. Biochem., 8, 8, 1958.

43. Elliott, A., Bradbury, E. M., and Zubay, G., J. Mol. Biol. 4, 61, 1962.

44. Arndt, U. W., and Riley, D. P., Phil. Trans. Roy. Soc. (London), Ser. A, 247, 409, 1955.

45. de Lozé, C. T., and Lenormant, H., Bull. Soc. Chim. Biol., 38, 450, 1956.

46. de Lozé, C. T., and Lenormant, H., Bull. Soc. Chim. Biol., 41, 331, 337, 1959.

47. Wilkins, M. H. F., Biochem. Soc. Symp., No. 14, p. 13, 1956.

48. Wilkins, M. H. F., Cold Spring Harbor Symp. Quant. Biol., 21, 75, 1956.

49. Franklin, R. E., and Gosling, R. G., Nature, 171, 740 and 172, 156, 1953.

50. Wilkins, M. H. F., Zubay, G., and Wilson, H. R., Trans. Faraday Soc., 55, 497, 1959.

51. Luzzati, V., and Nicolaieff, A., J. Mol. Biol., 1, 127, 1959.

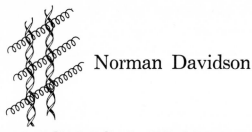

Norman Davidson

ELECTRICAL PROPERTIES
OF DNA IN SOLUTION

A study of the electrical properties of nucleic acids in solution and of the interactions of nucleic acids with small ions logically precedes the consideration of the properties of nucleohistones and of the interactions between the negative polyelectrolyte DNA and the positively charged histones.

The first point is that the hydrodynamic properties indicate that the large DNA's (molecular weights greater than about 10^7) in solution are random coils with a statistical segment length of the order of 1,000 Å. The theory is not very exact and the experimental data at present are not reliably accurate, but the qualitative picture is clear.

The appropriate limiting models for the consideration of the hydrodynamic properties of native DNA are a rod, a free draining random coil, and an impermeable random coil. The molecular weight dependence of the sedimentation coefficient, $\underline{s}$, and the intrinsic viscosity, $[\eta]$, are shown in Table 1.

TABLE 1

Molecular weight dependence of hydrodynamic properties for limiting polymer models

	Rod	Random coil, free draining	Random Coil, impermeable
$\underline{s}$	$M^{0.0}$	$M^{0.0}$	$M^{0.5}$
$[\eta]$	$M^{1.8}$	$M^{1.0}$	$M^{0.5}$

For a series of random coils intermediate between the free drain-ing and impermeable limits, it is expected that

$$\underline{s} = \underline{a} + \underline{b} \, M^{1/2}. \tag{1}$$

The first data available bearing on this problem were on native calf thymus DNA sonicates with average molecular weights from 3×10^5 to 8×10^6, as determined by light scattering [1]. The results were fitted to the equations

$$\underline{s} = 0.063 \, M^{0.37} \tag{2a}$$

$$[\eta] = 1.45 \times 10^{-6} \, M^{1.12}. \tag{2b}$$

The molecular weight dependences of $[\eta]$ and $\underline{s}$ were interpreted as indi-cating a structure in solution intermediate between a rod and a random coil. It is not known to what extent these results are misleading because of the heterogeneous molecular weight distribution produced by sonication and the difficulties in determining molecular weight by light scattering. In any case, the indications are that the semipermeable random coil model is preferable for the larger (and more homogeneous) viral DNA's.

The DNA of some bacterial viruses occurs as a single molecule per phage particle [2, 3]. These large molecules can be split into fairly homo-geneous halves and quarters by controlled stirring (shear breakage) and chromatographic separation [4]. Thus sources of homogeneous DNA of high molecular weight are now available. However, due to a number of technical reasons, accurate measurement of the sedimentation coefficient for these DNA's is difficult. It has been claimed that $\underline{s} \sim M^{0.55}$ [4] and, on the other hand, that $\underline{s} \sim M^{0.35}$ [5]. Thus the sedimentation coefficient data cannot be interpreted in precise detail, but in their general features they are consistent with equation 1, and point to the model of semiporous random coils for large DNA molecules.

A sufficiently extensive set of viscosity data for these DNA's, extrap-olated to zero shear gradient and zero concentration, is not yet published. The scattered measurements that are available for T2 DNA [6] and T4 DNA (Table 2) conform more closely to $[\eta] \sim M^{0.5}$ than to equation 2b.

A simple calculation of the size and statistical segment length for a random coil on the basis of the sedimentation coefficient data is instructive. We consider a "kinked-chain" model, that is, a molecule with a contour length of $\underline{L}$, consisting of $\underline{L}/\underline{k}$ segments, each of length $\underline{k}$, with a universal joint at each kink. By the random walk formula, the radius of gyration of such a molecule is

$$\underline{R_g} = (\underline{k}\ \underline{L}/6)^{1/2}. \tag{3}$$

For a random coil sufficiently large that its hydrodynamic behavior is close to the impermeable limit, the hydrodynamic friction factor is

$$\underline{f} = 6\pi\eta_0\ \underline{R_s}, \tag{4}$$

where $\underline{R_s}$ is the effective hydrodynamic radius for sedimentation. A more exact theory for gaussian coils gives

$$\underline{R_s} = 0.67\ \underline{R_g} \tag{5}$$

[7]. If this simple model is applied to T2 DNA with $M = 1.3 \times 10^8$, $\underline{L} = 63 \times 10^{-4}$ cm, $\underline{s} = 79$ or 55 [5, 8], one obtains $\underline{k} = 1,400$ Å or $\underline{k} = 2,700$ Å, that is, 410 or 800 base pairs per segment. There are then 450 or 230 kinks or segments per molecule. With this large number of segments, the molecules should be a pretty good approximation to a random coil. More detailed calculations indicate that such a molecule would in fact be intermediate between the free draining and impermeable limits so that the above calculation is at least roughly significant.

Hearst and Stockmayer [9] have made a detailed hydrodynamic analysis of this problem with essentially similar results. These authors also analyze the model of the wormlike chain and arrive at a persistence length of about 700 Å for such a continuously curved chain. Electron micrographs of large DNA's absorbed from solution onto a basic protein film strongly support the wormlike chain model [10, 11].

The next important point is that such a DNA molecule is a very dilute gel bead. That is, inside one statistically spherical, random coil molecule, the average concentration of monomer units is quite small. For simplicity, we neglect the gaussian distribution of chain segments and assume that there is a uniform distribution of chain segments out to a radius of

$\underline{R}_g$. For the T2 DNA model considered above, there are 4×10^5 monomer units with $\underline{R}_g \approx 1.5 \times 10^{-4}$ cm. The concentration of monomer units within the bead is then $4 \times 10^5 /(4\pi/3) \underline{R}^3$ or 2.8×10^{16} cc^{-1} or 5×10^{-5} molar in monomer units. In a homologous series of DNA's with varying molecular weight and a constant kink length, this concentration within the bead varies as $M^{-1/2}$ (M=molecular weight).

It is interesting to note that although DNA molecules are highly coiled in solution, a not negligible fraction of them are quite completely straightened out by the process of streaking an electron microscope grid or a glass slide through a DNA solution [12, 13].

We also note parenthetically that denatured DNA is a much less collapsed structure than would be expected if it were free jointed at every, or almost every, phosphate-to-sugar bond. For example, on heat denaturation of T7 DNA in the presence of formaldehyde, up to the point just preceding strand separation, the sedimentation coefficient changes from 30 to about 65 [14]. According to the kinked-chain model for an impermeable sphere, the kink length, $\underline{k}$, is inversely proportional to the square of the sedimentation coefficient. In this case, then, the kink length for denatured DNA is about one fifth of the kink length for native DNA or about 120 base pairs. The details of the above calculation are unreliable, but the general notion that denatured DNA is a highly expanded structure is important [15]. The expanded structure is partly due to residual base pairing and secondary structure, but it may also be partly due to other structural factors that are not yet understood.

We now consider the ion binding properties of the nucleic acids. In the first place, for a dilute polyelectrolyte gel bead with a spherical distribution of fixed negative charges, immersed in a solution containing a supporting electrolyte consisting of small ions, there will be a dilute counter-ion atmosphere in and around the bead. The charge density of this ion atmosphere can be calculated from the usual linearized Debye-Hückel approximation to the Poisson-Boltzmann equation [16]. The essential qualitative features of the ion atmosphere are displayed in Figure 1. The three important parameters are the Debye shielding length, $1/\kappa$, the density of fixed charges in the gel bead (for simplicity assumed to be a constant up to the radius $\underline{R}$ in this calculation), and the radius of the bead $\underline{R}$. The Debye shielding length depends on the ionic strength due to the small ions, and in water at 25 C is given by $(1/\kappa) = 3.0 \, \underline{I}^{1/2}$ Å, where $\underline{I}$ is the ionic strength. For the problem at hand, $\underline{R} >> 1/\kappa$. It is seen from Figure 1 that inside the gel bead and up to a distance of order $1/\kappa$ from the surface, the counter ions completely neutralize the fixed charge of the phosphate groups. That is, the inside of the bead is electrically neutral. There is some dissociation of positive ions from the surface of the bead and so there is an excess of fixed negative charges over the counter-ion charge in a shell $1/\kappa$ thick on the inner surface. There is a counterbalancing excess of positive ions within a distance of order $1/\kappa$ just outside the bead.

It is generally believed that in addition to this dilute ion atmosphere, which is calculated on the basis of a smeared-out continuous distribution

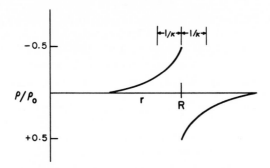

Fig. 1.—A qualitative sketch of the total charge density, ρ, (due to the fixed negative charges plus the mobile small ions of the supporting electrolyte) as a function of the distance, $\underline{r}$, from the center of a spherical polyelectrolyte gel bead according to the theory of Hermans and Overbeek [16]. The density of fixed negative charges is constant at $-\rho_o$ (charges cc^{-1}) out to a radius R and is zero outside. Other symbols are defined in text. The sketch is for the limiting case, R $\gg$ $1/\kappa$, when $\rho\,(\underline{r})$ = $-(\rho_o/2)$ exp $(-\kappa\,|\underline{R}-\underline{r}|)$ inside $(\underline{r} < \underline{R})$, and $\rho\,(\underline{r})$ = $(\rho_o/2)$ exp $(-\kappa\,|\underline{R}-\underline{r}|)$ outside $(\underline{r} > \underline{R})$.

of the fixed negative charges, there are a certain number of more tightly bound positive ions close to the surface of the DNA rod. The binding is still essentially electrostatic rather than covalent. This kind of binding, which may be called site binding, is particularly important for divalent ions such as Mg^{++} and Mn^{++} and for more highly charged ions. Although the binding is largely electrostatic, it may have some specific stereochemical characteristics. For example, it is not known whether Mn^{++} ions are bound as $Mn(OH_2)_6^{++}$ ions, each close to a PO_4^- group, or whether one of the water molecules of hydration of the octahedrally coordinated manganese ion is replaced by a phosphate oxygen to give a structure $O_3P-O-Mn(OH_2)_6^{++}$. There is some evidence that the latter is the case [17].

It is not easy to distinguish between dilute ion atmosphere binding and site binding. Experimentally, one measures the over-all binding. Figure 2, for example, displays the results of Shack and Bynum [18] on the binding of Mg^{++} by DNA. The essential results here are that native DNA binds somewhat more strongly than denatured DNA and that as the sodium ion concentration is raised, the magnesium binding is depressed. It should be noted that the conclusion that native DNA binds Mg^{++} ions slightly more strongly than denatured DNA does is not universally accepted. There is some conductimetric evidence that supports the opposite conclusion [19, 20]. I believe, however, that the interpretation of the conductimetric experiments is treacherous and unreliable; the chemical assay for free Mg^{++} used by Shack and Bynum is probably more reliable.

Figure 3 illustrates the dramatic effect of the stoichiometric binding of Mg^{++} to DNA in stabilizing the DNA against denaturation. For this particular DNA, the melting temperature at an ionic strength, due to $NaClO_4$, of 3 x 10^{-4} M is 37 C. It increases by 18° for every increase by a factor of 10 in NaClO4 concentration and is 81 C in 0.10 M NaClO4. However, addition of half an equivalent of Mg++ (about 2.5 x 10⁻⁵ M, the DNA concentration being about 10⁻⁴ M in monomer units) raises T_M to 58 C and 1

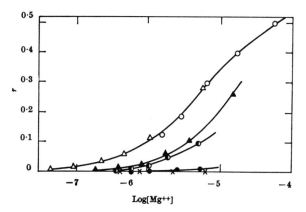

Fig. 2.—Binding of magnesium ions by DNA. The equivalents of magnesium bound per nucleotide is designated by r. o, from titrations at pH 9.04. All other points from titrations at pH 10.2. ▵, o, undenatured DNA in 0.002 M NaCl; ▲, denatured DNA in 0.002 M NaCl; o, undenatured DNA in 0.02 M NaCl; ●, undenatured DNA in 0.1 M NaCl; ✗, denatured DNA in 0.1 M NaCl. Concentration of nucleic acid phosphorous = 1.03 x 10⁻³ M. (From Shack and Bynum [18].)

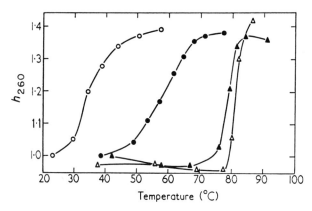

Fig. 3.—Effect of Mg++ on thermal denaturation of B, megaterium DNA, ionic strength = 3 x 10⁻⁴ M, pH 7. r = equivalents Mg++ per equivalent of DNA phosphorus; DNA = 10⁻⁴ M-(P), except for r = 2.0, where DNA = 5 x 10⁻⁵ M-(P). h = hyperchromicity referred to the native DNA. (From Dove and Davidson [21].)

	o–o	●–●	▲–▲	▵–▵
r	0	0.5	1.0	2.0
Tm °C	35.0	58.0	78.5	81.1

equivalent of Mg++ raises T_M to 78.5 C. That this stabilization is due essentially to stoichiometric binding is shown by the fact that a second equivalent of Mg++ has a very small additional stabilizing effect [21].

Figure 4 is from the quantitative studies of dye binding by Lawley [22]. The point here is that the binding is due partly to electrostatic interactions and partly to other forces. Thus, the binding of cationic dyes is depressed by Na+ and still more by Mg++ or Ba++. However, the strength of the binding by the two unipositive cationic dyes, 9-amino-acridine and rosaniline, differs by two orders of magnitude. Thus, forces other than electrostatic ones are playing a role. It has been proposed that acridines and related compounds bind to DNA by intercalation between normally neighboring base pairs [23]. If this is true, then London dispersion forces are playing an important role.

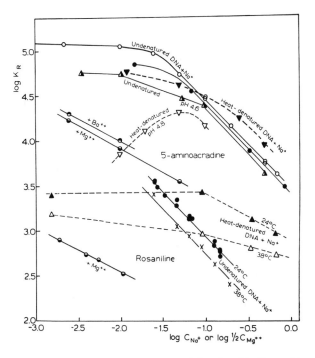

Fig. 4.—Values of the binding constant κ' for the binding of 9-aminoacridine (5-aminoacridine in the obsolete Richter numbering system used in the figure) and of rosaniline to DNA at various concentrations of metal ions. Black circles, calf-thymus DNA; open circles, herring sperm DNA; solid lines, native DNA; broken lines, heat-denatured DNA. (From Lawley [22].)

Several lines of evidence, including transport number measurements [24], and measurements with sodium ion electrodes [25] indicate considerable sodium ion binding by DNA. The binding is stronger by native DNA than by denatured DNA [25]. The binding by Mg^{++}, Mn^{++}, and Co^{++} (and probably by Cu^{++}) is almost certainly to the negatively charged phosphate groups. On the other hand, silver ion and mercury ion form covalent complexes with the pyrimidine and purine residues [26-28].

We now turn to a consideration of the electrophoretic properties of the nucleic acids in homogeneous solution (as contrasted with electrophoresis on a supporting medium). Most of the early work in this field was done with a Tiselius apparatus and schlieren optics [29-34]. The concentration of nucleic acid required is greater than 0.1% and corresponds to an absorbance at 260 mμ of greater than 40. For sedimentation and other hydrodynamic behavior, DNA does not begin to approximate to its behavior at infinite dilution until the concentration is lowered below $A_{260} = 1$. We [35] have therefore constructed the apparatus shown in Figure 5 for zone electrophoresis in free solution. Electrophoresis takes place through a solution with a uniform salt and buffer concentration. There is a sucrose density gradient for stability against convection. Concentrations corresponding to absorbance at 254 mμ of 0.10-2.0 are measured with a scanning ultraviolet optical system.

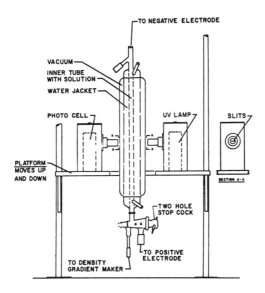

Fig. 5.—Electrophoresis apparatus for zone electrophoresis in homogeneous solution with scanning ultraviolet optics.

Figure 6 displays a typical good run in which a mixture of native and denatured DNA is separated into the two components.

Some general features of the electrophoretic properties of the nucleic acids are displayed in Table 2. The electrophoretic mobility of polymeric native DNA is independent of molecular weight, at least for $10^5 < M < 10^8$.

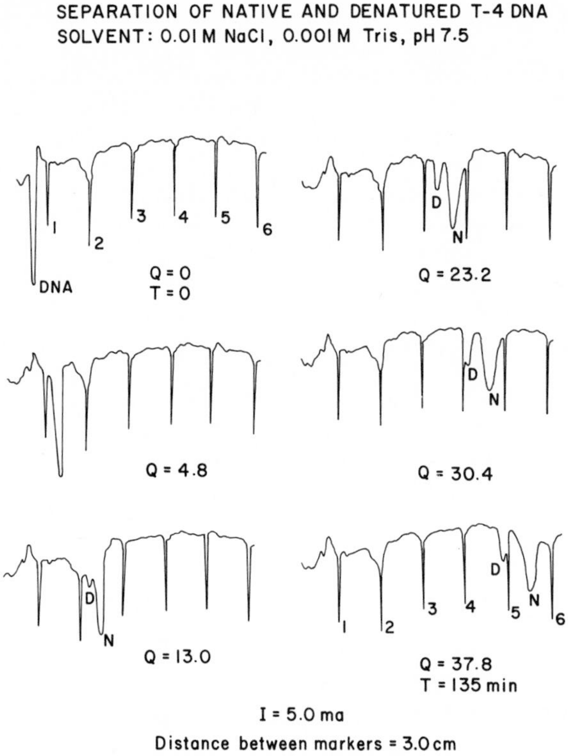

SEPARATION OF NATIVE AND DENATURED T-4 DNA
SOLVENT: 0.01 M NaCl, 0.001 M Tris, pH 7.5

I = 5.0 ma
Distance between markers = 3.0 cm

Fig. 6.—Results of an electrophoresis run on a mixture of native and denatured T4 DNA. Distance down the electrophoresis tube is the horizontal coordinate on each recorder display. Decreasing photocurrent is a vertical deflection downward. There are calibration markers every 3.0 cm along the tube. Total current passed in T minutes is given as Q (coulombs). In the upper left record, the DNA band is to the left of marker 1. At the end of the run, it has moved to the extreme right and resolved into its two components, denoted by D and N.

However, the electrophoretic mobility of the high polymer is 2.3 times that of the uninegative monomer, $dAMP^{-1}$ [36]. The electrophoretic mobility of denatured DNA, which is also independent of molecular weight, is about 15% less than that of native DNA. There is a small decrease when the ionic strength is increased; however, this is less than an inverse 1/2 power.

It was noted some time ago in experiments in a Tiselius apparatus, at nucleic acid concentrations of about 0.15%, that the mobility of native DNA is $-1.6(\pm0.1) \times 10^{-5}$ cm^2 sec^{-1} $volt^{-1}$ in 0.15 M NaCl at 0 C and that yeast RNA is about 30% slower than native DNA [34], which is in fair agreement with the data in Table 2 for much more dilute solutions. In the concentration range from 0.001% to 0.004%, we observe no dependence of electrophoretic mobility on concentration.

TABLE 2

Electrophoretic properties of nucleic acids

Sample	Mol. wt. $\times 10^{-6}$	$[\eta]$ dl g^{-1}	$\underline{s}$ $\times 10^{13}$	Ionic strength[a]	$\underline{u}$ (native)	$\underline{u}$ (heat denatured)
					\multicolumn{2}{c}{$\times 10^4$ cm^2 sec^{-1} volt^{-1}[b]}	
T2 DNA[c]	130		53	0.011	2.18	1.85
"	2.5	21.7		"	2.16	
"	0.45	3.2		"	2.14	
"	0.26	1.7	7.4	"	2.14	
T4 DNA	130	240[d]		"	2.18	1.86
calf thymus DNA	~8	90		"	2.17	1.90
d AMP^{-2}[e]						1.5
d AMP^{-1}[f]			~0.2	0.011		0.94
MS-2 RNA[g]	2×10^6		27	0.011		1.73
calf thymus DNA	~8			0.11	1.51	1.36
"				0.004	2.35	2.15

[a]Unless otherwise specified, the supporting electrolyte was at pH 7.5 and obtained by appropriate dilution of 0.10 M NaCl, 0.01 M tris buffer.

[b]Electrophoretic mobilities are corrected to water at 0 C.

[c]The T2 DNA samples are intact viral DNA and shear degradation products kindly supplied by Dr. Don Crothers of the University of California at San Diego. $[\eta]$ and $\underline{s}$ values are for the native material and were measured by him. (All sedimentation and viscosity values refer to the native DNA.) Molecular weights are estimated from empirical correlations with viscosity and $\underline{s}$ values.

[d]Measurements by Mr. H. Ohlenbusch in this laboratory.

[e]pH 7.5.

[f]pH 4.6; sedimentation coefficient calculated from hydrodynamic friction factor.

[g]From Mr. J. H. Strauss and Prof. R. L. Sinsheimer, who measured the other physical properties.

The effects of changing the pH are displayed in Table 3. The essential point is that the mobility decreases as native or denatured DNA is protonated in acid, but the mobility is not proportional to the "titration charge" of the molecule. The titration charge is calculated assuming complete ionization of the sodium ions, so each phosphate ester unit has a charge of -1 at pH 7.5.

TABLE 3

Effect of protonation on electrophoretic mobility of DNA[a]

pH	Ratio of $\underline{u}$ to that at pH $\overline{7.5}$[b]		Titration charge[c]	
	Native	Denatured	Native	Denatured
7.50	1.00	1.00	-1.00	-1.00
4.57	0.94	0.93	-0.87	-0.63
4.10	0.90	0.90	-0.74	-0.52

[a]Intact T4 DNA, native or heat denatured.
[b]0.010 M NaCl, 0.001 M buffer (tris or sodium acetate).
[c]Determined by a titration curve at 4° in 0.01 M NaCl; charges calculated assuming a charge of -1 per phosphate at pH 7.5 and adding the number of protons bound.

Several different theoretical interpretations provide insights into the electrophoretic mobilities of polyelectrolytes [37]. Hermans' sophisticated theory for semipermeable polyelectrolyte beads [38] takes into account the Debye-Hückel dilute ion atmosphere and the Kirkwood-Riseman [7] or Debye-Bueche [39] considerations about the hydrodynamics of semipermeable coils. The final result for polyelectrolytes of high molecular weights at reasonable supporting electrolyte concentrations (as for our measurements) is that the coil is always free draining (because of the shielding effect of the ion atmosphere) and the mobility is given by $\underline{u} \approx \underline{z}/\underline{f}$, where $\underline{z}$ is the charge on a monomer unit and $\underline{f}$ is the hydrodynamic friction factor for a monomer unit. Thus, this theory explains the independence of mobility on molecular weight, but it does not quantitatively explain the effect of acid titration displayed in Table 3.

It seems reasonable to us that the fault is not with the theory, but that the interpretation of the charge per monomer unit, $\underline{z}$, as -1 per phosphate group at pH 7 is probably wrong. To the extent that there is tight (site) binding of sodium ions, which is not accounted for by the dilute ion atmosphere theory, the effective charge is decreased. On protonation as the pH is lowered, the amount of sodium ion binding decreases. The overall predictions from this picture are in qualitative agreement with the facts, but a quantitative theory is not possible.

We know of no theoretical explanation of the difference between native and denatured DNA. Theoretically, the difference is small, but practically, it is sufficiently large to be readily useful.*

One other electrical property of the nucleic acids in solution to be discussed briefly is the phenomenon of electric birefringence. Because of the polarization of the counter ion atmosphere, the application of an electric field induces a large dipole moment in a rodlike segment of a polyelectrolyte in dilute ionic solution. The torque due to the interaction of the induced moment with the applied field is sufficient to produce a large degree of orientation under practical conditions [41-45]. The orientation effect can be observed by the negative birefringence of visible light or dichroism with ultraviolet light. The mechanism of counter ion polarization can be distinguished from the mechanism of orientation by a permanent dipole moment. In the latter case, the molecule must reverse its orientation if the field is reversed. This is a slow process. In the former case, on rapid reversal of the field, the counter ion atmosphere

---

*We have been stimulated by participation in this Histone Conference to investigate the electrophoretic mobility of nucleohistones. Although the histones themselves have been extensively studied by electrophoresis, there has been very little work on nucleohistones because of their tendency to aggregate at the concentrations needed with a Tiselius apparatus. Much lower concentrations (~0.004%) were used here. Native and reconstituted nucleohistones kindly provided by Drs. Bonner and Ru-Chih Huang have been studied. We find that native pea embryo nucleohistone is negatively charged at pH 7.5 and travels 60% as fast as native DNA. Because the percentage change in electrophoretic mobility is generally less than the change in charge, the implication is that the nucleohistone has less than 60% of the net negative charge of native DNA. Mobilities for reconstituted nucleohistones range from 60 to 90% of the mobility of native DNA. The mobilities of nucleohistones with histone fractions high in lysine and low in arginine (such as Ib) are lower than the mobilities of fractions high in arginine and low in lysine (such as IV). Since in all cases, the nucleohistone complex contained as many positively charged groups on the protein as negative phosphates on the DNA, we believe the net negative charge in these complexes is due to the glutamic and aspartic acid residues on the histones. The differences in mobilities between various reconstituted nucleohistones may be explained primarily on this basis: The work of Rasmussen [40] shows that the ratio of negative to positive groups in fraction IV is much greater than in Ib, accounting for the greater net negative charge and the increased mobility of reconstituted nucleohistone IV.

Preliminary electrophoretic studies on pea cotyledon chromatin using low concentrations show that electrophoresis proceeds without complications, and it is possible to separate the histone-DNA complex from other fractions that may contaminate it.

moves from one end of the macromolecule to the other, but the molecule retains its orientation. Our work has shown that DNA is indeed oriented by the polyelectrolyte orientation mechanism.

For a collection of thin rods of constant length, ℓ, and diameter, $2b$, the birefringence decay on turning off the field should be exponential with a single relaxation time, given by the equation

$$\tau = \frac{\eta \pi}{18kT} \frac{\ell^3}{\ln(\ell/b - 0.80)} .$$

For all of the DNA's examined by the several investigators listed above, the decay is not a simple exponential, and there is a spectrum of relaxation times. For example, for T4 DNA, which has a contour length of 60 μ, the first important component of the decay has a relaxation time of 5×10^{-4} sec, and there are other components extending out to about 5×10^{-3} sec [44]. These correspond to lengths calculated according to the above equation of 3,500 to 7,000 Å. The molecule is probably relaxing as a random coil with a complex spectrum of relaxation times.

For bacterial DNA's, such as E. coli or M. lysodeikticus, we find decays that differ from that of phage DNA in having a larger contribution from relaxation times of 10^{-2} to 10^{-1} sec. This indicates that the bacterial DNA is stiffer than the viral DNA, in keeping with the fact that it is less folded in vivo.

REFERENCES

1. Doty, P., McGill, B. B., and Rice, S. A., Proc. Natl. Acad. Sci. U. S. A., 44, 432, 1958.

2. Rubenstein, I., Thomas, C. A., and Hershey, A. D., Proc. Natl. Acad. Sci. U. S. A., 47, 1113, 1961.

3. Davison, P. F., Freifelder, D., Hede, R., and Leventhal, C., Proc. Natl. Acad. Sci. U. S. A., 47, 1123, 1961.

4. Burgi, E., and Hershey, A. D., J. Mol. Biol., 3, 458, 1961.

5. Burgi, E., and Hershey, A. D., Biophys. J., 3, 309, 1963.

6. Zimm, B. H., and Crothers, D. M., Proc. Natl. Acad. Sci. U. S. A., 48, 905, 1962.

7. Kirkwood, J. G., and Riseman, J., J. Chem. Phys., 16, 565, 1948.

8. Hearst, J. E., and Vinograd, J., Arch. Biochem. Biophys., 92, 206, 1961.

9. Hearst, J. E., and Stockmayer, W. H., J. Chem. Phys., 37, 1425, 1962.

10. Kleinschmidt, A. K., Lang, D., and Zahn, R. K., Z. Naturforsch., 16B, 730, 1961.

11. Kleinschmidt, A. K., Lang, D., Jacherts, D., and Zahn, R. K., Biochim. Biophys. Acta, 61, 857, 1962.

12. Beer, M., J. Mol. Biol., 3, 263, 1961.

13. Cairns, J., J. Mol. Biol., 3, 756, 1961.

14. Freifelder, D., and Davison, P. F., Biophys. J., 3, 49, 1963.

15. Doty, P., Marmur, J., Eigner, A., and Schildkraut, C., Proc. Natl. Acad. Sci. U. S. A., 46, 461, 1960.

16. Hermans, J. J., and Overbeek, J. P., Rec. Trav. Chim., 67, 32, 1948.

17. Eisinger, J., Shulman, R. G., and Szymanski, B. M., J. Chem. Phys., 36, 1721, 1962.

18. Shack, J., and Bynum, B. S., Nature, 184, 635, 1959.

19. Doty, P., and Zubay, G., Biochim. Biophys. Acta, 29, 47, 1957.

20. Zubay, G., Biochim. Biophys. Acta, 32, 233, 1959.

21. Dove, W. F., and Davidson, N., J. Mol. Biol., 5, 467, 1962.

22. Lawley, P. D., Biochim. Biophys. Acta, 22, 451, 1956.

23. Lerman, L. S., J. Mol. Biol., 3, 18, 1961.

24. Inman, R. B., and Jordan, D. O., Biochim. Biophys. Acta, 42, 421, 1960.

25.   Ascoli, F., Botré, C., and Liquori, A. M., J. Mol. Biol., 3, 202, 1961.

26.   Yamane, T., and Davidson, N., J. Am. Chem. Soc., 83, 2599, 1960.

27.   Yamane, T., and Davidson, N., Biochim. Biophys. Acta, 55, 609, 1962.

28.   Katz, S., Biochim. Biophys. Acta, 68, 240, 1963.

29.   Creeth, J. M., Jordan, D. O., and Gulland, J. M., J. Chem. Soc., 1406, 1409, 1949.

30.   Mathieson, A. A., and McClaren, J. D., J. Chem. Soc., 303, 1956.

31.   Ui, N., and Watanabe, I., Bull. Chem. Soc. Japan, 24, 210, 1951.

32.   Chargaff, E., and Saidel, H. F., J. Biol. Chem., 177, 417, 1949.

33.   Chargaff, E., and Zamenhoff, S., J. Biol. Chem., 173, 327, 1948.

34.   Zamenhoff, S., Leidy, G., Alexander, H. E., FitzGerald, P. L., and Chargaff, E., Arch. Biochem. Biophys., 40, 50, 1952.

35.   Olivera, B. M., Baine, P., and Davidson, N., 7th Annual Meeting, Biophys. Soc., New York, abstracts.

36.   Smith, J. D., In Chargaff, E., and Davidson, J. N., (ed.): The Nucleic Acids, (New York: Academic Press, 1955, p. 267).

37.   Rice, S. A., and Nagasawa, M., Polyelectrolyte Solutions, (New York: Academic Press, 1961).

38.   Hermans, J. J., J. Polymer Sci., 18, 527, 1955.

39.   Debye, P., and Bueche, A. M., J. Chem. Phys., 16, 573, 1948.

40.   Rasmussen, P. S., Murray, K., and Luck, J. M., Biochem., 1, 79, 1962.

41.   Benoit, H., Ann. Phys. (Paris), 6, 561, 1951.

42.   O'Konski, C. T., and Zimm, B. H., Science 111, 113, 1950.

43.   Stellwagen, N. C., Shirai, M., and O'Konski, C. T., J. Polymer Sci., submitted, 1963.

44.   Ohlenbusch, H., Huber, W., and Davidson, N., private communication, 1963.

45.   Ohlenbusch, H., work done in our laboratory, 1963.

Paul O. P. Ts'o

THE INTERACTIONS OF NUCLEIC ACID

It is generally recognized that the complicated problems of biology are being progressively carried to the molecular level. Coming from the other direction to study molecules of biological origin, the physical scientist is no longer satisfied merely to find out the composition, the molecular weight, shape, size, and other simple properties of such a molecule. He wants to know how these molecules interact with each other in solution or in the semi-solid state and whether this interaction is random or exhibits organization. By specific and coordinated interactions between molecules, especially molecules of the biopolymers, new properties can arise in the system due to organization. Indeed, in many cases the whole is more than the mere sum of its parts.

Of all biopolymers, proteins and nucleic acids appear to be of most importance in terms of the specific interactions which lead to information transfer. The significance and some of the general principles of the interactions of nucleic acids with one another are well known. These concepts and knowledge have served as the foundation for the development of molecular genetics. We wish to reexamine quantitatively the basic principles and the nature of the forces which govern the interactions of nucleic acids, and to do so by physical chemical studies.

The problem is approached at three levels of complexity: (1) interaction in solution between the monomeric unit of nucleic acid and its analogs and derivatives; (2) interaction between the monomeric unit and the nucleic acid polymer; (3) interaction between nucleic acid polymers. The present review is confined to investigations at the first two levels.

We concentrate first on interactions of neutral compounds and thus avoid complications due to the strong electrostatic interactions of charged molecules. Because both the sugar and the phosphate moieties are common to all nucleotide units, specific interactions of nucleic acids must reside in the purine and pyrimidine bases. Therefore, the experimental approach may quite justifiably be focused on the interaction of uncharged bases and nucleosides and their interaction with nucleic acid polymers.

The first level of interaction includes the following problems: Does a solution of monomeric units, such as free nucleosides, interact within

TABLE 1

Molal osmotic coefficients[a] of various solutes
determined in water at 25°[b]

Molal Conc.	Purine	Uridine	Cytidine
0.05	0.917	0 969	0.967
0.10	0.849	0.943	0.935
0.15	0.794	0.921	0.905
0.20	0.749	0.901	0.876
0.28	0.714	0.883	0.850
0.30	0.685	0.866	0.826
0.35	0.662	0.849	0.804
0.40	0.643	0.833	0.785
0.45	0.627	0.817	0.768
0.50	0.614	0.801	0.752
0.55	0.601	0.786	0.738
0.60	0.590	0.773	0.724
0.65	0.578	0.762	0.710
0.70	0.567	0.755	0.695
0.75	0.555		
0.80	0.544		
0.85	0.532		
0.90	0.522		
0.95	0.512		
1.00	0.505		
1.05	0.501		
1.10	0.501		

[a]Data from Ts'o [1].
[b]These are fitted osmotic coefficients computed from the experimental values.

itself? To what extent? By what mechanism? To answer these questions, three types of physical-chemical measurements have been made
using, because of solubility problems, pyrimidine nucleosides and purine.
    Vapor pressures of solutions of purine, uridine, and cytidine from
0.1 molal to approximately 0.8 molal have been measured thermoelec-
trically [1] . Osmotic coefficients, ϕ, were calculated from these data
(Table 1). Activity coefficients at 25 C were calculated from the osmotic
coefficients by the Gibbs-Duhem relationship using a computer which performed numerical integration on the fitted polynomials and related molal
concentration to ϕ (Table 2). The data clearly indicated that the properties
of purine, uridine, and cytidine in water are far from ideal. The values
of both the osmotic coefficients and of the activity coefficients are much

TABLE 2

Molal activity coefficients[a] at 25° computed from
the fitted osmotic coefficients[b]

Molal Conc.	Purine	Uridine	Cytidine
0.05	0.844	0.939	0.936
0.10	0.728	0.888	0.878
0.15	0.641	0.845	0.824
0.20	0.575	0.808	0.776
0.25	0.522	0.775	0.733
0.30	0.480	0.744	0.695
0.35	0.446	0.716	0.661
0.40	0.418	0.690	0.631
0.45	0.394	0.665	0.604
0.50	0.374	0.641	0.580
0.55	0.355	0.620	0.558
0.60	0.339	0.600	0.537
0.65	0.324	0.582	0.518
0.70	0.311	0.568	0.499
0.75	0.297		
0.80	0.286		
0.85	0.275		
0.90	0.264		
0.95	0.255		
1.00	0.247		
1.05	0.240		
1.10	0.235		

[a]Data from Ts'o [1].
[b]See Table 1.

below unity. These results establish the concept that purine and pyrimidine nucleosides do interact extensively in aqueous solution.

After further analysis for their congruence to different models for multiple equilibria, the thermodynamic data were found to be incompatible with the model which assumes that only dimers are formed. Thus, degree of association of these compounds may go beyond the dimer stage to higher degree of polymerization. The results are consistent with a model which assumes that the association process continues through many successive steps with the same equilibrium constant. Comparison of the equilibrium constants, and thus the standard free energy changes, shows that the tendency of purine to associate is much greater than that of pyrimidine nucleosides, which in turn is greater than that of urea. We have recently extended the measurement of osmotic and activity coefficients to 6-methyl purine and 5-bromouridine [2]. At comparable concentration, both the osmotic and the activity coefficient of 6-methyl purine are lower than those of purine, and both coefficients of 5-bromouridine are lower than those of uridine, indicating an even more extensive association of these compounds in water than those of the unsubstituted compounds.

The experiments detailed above concern solutions containing a single solute. They concern, then, interaction of the purine or the nucleoside with itself. What are the interactions between different compounds, for example, between purine and pyrimidine? The increase in solubility of the sparingly soluble adenine and thymine caused by the presence of the highly soluble purine or nucleoside was adopted as the method for investigation of interactions of this type [1]. As indicated in Table 3, the solubility of adenine is much enhanced by the presence of purine. The enhancement is moderate in the presence of cytidine, uridine, or pyrimidine and is practically nil in the presence of cyclohexanol, adonitol, and urea. Similarly, the solubility of thymine (Table 4) is enhanced by purine and to a lesser extent by uridine and cytidine. These data were also analyzed by multiple equilibria treatment. The assumption in the treatment is that the base interacts to the same extent with the free and the associated forms of the interactants. Equilibrium constants for such interactions between different compounds have been calculated and the general conclusions can be summarized as follows: Interaction between purines (i.e., 6-methyl purine with 6-methyl purine, purine with purine, purine and adenine, etc.) is stronger than interactions of purine with pyrimidine (purine with thymine, uridine or cytidine with adenine, etc.), which is in turn stronger than the interactions of pyrimidine with pyrimidine (cytidine with cytidine, uridine with uridine, thymine with uridine, etc.). These compounds all interact much more extensively, however, than does urea.

Interaction of the monomeric units then are clearly demonstrated by their thermodynamic properties in aqueous solution. Now we turn our attention to the mode of interaction which is studied by nuclear magnetic resonance spectroscopy. The resonance lines of the 2,6,8 protons of purine were first assigned experimentally by direct substitution of hydrogen by deuterium at the individual positions [3]. The concentration dependence of the chemical shifts of the purine protons was measured over a wide concentration range from 0.1 to 1 molal solution [2]. It was found that all of the proton signals are shifted significantly to higher magnetic field strengths as the concentration of solute is increased. This effect is being examined in the light of the hypothesis that the ring current of one purine molecule may influence the protons of the other purine in the associated form. These experimental observations completely exclude horizontal pairing as the mode of association of purine in water. The only reasonable model which fits the experimental observations is one in which there is a partial vertical stacking of the purine rings over one another in such a manner that an environment of diamagnetic anisotropy is created by the ring currents of these partially overlapped molecules. Similar ob-

TABLE 3

Solubility of adenine in the presence of interacting compounds[a]

Compounds Added	Concentration, molar	Solubility $\bar{S}$ molar x 10^3	
(A) 25.5°			
None	...	8.25 ± 0.30[b]	
Purine	0.19	22.8	1.1[a]
	0.39	37.9	1.6
	0.58	52.6	2.9
Cytidine	0.18	15.6	1.6
	0.36	22.3	1.5
	0.54	28.7	1.6
Uridine	0.18	14.5	0.9
	0.36	22.3	1.5
	0.54	30.9	1.2
Pyrimidine	0.20	11.1	0.23
	0.40	15.8	0.58
	0.60	19.6	0.52
Phenol	0.20	12.0	0.50
	0.40	19.0	0.74
Cyclohexanol	0.20	9.47	0.15
Adonitol	0.60	9.84	0.39
Urea	0.60	8.88	0.36
(B) 38°			
None	...	13.9	0.88[b]
Purine	0.193	29.1	1.33
	0.386	46.3	1.63
	0.58	60.9	1.70
Uridine	0.09	15.9	1.50
	0.18	20.1	1.26
	0.27	24.3	1.20
	0.36	30.5	1.33
	0.45	34.9	1.48
	0.54	42.7	1.11

[a]Data from Ts'o [1].
[b]Standard deviation.

servations have been made with 6-methyl purine. A more detailed presentation of the data and calculations is forthcoming.

In summary, investigations of the interaction of nucleic acid monomers have so far yielded two major conclusions: First, the uncharged bases and nucleosides do interact extensively in aqueous solution and their

TABLE 4

Solubility of thymine in the presence of interacting compounds at 25.5° [a]

Compounds Added	Concentration, molar	Solubility $\underline{S}$ molar x 10^3	
None	...	27.4 ± 0.70[b]	
Purine	0.095	33.5	1.20[b]
	0.19	40.2	0.87
	0.39	49.8	1.10
	0.58	56.3	1.03
	0.77	64.0	1.50
	0.97	70.7	2.10
Uridine	0.18	33.4	0.70
	0.36	39.7	0.95
	0.54	43.7	1.27
Pyrimidine	0.10	29.8	0.40
	0.20	32.6	0.55
	0.40	37.4	0.80
	0.60	41.2	1.50
	0.80	44.6	1.67

[a]Data from Ts'o [1].   [b]Standard deviation.

tendency of association can be ordered in the following series: purine-purine > purine-pyrimidine > pyrimidine-pyrimidine. Second, the mode of association of these compounds appears to be one of stacking in a partial overlapping manner. The tendency of association of these compounds is two orders of magnitude greater than that of urea in water. Furthermore, methyl substitution of these compounds appears to increase their tendency to associate. Together these findings strongly suggest that hydrophobic forces play a predominant role.

Two approaches have been taken for the study of interaction on the second level, i.e., interaction between the monomer and the polymeric nucleic acids. First, the effect of monomer on the conformation and properties of nucleic acids has been studied. Secondly, measurements have been made of the binding of the monomer to the nucleic acid polymer.

For the first approach, optical rotation has been shown to be a tool of value because it possesses the following advantages: One, optical rotatory power as measured at 436 or 589 mμ is not interfered with by the highly u.v. absorbing monomers which are, however, optically inactive. Two, the change of the optical rotation caused by the change of secondary structure of nucleic acid is very large. The rotation of the nucleoside, on the contrary, is weak and relatively independent of temperature. The relationships between the secondary structure of nucleic acid and its optical rotation have been fairly well studied and documented [4-6].

The effects of purine, purine nucleosides, pyrimidine, pyrimidine nucleosides, and analogs and derivatives of these compounds on the properties of nucleic acids in helical form have been studied [4]. The presence of these compounds causes no change of optical rotation nor viscosity of helical nucleic acid. There is simply no indication of interaction of native DNA or of helical poly A with these compounds in solution. Nevertheless, the helix-coil transition temperature, T_m, of both native DNA and of helical poly A is significantly reduced in the presence of these compounds (Fig. 1). For instance, in the presence of 0.3 M purine, the T_m of helical poly A is reduced as much as 14°C. A series of compounds has been tested for their effectiveness in lowering the melting temperature of poly A and of thymus DNA. The order of effectiveness was found to be: adonitol, methyl-riboside (both negligible) < cyclhexanol < phenol, pyrimidine, uridine, < cytidine, thymidine < purine,

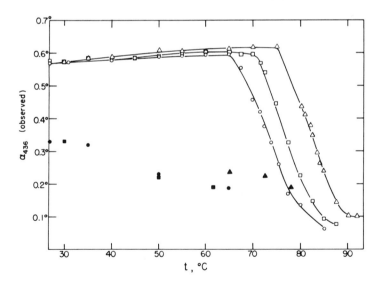

Fig. 1.—Helix-coil transition of DNA measured by optical rotation at 436 mμ. Buffer: 0.1 μ Na-phosphate, pH 6.5. DNA (- ▲ - ▲ -); with 0.3 M pyrimidine (- □ - □ -) or 0.3 M purine (-o-o-o). Empty symbols designate the heating curves and solid symbols designate the cooling curves. Data from Ts'o [4].

adenosine, inosine, deoxyguanosine < caffeine, coumarin, 2,6-dichloro-7-methyl-purine. Urea was found to be completely ineffective with poly A and only slightly effective with DNA. The relationship between the structures of these molecules and their effectiveness in reducing T_m again indicates that their denaturing effects do not appear to depend upon hydrogen bonding but rather upon hydrophobic interaction.

The effects of purine and related compounds on the physical properties of helical nucleic acids are not noticeable in the temperature range below the T_m. In contrast, the effect of purine on the physical properties of denatured DNA and on the coil form of poly A is quite striking. In the presence of 0.3 M purine, the specific rotation (at 20°C and at 436 mμ) of denatured DNA drops from 240° to 170°, and in the presence of 0.6 M purine, to 50°. Concurrently with the decrease of specific rotation, there is a significant increase of 30 to 60 percent in reduced viscosity. Similar effects of purine have also been observed for the coil form of poly A. From these facts, a coherent picture is emerging. Compounds such as purine and nucleosides do not appear to interact noticeably with the helical forms of nucleic acids. They do, however, interact significantly with the coil form. These interactions bring about further uncoiling and extension of the polymer with concomitant reduction of the base-base interaction of the nucleic acid itself. It is because of this preferential interaction of compounds such as purine with the coil rather than with the helical form of nucleic acid that causes the helix-coil transition of nucleic acid to be shifted to a lower temperature by their presence.

This picture is further confirmed by direct measurements of the affinities of purine and pyrimidine bases and related compounds to nucleic acids by equilibrium dialysis [7, 8]. Eight compounds were chosen for the binding studies. These included thymine, adenine, caffeine (a derivative of purine with mutagenic action), estradiol-β-17, testosterone (female and male sex hormone), diethylstilbesterol (a synthetic estrogen), and finally naphthalene and phenanthrene, representatives of the aromatic hydrocarbons. The biopolymers chosen were thymus nucleic acid, yeast soluble RNA, pea seedling ribosomal RNA, poly A, and poly U. The affinity constant, nk, of each of these compounds for each of the nucleic acids was determined from these experiments. In the constant nk, n is the number of binding sites per unit nucleotide of the nucleic acid and k is the binding constant of the unit nucleotide to the substrate of interest. The experimental condition was such that the concentration of the substrate was always low and the binding sites far from saturation due to a large ratio of polymer to substrate. In this situation, no information is obtained about n and k represents a number average value for all binding sites. Because the calculation is based on the unit nucleotide, the value of n is unlikely to be much larger or smaller than unity. The results of the binding study are given in Table 5.

The most significant discovery of the binding experiment is that the values of nk for the coil form of nucleic acids are much higher than those of the helical or native form. This fact clearly indicates that the affinity of a substrate for nucleic acid depends greatly on the secondary structure

TABLE 5

Binding constants of bases, steroids, and aromatic hydrocarbons to nucleic acids[a] at 5°[b]

$$n\underline{k}\ (M^{-1})^c = \frac{[\text{Complex}]}{[\text{free nucleotide-unit in nucleic acid}][\text{free substrates}]}$$

	Thymine	Adenine	Caffeine	Diethyl Stilbesterol	Estradiol-β-17	Testosterone	Naphthalene	Phenanthrene
Thymus DNA heat denatured[g]	<1[d]	9.0	7.0[e]	30	64	220	20	2800[f]
Thymus DNA[g] native	<1[d]	<1[d]	<1[d]	<1[d]	14	15	<1[d]	300
Poly A coil[j]	<1[d]	5.7[e]	5.8	...	6.2	7.0	...	30[d]
Poly A helix[h]	...	7.1	<1[d]	...	4.0	<1[d]	...	...
Poly U[g]	...	...	...	...	...	<1[d]	...	7[d]
Yeast s-RNA[g]	...	...	...	<1[d]	<1[d]	4[i]	...	63
Pea ribosomal RNA[g]	...	...	...	...	...	4[d]	...	65[d]

[a]The range of polymer concentration used in these experiments is around 0.01 M to 0.025 M of nucleotide unit. The concentration is around 0.005 M for the experiment with denatured DNA and steroids and aromatic hydrocarbons.

[b]All in 0.5 M NaCl in the presence of buffer. Data from [8].

[c]The standard error of measurement and computation of n$\underline{k}$ for a given sample of nucleic acid is estimated to be ±4% for n$\underline{k}$ values over 100, ±8% for n$\underline{k}$ values below 20, and ±12% for n$\underline{k}$ values below 10. For DNA, the value of n$\underline{k}$ is very sensitive to the helical content and random-coil content of the sample.

[d]Experiments were made only at one to three levels of the concentration of the radiochemicals. For values of n$\underline{k}$ less than 1, usually three repeats of the lowest workable concentration were taken.

[e]Points scattered more than usual, the standard error is around ±20%.

[f]The n$\underline{k}$ from the solubility data was 2800 ± 100, and from dialysis experiments varies from 1900 to 2800. Because of the difficulties in dialysis, the value of 2800 was taken.

[g]In 0.5 M NaCl, 0.01 M phosphate, pH 7.1.

[h]In 0.5 M NaCl, 0.1 M Na-acetate, pH 4.5.

[i]The n$\underline{k}$ values of 2 and 6 were obtained from two different preparations; an average is reported here.

[j]In 0.5 M NaCl, 0.05 M Tris buffer, pH 7.5.

of the nucleic acid. One notable exception to this general conclusion is listed in Table 5. The nk of adenine for the helical form of poly A appears to be higher than that for the coil form of poly A. At pH 4.5, however, adenine is partially protonated and therefore interacts with the negative phosphate group of poly A. This situation is unavoidable because the poly A must also be in the protonated form in order to assume the helical form. This exception is therefore based upon an interesting and logical reason. As for the other uncharged compounds, it is clear that they possess a greater affinity for the coil form of the nucleic acid than for the corresponding helical form. This conclusion substantiates the picture proposed above; namely, that the mechanism by which the T_m of nucleic acids is reduced is based on the preferential binding of the substrate to the coil form of the nucleic acid.

A second interesting conclusion from the binding experiments is that DNA exhibits a two orders of magnitude greater affinity for the substrates in question than does RNA, natural or synthetic. The data cannot be interpreted simply on the basis that ribosomal and yeast s-RNA possess more helical structure than denatured thymus DNA because the random coil forms of both poly A and poly U also possess a lower value of nk than does denatured DNA. Clearly, these vast differences between the affinity of purines and related compounds for DNA and their affinity for RNA may have profound biological significance although it is yet to be properly understood.

Binding of testosterone and phenanthrene by commerical calf thymus histone has also been studied [8]. At 5°C and in 0.5 M salt, pH 7.1, the value of nk for testosterone binding is 0.014 $(g/l)^{-1}$ and for phenanthrene binding is 0.3 $(g/l)^{-1}$. When the values are converted to the same unit of $(g/l)^{-1}$, the values for the binding of testosterone and phenanthrene by the denatured DNA are 25-35 fold higher than those for binding onto histone.

A comparison has also been made of the affinity of steroids for protein and for denatured DNA. The reported values of nk for testosterone binding to bovine serum albumin at 8°C is 1.7 x 10^4 m^{-1} [9]. Taking the molecular weight of albumin at 70,000 and the average molecular weight of the nucleotide unit in DNA as 350, and ignoring the small difference (3°) in temperature, the nk value of the binding of testosterone to denatured DNA appears to be 2.5 times greater on a weight basis than that for protein. Sandburg [10] has reported values for binding of steroids to various fractions of human plasma protein at 5°C. After proper corrections for molecular weight, the nk values for testosterone binding to DNA are ca. 2-30 times higher than those for the various fractions of plasma protein.

The biological implications of these two conclusions deserve reflection. They suggest three events as predictable when steroids or carcinogens enter into a living cell: (1) These compounds are more likely to interact with DNA than with anything else, once they penetrate into the nucleus. (2) They are most likely to interact with DNA in the uncoiled or uncoiling stage, i.e., DNA which is replicating or synthesizing RNA. Thus these compounds are expected to be more reactive in dividing cells or in cells actively engaged in RNA and protein synthesis. (3) Interaction of these compounds with DNA will lead to uncoiling of DNA. Therefore this interaction may be expected to trigger or modify any biological process in which the secondary structure of DNA is vitally involved.

Preliminary investigations have been made of the temperature dependency of the nk for testosterone binding to denatured DNA. In these experiments, the value of nk is 180 at 5°C, 110 at 18°C, and 90 at 27°C. In media 0.5 M in salt, the absorbancy of denatured DNA is unchanged within the temperature range of 5 to 27°C. This fact indicates that the secondary structure of the denatured DNA is not greatly affected over the range of temperature involved, at least as far as hypochromicity is concerned. All of these facts lead to the conclusion that the binding of testosterone to DNA exhibits a negative change both in enthalpy and in entropy as would be expected for a physical process.

What is the nature of the binding forces between the monomeric substrates discussed here and the polymeric nucleic acids? These forces cannot be electrostatic and are unlikely to be totally dependent on hydrogen bonding, especially in the case of aromatic compounds which have no hydrogen bonding sites. The order of affinities of different nucleic acids for these substrates appears to follow the same principles which govern effectiveness in the reduction of T_m. In a search for further insight into this question, measurements have been made of the partition coefficients between heptane and water of the substrates discussed here (Table 6). Table 6 lists these coefficients as well as the values of nk for these same substrates with denatured DNA. There is a certain correlation between partition coefficient and nk. For instance, hydrocarbons and steroids all have high partition coefficients and high values of nk as compared to purines and pyrimidines.

The highest partition coefficient and the highest value of nk among all steroids tested was found for testosterone, and among all hydrocarbons tested for phenanthrene. There are, however, discrepancies. For instance, naphthalene has a higher partition coefficient but a lower value of nk than do steroids. Adenine has lower partition coefficient but a higher value of nk than does thymine. The best conclusion seems to be that hydrophobic forces, such as interaction of water molecules, close-range van der Waal interaction, play an important role. Obviously, other factors must also be involved.

In conclusion, the investigations of monomer-polymer interaction have yielded two major points of new insight. First, bases and nucleotides interact with nucleic acids, preferentially with the coil form and predominantly through hydrophobic interaction. Second, many other compounds which are biologically active but chemically inert and hydrophobic, such as steroids and polycyclic carcinogens, interact strongly with nucleic acids.

It is now clear that the purine and pyrimidine moieties of the nucleic acids are endowed with a highly hydrophobic character. It is, however, certainly incorrect to think that this is the only parameter which determines the specificity and extent of interaction of polymers in the bio-

TABLE 6

Partition coefficients[a] of bases, steroids, and aromatic hydrocarbons
between heptane and aqueous buffer at 5 C[b]

Compound	Coefficient	$\underline{nk}$[c]
Adenine	~0.0004[d]	9.0
Thymine	~0.001[d]	<1
Caffeine	~0.01[d]	7.0
Estradiol-β -17	0.19	64
Diethyl stilbesterol	0.78	30
Testosterone	1.6	220
Naphthalene	8.2	20
Phenanthrene	800–1200[d]	2800

[a]Coefficient = conc. in heptane/conc. in 0.01 M phosphate, pH 7.1, 0.5 M NaCl.
[b]Data from [8]. For comparison, the values of $\underline{nk}$ for binding of these compounds to denatured DNA are also listed.
[c]Data from Table 5.
[d]The coefficient is too large or too small for accurate measurement.

logical processes considered here. Electrostatic interaction must play
a role since nucleic acids are polyelectrolytes. A nucleic acid, at neutral
pH, is not amphoteric as are proteins; the nucleic acid under these conditions contains only negative charges. Thus, the participation of electrostatic forces in the interaction of nucleic acids must be mainly repulsive.
The bases of nucleic acids can also participate in hydrogen bond formation, particularly by the well-known base-pairing scheme of Watson and
Crick. The unique specificity indicated for the interaction of nucleic acids
must require the participation of all of these forces as well as of other
forces, including π -electron attraction and stereochemical ones yet to
be explored. Any one of these forces alone is not adequate to define the
interactions of nucleic acids. We may imagine a junction created by the
meeting of all of the force vectors involved in the establishment of a
specific situation, for instance, that the hydrophobic interaction of the
bases of a nucleic acid takes these bases out of the environment of the
solvent and puts them in close contact with each other. At close range
and in the absence of solvent molecules such as water or hydrogen bonding, van der Waal's dispersion forces, π -electron interaction, and so on
can take hold and form specific bonds. The stereochemical and electrostatic interactions also participate in placing the bases in proper geometry
to each other. All of these forces therefore must work cooperatively with

one another to characterize the specificity required by the biological interaction. Because there is a big jump in complexity between the levels of
monomer-polymer interaction and that of the polymer-polymer interaction,
the phenomena of cooperative effect and of irreversible process must be
considered. We hope that these can be studied as we investigate stepwise
increases in complexity. For example, we can increase the degree of
polymerization of the polymer under investigation step by step. Thus,
by the study of the interaction of oligonucleotides we may gain an entrance
to this complex problem.

A further approach to the problem of interaction depends upon chemical modification of natural nucleic acids or upon the synthesis of new
polymers. These will be polymers designed for testing the relationships
between molecular structure and polymer interaction as well as for the
understanding of the properties of natural polymers. This approach is
well exemplified by the contribution synthetic polypeptides make to our
understanding of proteins.

Thus far, general attention has been focused only on the interactions
of homologous polymers; nucleic acids with nucleic acids, proteins with
proteins (as in case of antigen-antibody reactions). The day is at hand
when substantial effort should be made to study interaction between protein and nucleic acid, as in the case of soluble RNA and activating enzymes, or between DNA and histone. To launch such investigations and
particularly to explore the latter problem is the primary goal of this
volume.

REFERENCES

1.   Ts'o, P. O. P., Melvin, I. S., and Olson, A. C., J. Am. Chem. Soc., 85, 1289, 1963.

2.   Chan, S. I., Helmkamp, G. K., Schweizer, M. P., and Ts'o, P. O. P., paper presented at the Symposium on Molecular Structure and Spectroscopy, Columbus, Ohio, June 10–14, 1963.

3.   Schweizer, M. P., Chan, S. I., Helmkamp, G. K., and Ts'o, P. O. P., J. Am. Chem. Soc., In press, Feb. 5th, 1964.

4.   Ts'o, P. O. P., Helmkamp, G. K., and Sander, C., Proc. Natl. Acad. Sci. U. S. A., 48, 686, 1962.

5.   Ts'o, P. O. P., Helmkamp, G. K., and Sander, C., Biochim. Biophys. Acta, 55, 584, 1962.

6.   Helmkamp, G. K., and Ts'o, P. O. P., Biochim. Biophys. Acta, 55, 601, 1962.

7.   Ts'o, P. O. P., and Lu, P., Fed. Proc., 22, 583, 1963.

8.   Ts'o, P. O. P., and Lu, P., Proc. Natl. Acad. Sci., U. S. A., In press, Jan. 1964.

9.   Schellman, J. A., Lumry, R., and Samuels, L. T., J. Am. Chem. Soc., 76, 2808, 1954.

10.   Sandberg, A. A., Slaunwhite, Jr., W. R., and Autoniades, H. N., Recent Progress in Hormone Res., 13, 209, 1957.

Beal B. Hyde

A STRUCTURAL COMPONENT
OF CHROMATIN

Despite repeated observations of cell nuclei of all kinds, the ultra-structure of chromatin remains uncertain. For this reason it seemed worthwhile to look at isolated pea nuclei, which are prepared in our laboratory in large quantities and by routine methods [1].

The nuclei to be discussed here were purified once by spinning through 2 M sucrose containing 1 mM $CaCl_2$ and 4 mM $MgCl_2$. The pellet was resuspended in 0.4 M sucrose containing 1 mM sodium citrate. This suspension was usually fixed by 2 fold dilution with nonbuffered 2% O_sO_4. However, 3% glutaraldehyde in phosphate buffer pH 7.4 gives essentially the same type of preservation. Addition of Ca^{++} to the fixative causes clumping of the chromatin. It seems clear that the addition of sodium citrate, or perhaps a similar chelating agent, is essential to obtain the image to be described. It has been used routinely in our laboratory by Birnstiel [2] to destroy the nuclear membrane and to loosen the chromatin before isolation of purified nucleoli. Almost certainly, this method also results in the loss of a great deal of soluble material lying between the strands of chromatin. This material always makes interpretation of the structure of chromatin in nuclei in situ more difficult. It is also necessary to state that only interphase nuclei are isolated by this method; nuclei in other stages of mitosis have not been identified. Chromatin from the stages between the breakdown and reformation of the nuclear membrane would not be expected.

After fixation, the precipitated material was embedded in Epon or Maraglas, thinly sectioned, and post-stained with either Karnovsky's sodium plumbite [3] or lead citrate [4]. Photographs were made on a Philips 200 electron microscope, with the very convenient mechanism that allows one to take stereo pairs by tipping the specimen through an angle of 12°. Figure 1 is a low-power electron micrograph of a nuclear pellet prepared in this manner. The nuclear membrane is commonly destroyed, but the chromatin does not become entirely disorganized, as its continued location around the nucleolus indicates. Areas of chromatin to be photographed were selected from this type of nucleus. The cit-

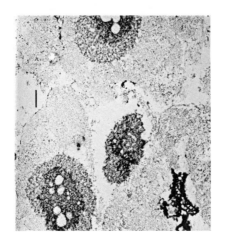 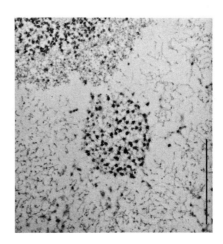

Fig. 1.—Survey of a pellet of isolated pea nuclei purified in sucrose and treated with weak citrate as described in the text. Note that the nuclear membrane is almost completely lacking, that the nucleoli are here characterized by a dense inner region and a lighter outer region, and that the chromatin is a mesh of fine strands. The scale line represents 1 μ.

Fig. 2.—A higher power electron micrograph of a similar nucleus showing the junction of the nucleolus with the chromatin. The two regions of the nucleolus may be seen more clearly. The ovoid structure in the center is commonly seen adjacent to, or attached to, the nucleolus. Its structure resembles the inner region of the nucleolus, but the large granules are invariably larger than those of the nucleolus. It may be the nucleolar organizer. The mesh of chromatin is clear. The scale line represents 1 μ.

rate treatment in some cases strongly elutes the nucleoli also, rendering their image only slightly different from the adjacent chromatin. Great care was sometimes necessary to be sure the background mesh of an eluted nucleolus was not confused with chromatin.

Figure 2 is a higher power micrograph of an isolated nucleus showing the junction of a nucleolus and the chromatin. The structure lying slightly separated from the nucleolus proper but resembling it in several ways is thought to be the heterochromatic nucleolar organizer. Figures 3 and 4 are stereomicrographs of regions of chromatin. The obvious strands are almost uniformly about 160 Å in diameter. With a stereoscopic viewer, one can readily see that the 160 Å strands can be subdivided into two, or sometimes four, helical strands about 20-25 Å in diameter. We believe that these helices are arranged paranemically, that is to say, the strands are not wound around each other, as are the two strands of a DNA double helix, but may easily be separated laterally. Two kinds of evidence lead us to this conclusion. First, where the strands appear to have been stretched lengthwise, they lie parallel to each other and show no signs

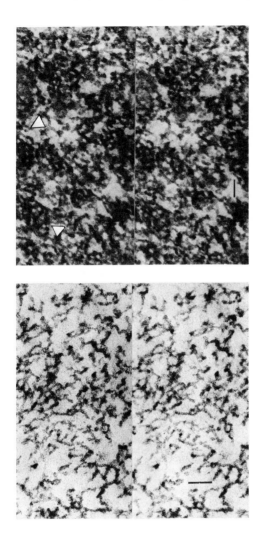

Figs. 3 and 4.—Stereomicrographs of chromatin from an isolated nucleus. The paired fine strands which make up the obvious meshwork may be seen most clearly where arrows have been placed. The scale line represents $0.1\,\mu$. Stereo viewers necessary to see the structure described may be obtained from Abrams Instrument Co., Lansing 1, Michigan.

of twisting. Second, when chromatin fractions prepared by this method are dried down on a grid and stained with uranyl acetate (Fig. 6 in Birnstiel, Chipchase, and Hyde [5]) intertwined strands are not seen. On the contrary, the strands (which are 35-40 Å in diameter) fray out or anastomose in a manner that suggests they may separate at random.

We have routinely seen the basic structure described here in thin sections of these nuclei. The 160 Å diameter of these strands is probably slightly larger than the true diameter in situ. The process of isolation, and particularly the citrate treatment, would be expected to swell and loosen nucleoprotein structure. It has been repeatedly stated that divalent cations play a role in chromosome structure and that the unit strand of chromatin is 100-120 Å [6].

Modifications of fixation and staining do not change the fundamental image. This is the only common structure we can see in the chromatin region of these nuclei. Particularly, we have seen no higher order of organization of these strands. For this reason we think it represents the basic unit of chromosome structure. We find it quite possible to speculate that this 160 Å, two-part, strand in the isolated nuclei is simply an uncoiled segment of a chromosome and that the two component helical fibrils measuring 20-25 Å in diameter are the chromatids. A metaphase chromosome with such a strand as its basic unit would have to be so enormously coiled and contorted as to appear to be without higher orders of structure in electron micrographs. These speculations more closely fit those hypotheses which attribute most of the structure of a chromosome to coiling of a unit strand than they do with the multiple-strand hypotheses of Kaufmann, Gay, and McDonald [7] and Ris [8] or the lampbrush hypothesis of Nebel and Coulon [9].

REFERENCES

1.   Rho, J. H., and Chipchase, M. I., J. Cell Biol., 14, 183, 1962.

2.   Birnstiel, M. L., Rho, J., and Chipchase, M. I. H., Biochim. Biophys. Acta, 55, 734, 1962.

3.   Karnovsky, M. J., J. Biophys. Biochem. Cytol., 11, 729, 1961.

4.   Reynolds, E. S., J. Cell Biol., 17, 208, 1963.

5.   Birnstiel, M. L., Chipchase, M. I. H., and Hyde, B. B., J. Cell Biol., 18, 41, 1963.

6.   Steffensen, D., Brookhaven Symp. Biol., 12, 103, 1959.

7.   Kaufmann, B., Gay, H., and McDonald, M. R., Intern. Rev. Cytol., 9, 77, 1960.

8.   Ris, H., Can. J. Genet. Cytol., 3, 95, 1961.

9.   Nebel, B., and Coulon, E. M., Chromosoma, 13, 272, 1962.

IV. HISTONE METABOLISM: CHROMOSOME STRUCTURE

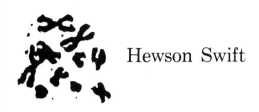 Hewson Swift

THE HISTONES OF POLYTENE CHROMOSOMES

INTRODUCTION

It is generally considered that gene action involves the formation of RNA on a chromosomal template. In cells engaged in active protein synthesis, cytochemical stains can demonstrate an RNA fraction closely related spatially to the DNA and often located between the areas of condensed chromatin [1]. Radioautography has shown this fraction to have a rapid rate of precursor incorporation [2-4]. This chromosomal RNA can be studied in a particularly favorable way in the giant salivary gland nuclei of Drosophila and other flies. Here interphase chromosomes occur in great bundles of more than a thousand strands, the familiar giant polytene chromosomes with their exact organization of bands and interbands. Upon this intricate framework changes in chromosomal RNA can be studied in far greater detail than is possible with the usual much smaller and less ordered nuclei. The RNA within polytene chromosomes is formed at specific regions, producing characteristic swellings or puffs. Puff formation is precisely timed and occurs at certain loci at exactly predictable stages in development [5], but it differs in different tissues or genetic strains [6]. These are the patterns one would expect if puffing were a morphological and chemical manifestation of gene action.

If histones somehow mediate gene action, we might also expect characteristic changes in the type or amount of histones during puff formation. With this problem in mind, we have been looking for changes in the histone levels of chromosome loci during various stages of the puffing process. Our present studies, still in progress, have demonstrated no detectable changes in histone amounts per band, using the binding of acid dyes at high pH [7].

Cytochemical observations are as good as the chemical reactions used. Present methods for the cytochemical demonstration of histones are certainly inadequate, particularly for localizing different types of histones. The present report outlines our attempts, based on the belief that functional changes in these important nuclear components need to be studied at the chromosomal level. At present even the comparatively crude cytochemical techniques available may add to our knowledge of histone function.

The first section of this paper contains a brief discussion of the nucleic acids in Drosophila chromosomes. The second part reviews a few of the problems of histone cytochemistry and gives some observations on histone levels in puff formation.

NUCLEIC ACIDS

Puff formation in Drosophila occurs without detectable changes in DNA amounts. As the puff increases in size there is a progressive decrease in DNA (Feulgen) concentration, entirely accountable by the dilution of a constant amount of DNA by labile puff components. Photometric measurements on whole nuclei stained with the Feulgen reaction fall into ten sharply defined classes in a 2:4:8....1024 series [8, 9], of which the four largest occur in the mature (late third larval instar) salivary gland. It is difficult to account for this discontinuous distribution of DNA amounts except by assuming that DNA synthesis takes place over a comparatively short period which involves the entire chromosomal set, and that marked metabolic fluctuations are absent. Apparently nine such synthetic periods, each resulting in a duplication of existing chromosomal material, have occurred during gland growth from minute diploid nuclei of the newly hatched larva.

This concept is supported by DNA radioautography with H^3-labeled thymidine. Most chromosomes either were unlabeled or were labeled throughout their length when the precursor was supplied to the tissues by feeding or when isolated glands were incubated in labeled medium for 30 minutes to 4 hours (see also [10]). In most cases the label showed the characteristic banding pattern expected if all the existing DNA underwent replication during the period of isotope presentation. In a few cells, there were deviations from this pattern, particularly where strongly staining bands and the chromocenter were involved, containing high concentrations of DNA. In some cases these regions alone were labeled, and in a few other nuclei these areas produced noticeably fewer grains than expected from their high DNA concentration (Figures 1 and 2). Similar results have been obtained in Chironomus by Sengun [11]. It has been repeatedly shown in several different cell types that DNA synthesis may be late in concentrated or heterochromatic chromosomal areas [12-14]. This situation also appears to exist in Drosophila salivary gland chromosomes. One may conclude that the cells in which intensely staining bands are only lightly labeled were probably fixed in the early phases of synthesis, and cells with these areas strongly labeled are representative of the later stages. Although the variations in labeling time may be of importance in maintaining the genetic balance of nuclei, as Taylor [15] postulates, it

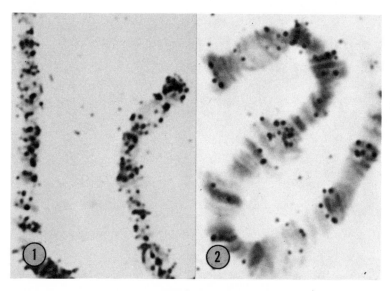

Figs. 1 and 2.—DNA labeling with H³ thymidine of chromosome 2 of <u>Drosophila</u> <u>virilis</u>. Figure 1 shows more the uniform label assumed to be associated with early stages in DNA synthesis. Figure 2 shows the label localized in a few areas where the DNA concentration is high. These areas probably represent late labeling regions. Magnification 2,400 X.

seems likely to us that areas condensed in interphase are late in labeling because of the steric interference one might expect within compact regions. We have found no evidence in <u>Drosophila</u> for zipper-like synthesis starting at chromosome ends. The pattern obtained certainly suggests that DNA synthesis may occur simultaneously in a variety of sites on the chromosome.

All of our findings on DNA in <u>Drosophila</u> indicate that DNA synthesis is related only to replication in the formation of the multistranded chromosome. No evidence has been found for localized "metabolic" DNA related to puff synthesis.

During larval development, the RNA component of salivary gland chromosomes changes in a complex manner as puffs form at certain loci and disappear at others (Figures 3 and 4). Becker [5] has described the varying sequence of puff patterns for chromosome 3L in <u>Drosophila</u> <u>melanogaster</u> during the third instar. Because these patterns are highly reproducible, it is possible to determine quite accurately from their appearance the developmental stage of a particular larva.

Most puff formation involves the localized accumulation of RNA as several workers [9, 10, 16-18] have shown for <u>Drosophila</u>, <u>Chironomus</u>, and <u>Sciara</u>. Two sciarid genera, <u>Rhynchosciara</u> and <u>Sciara</u>, also reveal certain puffs of a different type. In these puffs there is a localized increase in DNA [9, 19, 20] which is, however, not necessarily related to an

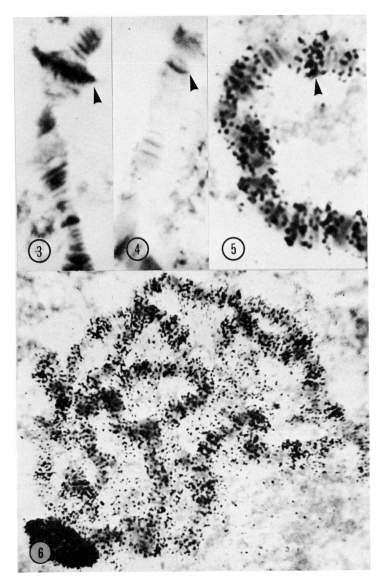

Fig. 3.—The end of chromosome 2, with the subterminal puff maximally expanded (arrow), stained for DNA and RNA with azure B. Magnification 1,800 X.

Fig. 4.—Chromosome 2 with the puff locus less expanded, stained for RNA with azure B, after DNA removal with deoxyribonuclease.

Fig. 5.—Chromosome 2 in explanted prepupal gland labeled for 15 minutes with H³ cytidine. The radioautograph was exposed for 50 days. Note strong label in the subterminal puff (arrow), as well as in other RNA containing regions of the chromosome.

Fig. 6.—Same as Figure 5, but at lower magnification to show entire cell. Heavily labeled nucleolus is at lower left. Magnification 600 X.

increase in total strandedness of the chromosome. This phenomenon of DNA puffs has not been found in Drosophila. Such localized DNA changes pose obvious problems to concepts of chromosome structure. DNA puffs may involve differential polyteny or may be a specialized case in which newly synthesized DNA, rather than RNA, represents a primary product of the gene. A report of DNA puff formation in a chironomid fly Glyptotendipes [21] has been reinterpreted as a localized condensation of a specific area rather than synthesis of new DNA [22].

One might expect that the complex morphology of RNA changes would be associated with complex patterns of precursor incorporation. Most radioautography in Drosophila has been carried out only on a random sample of chromosomal RNA obtained by sectioning whole glands [15, 23]. Although these studies on sections cannot be related to individual loci, they serve to demonstrate that puff RNA at times may be rapidly labeled and is thus probably synthesized on the chromosome. There is also a marked variability in incorporation rates. McMaster-Kaye [23] found that in mid to late third instar larvae chromosomal RNA becomes labeled less rapidly than does that of the nucleolus. However, if such experiments are extended into the prepupal period when a large number of new puffs arise in association with the final secretory activity of the larval gland, chromosomal RNA labels at a rate equal to that of the nucleolus (Figures 5 and 6). These studies suggest that puff RNA is most active when a new puff is forming and emphasize the fact that nucleolar RNA is at least partly independent of the chromosomal fraction, a point stressed by Leblond and Amano [24].

The fact that puff formation involves the accumulation of extra protein has been known for many years [8, 25]. It seems that a puff becomes an expanded region of the chromosome primarily because of the large amount of extra puff material formed at a particular locus within the chromosome, although the nature of this puff protein is still obscure. Its distribution closely parallels that of chromosomal RNA; it thus seems likely that this component is a ribonucleoprotein. It is not, in any case, a histone, if we define histones in terms of acid dye binding at high pH and acid extractability (see page 175). Radioautographic studies with labeled amino acids show this fraction labeled in Rhynchosciara after 5 hours [26], but in Chironomus no label was obtained [27]. Puff protein may be a gene-activating component synthesized elsewhere in the cell, such as the nuclear-cytoplasmic migratory protein described by Goldstein [28] and Prescott [29], and may be due to the association between hormone and chromosome as postulated by Clever [30]. On the other hand it may be an enzyme, such as RNA polymerase, necessary for the synthesis of puff RNA. A third possibility is that it is a protein needed in the transfer of chromosomal RNA to the cytoplasm. A ribonucleoprotein component, probably homologous with puff material, occurs in the loops of the lampbrush chromosomes of amphibian oocytes [31]. The loop protein is rapidly labeled and appears to be at least partly synthesized on the chromosome.

In electron micrographs, puff material exists at least partly as a particulate ribonucleoprotein component. An individual locus possesses particles of a characteristic size, in some cases smaller than ribosomes of the cytoplasm, and, in other cases, larger [9, 32, 33]. This morpho-logical heterogeneity is almost certainly a manifestation of a chemical heterogeneity in chromosomal ribonucleoproteins.

The puff thus contains three distinguishable components, DNA, RNA, and non-histone protein, with which we can compare the behavior of histones. The DNA appears stable except for the complex patterns of replication, pos-sibly influenced by the aggregation state of the chromatin substance. The RNA appears linked to a non-histone protein, to form small nucleoprotein particles within the puff. Together the RNA and non-histone protein form a variable but predictable complex, the RNA portion of which has a high incor-poration rate suggesting that it is formed on the chromosome.

HISTONES

Histone reactions for cytochemistry have depended either on amino acid staining reactions used with differential extraction procedures, or on the differential affinity of histones for acid dyes. Although both the Millon reaction for tyrosine and tryptophane [34, 35] and the Sakaguchi reaction for arginine [36, 37], stain nuclear proteins intensely, they cannot be considered as reactions for histones alone. Pollister and Ris [34] and Pollister [38], were among the first to attempt the cytochemical study of histones. These works compared tissues subjected to a sulfuric acid Millon reaction, by which histones were presumably removed, with tissues treated with trichloroacetic acid, by which histones were considered to be left intact. However, the solubility characteristics of proteins denatured by normal fixation are altered and such procedures probably cannot be relied on to give interpretable results. On the other hand, the application of the Millon or Sakaguchi reaction to selectively extracted fresh, frozen-dried, or other special preparations may prove useful. The application of these techniques can provide indications of shifts in the protein composition of nuclei, such as the replacement of histones by protamine-like proteins in spermatogenesis [39, 40].

The cytochemical method for histones now most widely used involves acid dye binding at high pH [7]. This reaction depends on the extremely basic nature of histones, and also on their highly concentrated occurrence in chromatin. Under appropriate conditions, histone aggregates in tissues are capable of producing strong anionic fields which can be selectively stained by cationic dyes. Where the relation between dye and substrate is predominantly electrostatic, staining reactions are subject to a number of variables. Studies [41, 42] have emphasized that such dye bind-ing reactions are a result of the total charge density of the tissue compo-nents as well as of the ion spectrum of the staining solution. Thus these reactions represent equilibria between a variety of factors, only one of which is the concentration of the substrate. For example, the basic dye binding of nucleic acids can be markedly enhanced by treatment of tissues with nitrous acid. Such treatment should not effect the anionic nucleic acid phosphoryl groups that bind the dye, but does deaminate certain of the cationic amino groups of the protein so that the total nucleoprotein carries an increased negative charge. The concentration of basic dye molecules is then increased at the tissue interface, and more dye is bound by the nucleic acid.

Histones can be stained more or less specifically by acid dyes under the following conditions: (1) The pH of the staining solution must be high enough so that the staining of other tissue proteins is negligible. (2) The negative charge of the chromatin must be greatly reduced. This can be achieved by DNA extraction, or less effectively, by blocking of the nucleic acid phosphory groups, as for example, with azure B which can later be extracted with ethanol. (3) Protein amino groups must be partially blocked by short formaldehyde fixation or postfixation treatment. (The more extreme deamination with nitrous acid results in a negative reaction for histones.) (4) The concentration of chromatin must be reasonably high. (The weak to negative reaction in early cleavage stages of some oocytes has been attributed to dilution [43].)

Under these rather special conditions many tissues can be prepared so that only their chromatin binds acid dyes. The reaction cannot be considered entirely specific for histones because other basic proteins, such as those of the cytoplasm of Tetrahymena [44] or of certain secretory granules of Drosophila salivary glands, also stain. These other basic proteins can often be distinguished from histones because the removal of DNA is not essential to their staining and they respond differently to methods of acid extraction.

Extraction techniques are often useful for increasing the specificity of cytochemical methods, or providing more confidence in the specificity of a reaction. Histones can be extracted with dilute mineral acids in tissues prepared so that the proteins are not denatured or only partially so; e.g., after fixation in cold methanol [45], cold acetone, freeze drying, or smearing in dilute acetic acid. Where customary fixatives employing formalin or metal salts are used, such extraction is difficult or impossible. Under these conditions either the histones may be incompletely extracted or the treatment must be so prolonged that other proteins as well are removed. More work certainly remains to be done on extraction techniques for histones, work preferably employing parallel biochemical analyses of the materials extracted and remaining. Such studies should afford a picture of the morphological position of different histones in the nucleus.

As determined by acid dye binding techniques, histone protein can thus be defined empirically as nuclear basic protein that stains with alkaline solutions of acid dyes, after but not before, blockage or removal of DNA. In addition, extraction of the protein in question from the tissue by dilute mineral acids must abolish the reaction.

One can obtain good localization of basic chromosomal proteins in Drosophila salivary glands (Figure 7 [9, 16, 46]). The technique used was: (1) Salivary glands were removed from late third instar or prepupal larvae of Drosophila virilis in Ringer's fluid, transferred to a drop of 45% acetic acid, and squashed between slide and coverslip. (2) The slide was

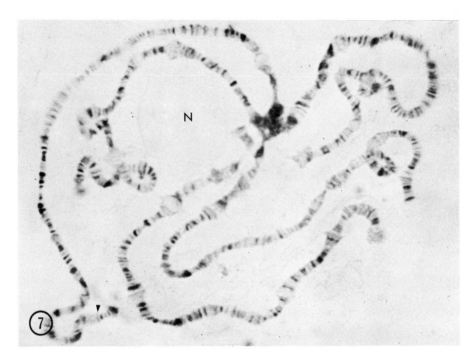

Fig. 7.—Fast green–histone reaction on a squash of <u>Drosophila</u> <u>virilis</u>. The nucleolus (N) and cytoplasm are virtually unstained. The end of chromosome 2 is at the lower left. (Preparation by M. Gorovsky.)

frozen on dry ice and the coverslip pried off. (3) Fixation time was one to four hours in 10% formalin in Sorenson phosphate buffer, pH 7.4 at 4 C. (4) The tissue was rinsed in hot water of 90 C for 15 minutes and treated with deoxyribonuclease (Worthington, 0.2 mg. per ml. in deionized water containing 0.003 M magnesium sulfate, adjusted to pH 6.5) for 1 hour at 20 C. (5) The slide was rinsed in water and then stained in an 0.1% solution of fast green FCF (National Aniline) in distilled water adjusted to pH 8.1 for 1 hour at 20 C. (6) This was followed by two five minute changes of distilled water at pH 8.1, after which the slide was dehydrated and mounted in oil of the appropriate refractive index, (usually 1.552) for microdensitometry.

To test for the possible removal of histones by 45% acetic acid, we have compared glands treated with 45% acetic acid for 12 hours with glands treated for only 10 seconds--the minimum time needed for squashing, freezing in liquid nitrogen and coverslip removal, and immersing the slide in formalin phosphate solution. Because good preparations with intense band staining are obtainable under both conditions, it may be concluded that the 45% acetic acid does not appreciably extract histones, or does so almost instantaneously. The latter possibility probably can be ruled out, because chromosome staining may also be obtained on squashes made in 50% ethanol and without the use of acetic acid. Such treatment, however, yields chromosomes which do not spread well and are not suitable for band analysis. The alcoholic smear will still show good histone localization after the required freezing in liquid nitrogen for coverslip removal. Thus we conclude that treatment of salivary gland tissue with 45% acetic acid prior to squashing removes little or none of the stainable basic proteins of chromosomes.

Preparations have also been made in fixatives in which formalin has been replaced by 95% ethanol, or ethanol-acetic acid (3:1). These smears generally yield more intense staining than those fixed in formalin, but also exhibit more staining of non-histone proteins of nucleus and cytoplasm. Apparently formalin adds a degree of specificity to the reaction by blocking protein amino groups [7]. In spite of the greater staining intensity of the ethanol smears, band patterns were similar in the two preparations except for the increased staining of puff areas, as would be expected from the loss in specificity. This staining was readily distinguishable as non-specific since it was independent of DNA removal.

Histone staining can readily be eliminated by extraction with hydrochloric acid. After coverslip removal and before formalin fixation, smears were treated with 0.2 $\underline{N}$ hydrochloric acid for one to four hours at 20 C. This extraction procedure rendered the subsequent histone reaction negative. Extraction of whole salivary glands before squashing were generally unsuccessful. Interestingly enough, after histone extraction total protein stains, such as fast green at pH 2.0, still showed a considerable amount of protein in the chromosomes. Much of this occurred in the puff areas in which the unextracted non-histone protein is concentrated, but other regions showed some staining as well. The question of whether or not the chromosome contains a "backbone" or residual protein in addition to histone needs further study. Good preparations of polytene chromosomes, isolated and free of contaminating nucleoplasm, would seem to be necessary for an adequate answer to this question.

We have defined histones in Drosophila polytene chromosomes as that basic protein fraction stainable with 0.1% fast green at pH 8.1 after DNA removal. There must be no staining without removal of DNA, or after extraction before fixation with 0.2 $\underline{N}$ hydrochloric acid.

If puffing represents gene action, it is important to know the behavior of histones during puff formation. Therefore we have measured the amount of fast green bound to a particular band in chromosome 2 of Drosophila virilis during the puffing process. Photomicrographs of fast green-stained smears were taken at a wavelength of 630 mμ in light from a Zeiss M4-QII monochromator with a slit width of 0.2 mm. Magnification on Kodak M plates was 4,000 X. The plates were scanned in a Joyce-Loebel 3-B recording densitometer, and the relative amount of dye determined both for the puffed band and an immediately adjacent unpuffed locus. An attempt was made to study well-spread chromosomes to avoid band overlap, and only the largest chromosomes (class 1024C, see Swift [9]) were measured. Figures 8 to 11 show representative micrographs, and Figures

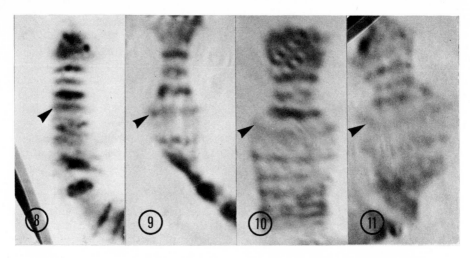

Figs. 8 to 11.—Ends of chromosome 2, stained with the fast green-histone reaction, showing different stages in puffing of the band marked with an arrow. Dark regions in the corners of Figures 8 and 11 are portions of the rotating sector step wedge for plate calibration. Magnification 4,200 X. (Preparations by M. Gorovsky.)

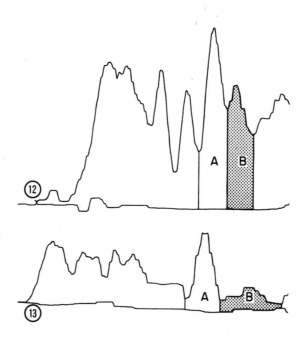

Figs. 12 and 13.—Sample densitometer traces made lengthwise along micrographs shown in Figures 8 and 10. Absorption associated with an unpuffed band is shown at A, and with puffed band at B.

TABLE I

Amounts of fast green bound to basic proteins in two adjacent bands
in chromosome 2 of Drosophila virilis. Locus A remains
unpuffed while locus B undergoes puff formation.*

	N	Mean	Range	Ratio $\frac{A}{B}$
Locus A		104	85–120	
	6			0.98
Locus B (no puff)		106	86–127	
Locus A		76	65–87	
	4			0.95
Locus B (small puff)		80	60–98	
Locus A		88	80–99	
	5			0.98
Locus B (full puff)		90	70–102	

*Micrographs were made as described in text. Each measurement is the mean of
from 3 to 5 densitometric traces taken through the chromosome parallel to its
long axis. After correction for non-linearity of emulsion, the area related to each
band was determined on graph paper with the lowest absorption points used as
arbitrary limits. Areas were then multiplied by chromosome width in band region.
The density of the slide containing small puffs was slightly lower than the others.
The ratios of band to puff should not be affected, however.

12 and 13 show sample densitometric traces. Table 1 gives the values
obtained.

Present in the band at all stages of the puffing process is a basic
protein fraction. It is stainable with fast green and extractable with hydrochloric acid and has a localization precisely similar to that of the DNA.
Like the DNA, this fraction is diluted by the accumulation of RNA and non-
histone protein as the puff forms, but a significant change in the amount
of protein-bound dye was not found. If the histones had disappeared or
been markedly reduced in amount during puff formation, we feel that our
techniques would have detected the change. If a lysine-rich histone replaced an arginine-rich histone, we would also expect a marked change
in the charge density at pH 8.1, and a similar alteration in the amount
of dye bound. As Table 1 indicates, our measurements of amount of dye
binding by chromosomes in similar stages vary by about ±20%. Changes
in histone amount or kind smaller than this might, therefore, remain un-
detected.

It might be argued that a loss in basic protein actually does occur but that this is exactly offset by the increase in non-histone puff protein. Puff protein is, however, not extracted to a detectable extent by 0.2 $\underline{N}$ hydrochloric acid. The non-histone puff protein also resists the more stringent acid treatment required for Feulgen hydrolysis of DNA. Dilute acid extraction, however, removes all of the chromosomal proteins in both puffed and unpuffed areas which stain at pH 8.1.

The reaction might also be criticized on the grounds that a DNA-protein artifact is formed on fixation of the tissue. Such an artifact might involve an unnatural binding of denatured protein basic groups to the phosphoric acid groups of DNA. The basic groups linked to DNA might be protected from attack by formalin; thus DNA removal would uncover clusters of new basic groups ipso facto equivalent to the DNA removed. Several facts refute this argument. Increasing biochemical evidence, much of it summarized in this volume, supports the reality of a DNA-histone complex in the living cell. Furthermore, much cytochemical data exists concerning the equivalence of DNA and histone amounts in cell nuclei. This has been shown by microphotometry of fast green-stained nuclei for a wide variety of tissues [45, 47]. Together these data suggest that the DNA-histone complex is a real biological entity and not an artifact of preparation.

It will be impossible to have complete confidence in the cytochemical reactions for histones until accurate comparisons with biochemical studies can be made on the same material. It is quite possible, for example, that the fast green reaction stains only one specific component of the histone spectrum, such as the arginine-rich fraction, and that other histones are unaccounted for in the preparations. Specific comparison studies are needed and are presently being conducted in several laboratories.

From these as-yet preliminary studies on $\underline{Drosophila}$ histones we can conclude that there is a particular acid extractable basic protein fraction in the salivary gland chromosome, and that, like the DNA, this component probably remains constant in amount during the activation of a band into a puff. These facts suggest that the function of this protein lies in neutralizing the charges of the DNA, and possibly also in chromosome structure, rather than in the mediation of gene activity.

Summary

Cytochemical studies on the giant chromosomes of $\underline{Drosophila\ virilis}$ larvae have demonstrated the following: (1) Radioautography with H^3 thymidine has shown that the DNA of some chromosomes became uniformly labeled, but that in others the label was largely restricted to densely staining areas. It is suggested that these restricted regions represent areas of late DNA synthesis. (2) Radioautography with H^3 cytidine has shown that the chromosomal RNA became labeled after 15 minutes of precursor presentation. With other workers, we conclude that RNA is synthesized on the chromosome during the formation of puffs. (3) The nature and specificity of the fast green histone reaction has been discussed, and a method for staining salivary gland squashes given. This method has been used to measure the amount of reactive protein present in a specific band near the tip of chromosome 2 and at different stages of puff development, employing photographic microdensitometry. We have found no measurable difference in amount of stainable basic protein per band during the puffing process. Our measurements support the concept that histones may play a role in neutralizing charges or DNA or in chromosome structure.

Acknowledgments

These studies were begun by Dr. M. F. Schurin and our early results form a portion of her thesis [16]. Mr. Irvin Heilmann made some of the radioautographs and Mr. Martin Gorovsky made the histone preparations as well as some modifications in technique. The author is indebted to these workers for their valuable assistance. Special thanks are due to Dr. Michel Rabinovitch for his advice and collaboration in some of the work on histones. This research has been aided by grants from the NSF and U. S. Public Health Service.

REFERENCES

1. Swift, H., Rebhun, L., Rasch, E., and Woodard, J., In D. Rudnick (ed.), Cellular Mechanisms of Differentiation and Growth (Princeton: Princeton Univ. Press, 1956), p. 45.

2. Ficq, A., Pavan, C., and Brachet, J., Exp. Cell Res. Suppl., 6, 105, 1958.

3. Swift, H., In W. McElroy and B. Glass (eds.), The Chemical Basis of Development (Baltimore: Johns Hopkins Univ. Press, 1958), p. 174.

4. Goldstein, L., and Micou, J., J. Biophys. Biochem. Cytol., 6, 301, 1959.

5. Becker, H. J., Chromosoma, 7, 508, 1959.

6. Beermann, W., Protoplasmatologia, 6D, 1, 1962.

7. Alfert, M., and Geschwind, I., Proc. Natl. Acad. Sci. U.S.A., 39, 991, 1953.

8. Swift, H., and Rasch, E., In Alfert, M., Int. Rev. Cytol., 3, 131, 1954.

9. Swift, H., In J. Allen (ed.), The Molecular Control of Cellular Activity (New York: McGraw Hill, 1962), p. 73.

10. Rudkin, G. T., and Woods, P., Proc. Natl. Acad. Sci. U.S.A., 45, 997, 1959.

11. Sengun, A., Path. et Biol., 9, 753, 1961.

12. Lima-de-Faria, A., J. Biophys. Biochem. Cytol., 6, 457, 1959.

13. Taylor, J. H., J. Biophys. Biochem. Cytol., 7, 455, 1960.

14. Woodard, J., Rasch, E., and Swift, H., J. Biophys. Biochem. Cytol., 9, 445, 1961.

15. Taylor, J. H., and Woods, P. S., In T. Hayashi (ed.), Subcellular Particles (New York: Ronald Press, 1959), p. 172.

16. Schurin, M., Ph. D. Thesis 3065, Univ. of Chicago, 1957.

17. Beermann, W., Cold Spring Harbor Symp. Quant. Biol., 21, 217, 1957.

18. Swift, H., In R. Zirkle (ed.), Symposium on Molecular Biology (Chicago: Univ. of Chicago Press, 1959), p. 266.

19. Breuer, M. E., and Pavan, C., Chromosoma, 7, 371, 1955.

20. Rudkin, G. T., and Corlette, S. L., Proc. Natl. Acad. Sci. U.S.A., 43, 964, 1957.

21. Stich, H. F., and Naylor, J. M., Exptl. Cell Res., 14, 442, 1958.

22. Keyl, H. G., Exp. Cell Res., 30, 245, 1963.

23. McMaster-Kaye, R., J. Biophys. Biochem. Cytol., 8, 365, 1960.

24. Leblond, C. P., and Amano, M., J. Histochem. Cytochem., 10, 162, 1962.

25. Schultz, J., Cold Spring Harbor Symp. Quant. Biol., 12, 179, 1947.

26. Ficq, A., and Pavan, C., Path. et Biol., 9, 756, 1961.

27. Clever, U., Chromosoma, 12, 607, 1961.

28. Goldstein, L., Exp. Cell Res., 15, 635, 1958.

29. Prescott, D. M., In J. Bonner and Paul O. P. Ts'o (eds.), Nucleohistones (San Francisco: Holden-Day, Inc., 1963), p. 193.

30. Clever, U., Develop. Biol., 6, 73, 1963.

31. Gall, J. G., and Callan, H. G., Proc. Natl. Acad. Sci. U.S.A., 48, 562, 1962.

32. Beermann, W., and Bahr, G. F., Exp. Cell Res., 6, 195, 1954.

33. Swift, H., Exptl. Cell Res. Suppl., 9, 54, 1963.

34. Pollister, A. W., and Ris, H., Cold Spring Harbor Symp. Quant. Biol., 12, 147, 1947.

35. Rasch, E., and Swift, H., J. Histochem. Cytochem., 8, 4, 1960.

36. McLeish, J., Chromosoma, 10, 686, 1959.

37. Deitch, A. D., J. Histochem. Cytochem., 9, 477, 1961.

38. Pollister, A. W., Revue d'Hematologie, 5, 527, 1950.

39. Alfert, M., J. Biophys. Biochem. Cytol., 2, 109, 1956.

40. Bloch, D. P., and Hew, H., J. Biophys. Biochem. Cytol., 7, 515, 1960.

41. Singer, M., Int. Rev. Cytology, 1, 211, 1952.

42. Swift, H., In E. Chargaff and J. N. Davidson (eds.), The Nucleic Acids, Vol. 2, (New York: Academic Press, Inc., 1955), p. 51.

43. Moore, B. C., J. Histochem. Cytochem., Abs., In press, 1963.

44. Alfert, M., and Goldstein, N. O., J. Exp. Zool., 130, 403, 1955.

45. Rasch, E., and Woodard, J. W., J. Biophys. Biochem. Cytol., 6, 263, 1959.

46. Horn, E. C., and Ward, C. L., Proc. Natl. Acad. Sci. U.S.A., 43, 776, 1957.

47. Bloch, D. P., and Godman, G. C., J. Biophys. Biochem. Cytol., 1, 17, 1955.

George T. Rudkin

THE PROTEINS OF
POLYTENE CHROMOSOMES

INTRODUCTION

Chromosomal proteins have proved much more elusive than the nucleic acids to the biochemist and, as a result, to the cytochemist or histochemist who usually depends on biochemical characterization for the bases of his experimental methods. The role of the proteins, the functions of the different types of protein in the structural and functional changes undergone by chromosomes and their differentiated parts, are still, for the most part, unresolved questions. The present discussion is an account of attempts to learn something about quantitative differences in protein content of chromosome regions in different states of activity. The methods of measurement were designed to take advantage of a specific attribute of the nucleic acids—their ultraviolet absorption—which Caspersson has developed into a most useful cytophotometric tool. The analogous property of the proteins is less effective for purposes of measurement at the intracellular level, because absorption coefficients dependent on cyclic amino acids are far lower than those of the nucleic acids, and the relatively high "end-absorption" occurs in a region of the spectrum technically difficult to work with (below 240 mμ). None the less, with an ultraviolet microspectrophotometer as the principal measuring tool, it has been possible to demonstrate differences between various states of functional activity in chromosome regions with respect to proteins as well as the nucleic acids. The question of what kinds of protein would be involved and their possible function will be left until later, except to point out the likelihood that a large fraction of the original basic protein content of the material would have been extracted by the acid fixative employed (50% aqueous acetic acid).

DROSOPHILA MELANOGASTER

Giant X Chromosome in Male and Female

Differences in functional activity within chromosomes have been the objects of intense study in recent years, since Beermann [1] and Breuer and Pavan [2] pointed out that swollen regions are likely to be manifestations of genic or chromosomal activity. We shall speak of such regions later, but let us first examine situations in which whole chromosomes occur in relatively more or less swollen states. In these cases also, a greater degree of swelling is associated with the greater activity. Such a case is the X chromosome of Drosophila melanogaster, which in the polytene cells of the larval salivary gland, appears to have approximately the same diameter as the autosomes, regardless of the sex of the larva. Since the Y chromosome does not undergo polytene growth in this tissue, the euchromatic X of the male is haploid; there is only half as much chromatin material as in the closely paired diploid X's in the female. The autosomes are diploid in normal animals of both sexes, so the similarity in size between them and the sex chromosomes in each sex implies that in the male the X is larger than in the female. In preparations stained to reveal DNA—for example, by aceto-carmine or aceto-orcein or the Feulgen reaction—a paler color in the male indicates that its X chromatin is more dilute.

The view that the activity of sex-linked genes is different in the two sexes goes back to Bridges' demonstration of "genic balance" [3, 4] and Muller's concept of "dosage compensation" [5], according to which the phenotypic effect of a gene is different, depending on how many copies of it are present in relation to the rest of the genome. In essence, the single dose in the male is as effective as the double dose in the female, from which it is concluded that the genetic material of the X chromosome must operate at a higher average level in the male. That the over-all synthetic capacity in salivary glands is sex dependent is directly evident from the work of Patterson et al. [6, 7], who found lower amounts of total protein, RNA, and peptidase activity per cell in male (where cells are smaller), compared to female larvae. It is likely that the differences in cell metabolism are traceable directly to the X chromosome itself.

The above cytological picture (first described by Offermann [8]) has been studied in more detail by my associates and me. The results, already reported briefly and in part [9], will be published in more detail elsewhere. Our experiments were designed to find out whether there is a difference in the content of ultraviolet-absorbing material in polytene X chromosomes of male and female Drosophila larvae; we used 257 mμ to study the nucleic acids and 275 and 231 mμ to study proteins. In addition, quantitative measurements of bound Feulgen dye gave a measure of DNA alone for comparison with total nucleic acid represented by absorption at 257 mμ. Caspersson's photographic method as modified by us [10] was used throughout these measurements and others to be described later. The lenses used for taking the photomicrographs from which the measurements were made were corrected for single wavelengths in the ultraviolet (275 $m\mu$ for use at 275 $m\mu$; 257 $m\mu$ for use at 257 and 231 $m\mu$; both with numerical apertures of 1.25) or were apochromatic (N.A. 1.32) for use in the visible (546 $m\mu$ Hg line) to measure bound Feulgen dye. Condenser numerical apertures were set between 0.3 and 0.4.

The experimental design called for measurement of only a small representative part of each giant chromosome, the terminal portion designated section 1 of the 20 sections on Bridges' [11] map of the X. Possible variations in total absorbance from cell to cell (e.g., because of different grades of polyteny or states in the cycle of polytene replication) were controlled by making identical measurements on an autosome, in Bridges' section 60 [12], the terminal section of the 20 sections in the right arm of the second chromosome (2R).

The measurements were carried out on a strain of D. melanogaster in which the females were heterozygous for a translocation involving the tip of one of the X chromosomes; the tip of the other, normal, X chromosome very frequently failed to pair with its translocated homolog and was measured in the haploid state, directly comparable with the haploid X in the male. In Table 1, the value expected on the hypothesis that X chromosomes are identical in both sexes is 0 (or $\log_{10} 1$).

The summary (Table 1) shows the results of the statistical analysis. Since the variance of one of our measurements is roughly proportional to

TABLE 1

Comparison of X chromosomes in salivary gland nuclei
of male and female Drosophila melanogaster larvae.*

Measured Parameter	$\log_{10}$ Corrected Ratio, ♂/♀
Area	0.075 ± 0.017**
A_T, 275 $m\mu$	0.009 ± 0.020
A_T, 231 $m\mu$	0.045 ± 0.021[†]
A_T, 257 $m\mu$	0.006 ± 0.020
A_T, 546 (Feulgen)	0.017 ± 0.018

*Entries are differences between mean values (N = 8–14) of the logarithms of measurements of X chromosomes in male larvae and female larvae, corrected for measurements made in chromosome 2R of each nucleus (see text). From unpublished data of Rudkin, Aronson, and Schultz.
**Significantly different (P<.001) from zero.
†Significantly different (P<.05) from zero.

the measurement itself, the analysis was performed on logarithms of the original data. The $\log_{10}$ of the ratio of a value for the autosome to a value for the X chromosome was calculated for each nucleus. The mean of those log ratios for a given set of female larvae was subtracted from the corresponding mean from a set of male larvae. The differences, entered in Table 1, are thus the logarithms of the ratios of X chromosomes of males to those of females "normalized" to identical autosomal values.

The first row of the table gives an objective measure of the difference in size attained by the X chromosome in male and female. The area of the segment is significantly larger in the male although the length as shown by other measurements was identical (within 5%) in the two sexes.

The nucleic acid contents are the same, confirming the earlier measurements [9] (last two rows). Since neither DNA (Feulgen) nor total nucleic acid (257 mμ) is different, the conclusion might be drawn that RNA content is also the same; but, as we shall see later, RNA contributes only a small portion to the 257 mμ absorption of these chromosomes, and further study is necessary to establish the relative RNA contents of the X's in the two sexes.

Only in the end-absorption of the proteins (231 mμ) was a significant difference observed; the antilog of the value in Table 1 gives a ratio of 1.11 for male to female, i.e., 11% more absorbing material in the male. Sensibly identical chromosomal contents of 275 mμ-absorbing material (observed difference only 2%) indicates that the end absorption is not increased in the male by a protein with a high cyclic amino acid content.

Puffs

An essentially similar result has been observed in short regions of giant chromosomes that undergo extensive swelling at certain stages of the development of the larvae. These swollen regions, called puffs, are now accepted as regions of high functional activity of genetic material within them (see Beermann [13] for review). A study of one such region [14, 15] included measurements similar to those outlined above on a puff region before and after it had swollen and compared them with adjacent chromosome regions in which no puff formed. The measurements were less precise (for technical reasons), and fewer individual measurements were made than for the X chromosome. Here a higher relative integrated absorbance value was found at all three wavelengths (no Feulgen measurements were carried out) when the region was puffed than before it had puffed; about 20% higher at 257 and 275 mμ (not significant in these data), but 31% higher at 231 mμ (considered significant) (Table 2). Experiments in which autoradiographic methods and ribonuclease treatment were combined with microphotometry showed that the changes at the two longer wavelengths could be completely accounted for by the synthesis of RNA in the puffed region. The increase at 231 mμ remains unaccounted for except in terms of the end absorption of chromosomal protein.

Our information about the nature of the protein is very meager, beyond

TABLE 2

Comparison of puffed and nonpuffed states of two puff
regions in <u>Drosophila</u> <u>melanogaster</u>, chromosome 2R*

Parameter[‡]	Puff 1 (60 B8–C5) ratio to nonpuffing region		ratio puffed to prepuff	Puff 2 (60 A6–B7)[†] ratio puffed to prepuff
	prepuff	puffed		
Area	0.728	1.35	1.86[§]	1.56[§]
A_T, 257 mμ	0.550	0.664	1.21	1.12
A_T, 275 mμ	0.520	0.642	1.23	1.20
A_T, 231 mμ	0.522	0.675	1.30[§]	0.94

*Calculated from data in Rudkin [15].
[†]Only the final ratios are given for puff 2.
[‡]A_T = integrated absorbance at indicated wavelength.
[§]Significantly different from 1.00.

an indication that it must be poor in cyclic amino acids; this fact would
seem to exclude the residual, tryptophane-containing protein of Mirsky and
Ris [16, 17]. The ultraviolet absorption curve of histones, very poor
in cyclic amino acids [18] would suggest that they might be involved. They
have been demonstrated in these chromosomes by the alkaline fast green
test [19]; the distribution of the fast green stain parallels the distribution
of DNA (Feulgen reaction) in the chromosomes [20, 21]. The fixatives
normally used for the demonstration of histones are not suitable for the
preparation of squashes in which chromosomes are free of cytoplasm
and otherwise suitable for microspectrophotometric analysis. The alkaline
fast green test is negative after the fixative we used, so there is some
doubt that histones could make up an appreciable fraction of the protein that
we detect; the biochemical reasons for the negative reaction do require
more study.

Acidic proteins can be detected by staining with fast green at low
pH. Swift [21] has found a strong acid fast green reaction in an RNA puff
in a different species of <u>Drosophila</u>, suggesting that accumulation of an
acidic protein may be of common occurrence in RNA puffs.

Two reasonable suggestions concerning the function of the unknown
protein come to mind. Since, as Swift has pointed out, restriction to a
short chromosome region and rapid change in amount with time argue
against the protein being a permanent structural feature, it must have
something to do with activity. Beyond that, the choice between a product,
a necessary intermediary with, for example, enzyme activity, or a nec-

essary prerequisite for activity cannot be made on the basis of available evidence. The last possibility is an interesting one in the light of the currently popular view of Stedman [22] that histones have a regulatory function: the protein we detect could serve to release a histone block from the DNA, either enzymatically or by complexing with the histone itself.

Against the view that the regulatory function is a general one, is our finding of no change in protein in other puff regions. An area of the second chromosome just proximal to puff 1 (section 60 B8-C5) discussed above puffs at a slightly later time. A similar progression of puffing along a chromosome in Acricotopus has been described by Mechelke [23]. The protein content in this second region (section 60 A6-B7) did not increase with area (Table 2, puff 2) when compared to the nonpuff regions. Here, then, either the mechanism for activating the genetic material cannot involve the sequestering of histone by an acid protein or the complexed proteins are removed from the site of the puff.

RHYNCHOSCIARA ANGELAE: DNA PUFFS

An analogous situation has been studied in a different organism and in a pair of puffs that differ in their chemistry from those in the second chromosome of Drosophila. In Rhynchosciara angelae, chromosome B, two puffs appear, in which disproportionate synthesis of DNA occurs [2, 24], in contrast to synthesis of RNA while DNA remains constant, as in the Drosophila puffs we have just discussed [25]. In Rhynchosciara we measured protein by its absorption at 275 mμ after the nucleic acids had been removed with hot 5% trichloracetic acid, thus certainly removing all histones but removing interference with the measurements by nucleic acids [24, 26]. We could as well compare the active or puffed state with an earlier stage before the puff had arisen and with a later "inactive" state after the puff had regressed. It was not, however, possible to distinguish the adjacent puff regions from one another in the puffed condition. Protein was synthesized in both regions, ending up with relatively twice as much as appeared in the adjacent nonpuff regions (Table 3). At an intermediate puffed stage the relative protein content of the two regions together was 1.78, intermediate between the prepuff values (arbitrarily taken as 1.0) and the postpuff value of about 2 in Table 3. Here, there is no question of activity, for that is presumed to have returned to prepuff levels when the puff has regressed and the function of the new protein is an open question.

That leads us to another problem, one relating to the organization of the materials in the DNA puff, which may shed some light on the question. We know that DNA is approximately doubled in the puffs with which we have worked [24], so the acid-insoluble protein, measured on the same chromosomes, increases approximately in proportion with it. Swift [21]

TABLE 3

Comparison of protein residue after hot TCA extraction in puff and
nonpuff regions of chromosome B in <u>Rhynchosciara angelae</u>,
measured by integrated absorbance at 275 mμ.*

	A_T† 275 mμ		Ratio after to before	Ratio of change†; puff to nonpuff regions
	before puff	after puff		
nonpuff region	34.3	63.5	1.9	(1.0)
Puff 1 region	14.3	57.4	4.0	2.1
Puff 2 region	9.0	32.0	3.6	1.9

*Taken in part from data presented graphically in Rudkin [26] and in part from
unpublished data.
†A_T = integrated absorbance at indicated wavelength.
‡The fourth column gives the ratio of the values in the third column to the nonpuff region value. It represents the changes in the puff regions relative to a
region that did not puff. (See text.)

has presented evidence (not quantitative) that histone stainability increases
in DNA puffs in a related species. If we assume that the histones are
indeed synthesized in proportion to the DNA within the puff period, then
it would appear that the extra or puff DNA is integrated into a structure
of its own, presumably comparable with the already existent chromosome
on which it arose. On that basis, the nonhistone protein we have measured
in this chromosome region might be construed as a structural one, required in the over-all organization of chromosomal material.

CONCLUSION

These data, as far as they go, demonstrate possibilities for studying
chromosomal proteins and suggest directions in which such studies might
lead. As manifested in puffs, chromosomal activity involves nucleic acids
in very different ways in different chromosome loci. The present data
suggest that the protein moieties can be at least equally varied, even when
only acid-insoluble fractions are studied. The protein changes in RNA
puffs are small or nonexistent, compared to an over twofold increase in
puff RNA. A disproportionate increase of 2-3 fold in DNA is accompanied
by a doubling in the acid-fast protein as well. The significance of these

changes, the nature and functions of the proteins, the relationship of them to the nucleic acids and to the proteins that "got away" during the preparative procedures, the relationship of them to the functional activity of the chromosome, and other like problems are just beginning to be approachable by modern methods. The data reviewed here create more questions than they answer and emphasize the need for more discriminating quantitative cytochemical methods for the study of chromosomal proteins.

Acknowledgments

This work was supported by a research grant (C1613) from the National Institutes of Health to Dr. Jack Schultz, by an institutional grant from the American Cancer Society, and by grant NSF G-18953.

REFERENCES

1.   Beermann, W., Chromosoma, 5, 139, 1952.

2.   Breuer, M. E., and Pavan, C., Chromosoma, 7, 371, 1955.

3.   Bridges, C. B., Sex and Internal Secretions (1st ed.; New York: Williams & Wilkins, 1932), chap. 3, p. 55.

4.   Bridges, C. B., Sex and Internal Secretions (2nd ed.; New York: Williams & Wilkins, 1939), p. 15.

5.   Muller, H. J., Harvey Lectures, Ser. 43 (Springfield, Ill.: Charles C. Thomas, 1950), p. 165.

6.   Patterson, E. K., Dackerman, M. E., and Schultz, J., J. Gen. Physiol., 32, 623, 1949.

7.   Patterson, E. K., Lang, H. M., Dackerman, M. E., and Schultz, J., Exptl. Cell Res., 6, 181, 1954.

8.   Offermann, C. A., J. Genet., 33, 103, 1936.

9.   Aronson, J. F., Rudkin, G. T., and Schultz, J., J. Histochem. Cytochem., 2, 458, 1954. (Abstract.)

10.   Rudkin, G. T., Aronson, J. F., Hungerford, D. A., and Schultz, J., Exptl. Cell Res., 9, 193, 1955.

11.   Bridges, C. B., J. Heredity, 29, 11, 1938.

12.   Bridges, C. B., and Bridges, P. N., J. Heredity, 30, 475, 1939.

13.   Beermann, W., _Protoplasmatologia_ 6D (Wien: Springer-Verlag, 1962).

14.   Rudkin, G. T., Genetics, 40, 593, 1955. (Abstract.)

15.   Rudkin, G. T., Ann. Histochim., Supp. 2, 77, 1962.

16.   Mirsky, A., and Ris, H., J. Gen. Physiol., 31, 7, 1947.

17.   Mirsky, A., and Ris, H., J. Gen. Physiol., 34, 475, 1951.

18.   Phillips, D. M. P., Progr. Biophys. Biophys. Chem., 12, 213, 1962.

19.   Alfert, M., and Geschwind, I. I., Proc. Natl. Acad. Sci. U. S. A., 39, 991, 1953.

20.   Schurin, M., Ph. D. Thesis 3605, Univ. of Chicago, 1957.

21.   Swift, H., In J. M. Allen (ed.), _The Molecular Control of Cellular Activity_ (New York: McGraw-Hill, 1962), p. 75.

22.   Stedman, E., and Stedman, E., Nature, 166, 780, 1950.

23.   Mechelke, F., Naturwissen schaften, 48, 29, 1961.

24.   Rudkin, G. T., and Corlette, S. L., Proc. Natl. Acad. Sci. U. S. A., 43, 964, 1957.

25.   Rudkin, G. T., and Woods, P. S., Proc. Natl. Acad. Sci. U. S. A., 45, 997, 1959.

26.   Rudkin, G. T., Proc. 7th Microscopy Symp., Chicago, 1958 (Chicago: W. C. McCrone Associates), p. 60.

 David M. Prescott

TURNOVER OF CHROMOSOMAL
AND NUCLEAR PROTEINS

The experiments described in this paper deal with three general questions about proteins of the cell nucleus: (1) Are there any nuclear proteins that show no turnover in the same sense that DNA shows no turnover ? (2) What is the pattern of segregation of isotopically labeled proteins in metaphase chromosomes over several cell cycles ? (3) How rapid is the turnover of total nuclear protein during interphase and what is the fate of nuclear proteins during mitosis ?

Proteins of mammalian chromosomes were studied autoradiographically by the procedure of Taylor, Woods, and Hughes [1] for labeling DNA and tracing its segregation over a series of cell cycles. Cultures of Chinese hamster fibroblasts were used for this work. A full description of materials, methods, and results has been reported elsewhere [2, 3].

To establish the technical procedures, the experiments of Taylor, Woods, and Hughes [1] on the chromosome segregation of labeled DNA were repeated. In addition, a method was developed for isolating metaphase chromosomes [4] so that autoradiography could be carried out without interference from cytoplasm or the mitotic spindle. In all respects, the results [2] confirmed those of Taylor, Woods, and Hughes [1]. DNA labeled with H^3-thymidine segregated in a semiconservative fashion over the four cell cycles studied. At the first metaphase after DNA was labeled with H^3-thymidine, both chromatids of each chromosome contained radioactive DNA. At the second metaphase (Fig. 1), only one chromatid of each chromosome was radioactive. At the third metaphase, only one half of the chromosomes were labeled, and in these the radioactivity was restricted to one chromatid. By the fourth metaphase only one fourth of the chromosomes contained a labeled chromatid.

With these experiments on labeled DNA segregation as a base line, cells were labeled with a mixture of H^3-amino acids (lysine, leucine, histidine, proline, tyrosine, and phenylalanine (see Prescott and Bender [3] for technical details), and chromosomes were isolated from metaphase cells at the first, second, third, and fourth divisions after labeling. Even with incubations with the H^3-amino acids for several hours, the amount of radioactivity in the metaphase chromosomes was very low, and in some

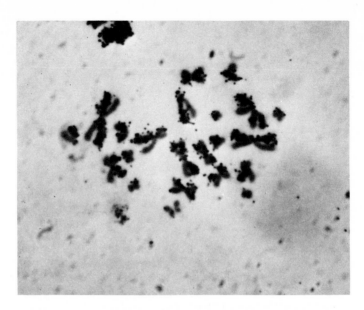

Fig. 1.—An autoradiograph of Chinese hamster chromosomes taken from a fibroblast in the second metaphase after labeling with H³-thymidine. One chromatid of each chromosome is labeled.

cases six months were required to produce an autoradiographic image. Radioactive proteins were distributed equally between the two chromatids of each chromosome at the first metaphase after labeling. At the second metaphase (Fig. 2), the amount of radioactivity was reduced by more than could be accounted for by dilution through chromosome reproduction. The radioactive protein was equally divided between the two chromatids of each chromosome. At the third metaphase, only some chromosome sets still contained label, and by the fourth metaphase, all chromosomes were free of radioactive protein.

In summary, labeled proteins segregated dispersively between chromatids at the second metaphase, but replacement of radioactive proteins was complete in all chromosomes by the fourth metaphase.

In these experiments, the chromosomes were isolated from metaphase cells by fixation in neutral formalin for 60 seconds followed by a second fixation and rupture in ethyl alcohol-acetic acid (3:1). Since this solvent treatment might extract proteins from the chromosomes during isolation, an experimental approach not involving acid extraction was devised to examine turnover of total nuclear protein (including proteins of the chromosomes) in Amoeba proteus [3, 5].

The procedure is most easily outlined by describing the control experiment. Amoebae were incubated in medium with H³-thymidine. Since amoebae normally contain a large number of self-replicating, DNA-containing particles of a rickettsial nature in the cytoplasm [6, 7], auto-

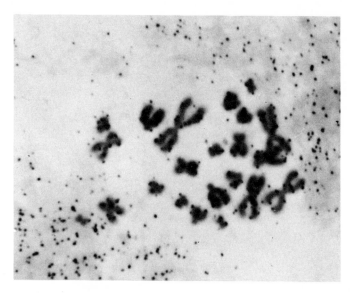

Fig. 2.—An autoradiograph of Chinese hamster chromosomes isolated from a fibroblast in the second metaphase after labeling with H³-amino acids. Both chromatids of each chromosome are labeled. The radioactivity on each side of the complement of chromosomes is from dispersed cytoplasm.

radiographs showed heavy labeling of both the cytoplasm and the nucleus [8]. Amoebae labeled with H³-thymidine were washed and transferred to nonradioactive nutrient conditions, and approximately every 36 hours one half of the cytoplasm was cut away with a glass needle. Between these operations, the lost cytoplasm was regained through growth, and, in effect, by a series of operations, the cytoplasm could be replaced without any direct disturbance to the nucleus. Ten successive operations produced a 99.9% replacement of the original cytoplasm. The cytoplasmic amputations have the second useful effect of preventing amoebae from reaching mitosis. In the case of H³-thymidine-labeled amoebae, the result conformed to prediction. With ten operations the labeled cytoplasmic particles had been replaced with unlabeled particles, and the cytoplasm was therefore free of radioactivity. During this time there was no loss of label from DNA in the amoeba nucleus.

This type of experiment was next carried out with amoebae incubated in a medium containing six H³-amino acids (lysine, leucine, histidine, proline, tyrosine, and phenylalanine). This heavily labeled both nuclear and cytoplasmic proteins. When such amoebae were subjected to the cytoplasmic replacements, the amount of radioactivity decreased in both the nucleus and cytoplasm, but much more rapidly in the latter. At the end of 15 operations, the nucleus was still very radioactive (Fig. 3) but less than 0.005% of the original cytoplasm should have remained. On the

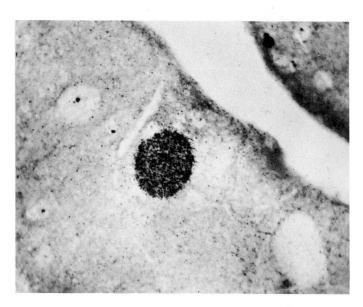

Fig. 3.—An autoradiograph of an amoeba labeled with H^3-amino acids and cut 15 times to produce replacement of the cytoplasm. The nucleus contains a high concentration of radioactive protein, and the cytoplasm a very low concentration.

basis of this calculation, the original cytoplasmic radioactivity should have been decreased below a detectable level, but autoradiography showed that the cytoplasm was still weakly labeled. These findings led to the initial conclusion that there must be a slow, net transfer of proteins or their breakdown products from the nucleus to the cytoplasm. The situation, however, has been elucidated by Goldstein's [9] nuclear transplantation experiments in amoeba. These have clearly demonstrated that a substantial fraction of nuclear protein is constantly shuttling in and out of the nucleus during interphase; this protein fraction probably accounts for the weak cytoplasmic labeling after 15 operations. The protein fraction described by Goldstein has a high affinity for the nucleus and at any one moment is present in much higher concentration in the nucleus than in the cytoplasm. The distribution of Goldstein's protein conforms with what is seen in amoeba after 15 cytoplasmic cuttings (Fig. 3).

Some clarification of the relation of this nucleus-specific protein to the chromosomes was achieved in the following manner. Cells that had been labeled and cut 15 times (Fig. 3) were allowed to enter mitosis (by suspending the cytoplasmic cuttings) and then autoradiographed. In such dividing cells the radioactive, nucleus-specific proteins were found to be evenly distributed throughout the cytoplasm, with no concentration of radioactivity in the region of the chromosomes and spindle (Fig. 4). In cells that had reached late telophase the radioactive proteins had begun to reaccumulate in the daughter nuclei. By very early interphase (Fig. 5),

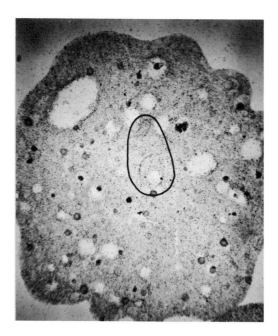

Fig. 4.—An autoradiograph of an amoeba treated as in Figure 3 but allowed to reach early telophase. The two groups of chromosomes are within the indicated circle. The nucleus-specific protein has become dispersed throughout the cytoplasm.

the transfer back into the nucleus had re-established the premitotic ratio of nuclear to cytoplasmic radioactivity.

The latter experiments demonstrate that the nucleus-specific proteins do not contribute detectably to the structure of mitotic chromosomes. Goldstein [9] has shown that these proteins are not associated with the interphase nuclear membrane, and our own observations have revealed that they are not contained in the nucleoli. Undoubtedly these proteins contribute to interphase functions of the nucleus, but to which nuclear functions remains to be determined. The shuttling of the nucleus-specific proteins in and out of the nucleus during interphase suggests they may be involved in coordinating nuclear and cytoplasmic activities.

In some experiments, amoebae labeled with H^3-amino acids were subjected to 30 operations (over 45 days). During this treatment radioactivity declined steadily, and by 30 cuts, all detectable radioactive protein had been lost from both the nucleus and cytoplasm. From on-grain counts of autoradiographs, it has been calculated that any radioactive protein remaining in the nucleus after 30 operations could occupy no more than 1 out of 10^8-amino acids of the nucleus. These cutting experiments are concerned with total nuclear protein, and it is concluded that complete turnover of all nuclear proteins, including histone, can take place without an intervening mitosis.

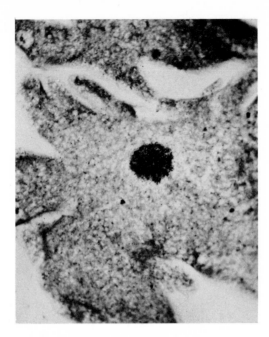

Fig. 5.—An autoradiograph of an amoeba treated as in Figure 3 but allowed to complete cytokinesis. The nucleus-specific protein has largely returned to the daughter cell nucleus.

In summary, the experiments on H^3-amino acid-labeling of mammalian chromosomes and amoeba nuclei have led to the following conclusions. The proteins of the chromosome segregate dispersively at mitosis. There is no detectable retention of labeled protein in chromosomes after a few cell cycles. The nucleus of amoeba contains a nucleus-specific protein, which probably shuttles in and out of the interphase nucleus. This protein is lost to the cytoplasm during mitosis but rapidly returns to the nucleus after division. All proteins, including histones, of the amoeba nucleus are constantly turning over in the sense that they are destroyed or become irreversibly displaced from the nucleus.

REFERENCES

1. Taylor, J. H., Woods, P. S., and Hughes, W. L., Proc. Natl. Acad. Sci., U. S. A., 43, 122, 1957.

2. Prescott, D. M., and Bender, M. A., Exptl. Cell Res., 29, 430, 1963.

3. Prescott, D. M., and Bender, M. A., J. Cellular Comp. Physiol., in press, 1963.

4. Prescott, D. M., and Bender, M. A., Exptl. Cell Res., 25, 222, 1961.

5. Prescott, D. M., In R. J. C. Harris (ed.), Intern. Soc. Cell Biol. (New York and London: Academic Press, Inc., 1963), vol. 2, p. 111.

6. Rabinovitch, M., and Plaut, W., J. Cell Biol., 15, 525, 1962.

7. Rabinovitch, M., and Plaut, W., J. Cell Biol., 15, 535, 1962.

8. Plaut, W., and Sagan, L. A., J. Biophys. Biochem. Cytol., 4, 843, 1958.

9. Goldstein, L., In R. J. C. Harris (ed.), Intern. Soc. Cell Biol. (New York and London: Academic Press, Inc., 1963), vol. 2, p. 129.

 Roberto Umaña, Stuart Updike,
John Randall, and Alexander L. Dounce

HISTONE METABOLISM

INTRODUCTION

The chief purpose of the work to be reported in this paper was to investigate the metabolic behavior of the histones in relation to the mitotic cycle. It had been noticed that the histone content of isolated rat liver nuclei [1] was approximately twice that of isolated rat liver or thymus chromosomes [2-4], and this observation lead to the idea that there might be a more easily and a less easily extractable histone fraction in whole liver nuclei, the more easily extractable fraction being lost during the isolation of the chromosomes. The latter idea in turn raised the question whether there might be a difference in the disposition and metabolism of these hypothetical fractions.

At the outset, it was realized that the quantitative isolation of relatively undegraded histone fractions or even of total histone might be technically difficult, owing to the presence of proteolytic enzymes in cell nuclei. Hence the first part of the work involved a study of the proteases of rat liver nuclei, with the purpose of attempting to minimize possible proteolytic action during isolation of the nuclei. This work has already been reported in part [5, 6].

This paper consists of four sections. The first covers certain aspects of the chemistry of the histones; the second deals with the ratio of total histone to DNA during various phases of the mitotic cycle; the third takes up the incorporation of isotopic leucine by the histones following hepatectomy; and the last contains a few speculations on the possible function of the histones. The findings in the second section have already been reported briefly [7].

I. SOME CHEMICAL CHARACTERISTICS OF HISTONES EXTRACTED FROM RAT LIVER NUCLEI ISOLATED IN 0.44 M SUCROSE AT pH 5.8

In previous work [6, 8], conditions for isolation and extraction of rat liver nuclei with minimal degradation of the nuclear proteins were investigated. From nuclei isolated under these conditions, it is possible to extract three different protein fractions [1]. The first, the globulin fraction, is extracted with 0.14 M NaCl at pH 5.8. After removal of the globulins, the histones are obtained as a second fraction by extraction with 0.1 N HCl. The HCl extract is fractionated into two different histones by adjusting the pH to about 10.5.* The P-histone (precipitable histone) is isoelectrically precipitated at this pH value, and the S-histone (soluble histone) is precipitated by adding 3 volumes of ethanol to the supernatant from precipitation of the P-histone. Both the globulin and the histone fraction are extracted from the isolated nuclei at a temperature as close to 0 C as possible.

A third fraction, which is the residue remaining after the extraction of the globulins and the histones, includes the residual protein of the nuclei. Residual protein can be obtained by treating this fraction with DNAase I before or after extraction of the lipid, or for analytical purposes, by extracting lipid and then extracting nucleic acid with hot trichloroacetic acid. The insoluble residue constitutes the residual protein.

This section deals with some chemical characteristics of the histones and the differences between the histone fraction and the other nuclear proteins.

Experimental

Rat liver nuclei were isolated in an aqueous medium by the method of Dounce et al. [9] as modified by Umaña [6]. In this method, the mechanical, chemical and osmotic damage to enzyme-containing organelles, especially lysosomes, is minimized by homogenization of the livers with the ball-type homogenizer in a medium of 0.44 M sucrose at pH 5.8, attained by the addition of dilute citric acid. The low proteolytic activities of the soluble phase of the homogenate and the nuclear fractions [8] obtained by this method are taken as an index of the gentleness of the homogenization technique.

The bulk of the cytoplasmic particulates is discarded within 30 minutes after the initial homogenization of the livers, leaving the nuclear fraction contaminated chiefly with whole cells that are not broken during the homogenization, together with some red cells. The whole cells are re-

---

*This value is lower than the true pH, since an ordinary glass electrode was used in making the determination.

moved by centrifugation in 2.2 M sucrose (specific gravity flotation step of Chauveau [10]), and the red cells by washing with 1% gum arabic of pH 5.8. The over-all time taken for isolating and extracting the nuclei is about 3-4 hours.

Once the nuclei are obtained in pure form, the globulin fraction is extracted with 0.14 M NaCl at 0 C, and subsequently the histone fraction is extracted with 0.1 N HCl, at a temperature as close to 0 C as possible. The residue consists of protein firmly bound to DNA, and lipids. After removal of the lipids with chloroform-methanol (3:1 by volume), the total nucleic acid is removed by heating with 5% trichloracetic acid at 95 C. The insoluble material left is considered as the residual protein fraction. Details of the method have been given elsewhere [6, 8].

The HCl extract is fractionated by adjustment of the pH to 10.5 with concentrated ammonia. The precipitate constitutes the P-histone. Addition of 3 volumes of 95% ethanol to the supernatant from the precipitated P-histone causes precipitation of the S-histone.

The Millon reaction as described by Mirsky and Pollister [11] was used for determining the purity and the concentration of the histones in the HCl extract.

The Hopkins-Cole test [12] was used for detecting tryptophan in the nuclear protein fractions.

The ultraviolet spectrum of the histone fractions was determined with the Model DU Beckman spectrophotometer, with water solutions of the histones adjusted with dilute HCl to pH 3.0.

Five to 10 mg of each protein fraction was hydrolyzed in 6 N HCl (boiling point 104), as described by Hirs, Stein, and Moore [13]. With these hydrolysates, two-dimensional paper chromatograms and a quantitative amino acid analysis were run.

Paper chromatograms of the acid hydrolysates were run with methanol-water-pyridine (80:20:4 by volume) in one dimension [14] and n-butanol-acetone-water-dicyclohexylamine (40:40:20:8 by volume) in the second dimension [15].* The amino acid spots were developed with 0.5% ninhydrin in 7% acetic acid in a spray form.

Quantitative amino acid analysis of the protein hydrolysates were carried out by the method of Moore and Stein [16], using a Spinco amino acid analyzer.†

The N-terminal amino acids of the nuclear fractions were converted to 2,4 dinitrofluorobenzene derivatives by the method of Sanger [17] as described by Biserte et al. [18]. The dinitrophenyl derivatives of the N-terminal amino acids were identified by paper chromatography by the system developed by Pairent [19]. No quantitative estimation of the

---

*We are indebted to Mr. Manning Richards for this combination of two previously published methods, which gives a rapid and convenient system of paper chromatography of the amino acids.

†We are indebted to Dr. Dale Goldsmith of the Department of Physiology for these analyses.

N-terminal amino acids was attempted because the relatively small amounts of pure proteins that could easily be obtained were not large enough for this purpose.

The protein fractions were separated by electrophoresis in poly-acrylamide gels [20]—the globulin and residual protein fractions in gels of pH 9.0, and the histone fractions in gels of pH 2.3, to avoid aggregation. The procedure has been described in detail by Ornstein and Davis [20]. In spite of the impossibility at the present time of quantitatively measuring protein components separated by gel electrophoresis, this method was preferred over others because of the high resolving power and the short time needed for the separation (30 minutes to 2 hours).

Results

When isolated nuclei were extracted with 0.1 N HCl without previous extraction of the globulin fraction, the globulins were extracted together with the histone fraction. When HCl extracts of whole nuclei (globulins plus histones) were titrated with 0.1 N NaOH, a precipitate formed at pH 6.4 accounted for more than 50% of the dry weight of the nuclei. A second precipitate obtained at pH 8.6 accounted for an additional 2%. A further increase in the pH to 10.5 or higher did not produce a histone precipitate, nor did addition of 3 volumes of alcohol to the supernatant obtained after collection of the precipitate formed at pH 8.6 show any soluble histone. The precipitates obtained at pH values of 6.4 and 8.6 were insoluble in distilled water, in 0.9% NaCl, and in dilute HCl. Salt fractionation with ammonium sulphate of HCl extracts of nuclei containing both globulins and histones showed that the two protein fractions coprecipitate when the concentration of $(NH_4)_2SO_4$ reaches 50% saturation.

These results seem to indicate that during the titration of the HCl extract with NaOH, insoluble complexes are formed between globulins and histones, which precipitate at pH values higher than the isoelectric points of the globulins but lower than the isoelectric point of the precipitable histone.

The titration of HCl extracts containing only the total histone fraction with 0.1 NaOH gives only one precipitate, which forms over a pH range of 9.6-10.5. As the pH is raised above 10.5, the precipitate redissolves completely. Since the appearance of the precipitates at pH values of 6.4 and 8.6 in the HCl extract containing the globulins and histones must be attributed to the formation of complexes between these two protein fractions, the absence of precipitates at these pH values in the HCl extract made after removal of the globulins seems to indicate that no gross contamination of the histones with globulins occurs under these conditions.

When HCl extracts containing only the total histone fraction are diluted with 2 volumes of Mirsky's reagent and heated to 60 C for 15 minutes, only a very slight cloudiness appears, indicating the existence of only traces of contaminants. The Hopkins-Cole test for tryptophan when carried out in HCl extracts containing both globulins and histones gives a strongly positive result, whereas the same test when carried out on HCl extracts containing only the histone fraction is very weak. This also indicates that the histones extracted from isolated nuclei after the extraction of the globulins as previously described are not grossly contaminated with globulins or residual protein.

Precipitable histone. This histone fraction constitutes from 20 to 28% of the dry weight of the nuclei and at least 80% of the total histone of the nucleus.

This histone fraction is partially soluble in water and readily soluble in dilute acid, and in cold or warm Mirsky's reagent (1.88 M H_2SO_4-0.33 M H_gSO_4) after being dissolved in dilute HCl. The isoelectric point of P-histone is about 10.5, at which it can be precipitated out of solution. Raising the pH of the solution above 10.5 with dilute NaOH causes rapid solution of the precipitated histone; readjustment of the pH with dilute HCl back to 10.5 causes a reprecipitation of histone, but this time the recovery is only about 10% of the amount of P-histone originally precipitated.

The ultraviolet spectrum of the P-histone fraction is presented in Figure 1. An absorption maximum is found at 274 mμ and an absorption minimum at 248 mμ. The ratio of optical density at the absorption maximum to optical density at the absorption minimum is 1.31. The extinction coefficient, $E_{1cm}^{1\%}$, calculated for the absorption maximum of 274 mμ, is approximately 5.9.

Paper chromatograms of acid hydrolysates of P-histone showed no detectable differences from chromatograms of acid hydrolysates of the other nuclear proteins, except for the absence of the spot corresponding to cysteine.

Quantitative amino acid analyses of the P-histone and those of the

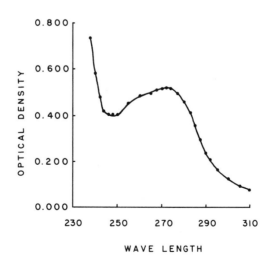

Fig. 1.—Ultraviolet spectrum of P-histone in water at pH 3.0.

TABLE 1

Quantitative amino acid composition of the nuclear proteins*

Amino Acids	Globulins	P-histone	S-histone	Residual Protein
Lysine	5.3	9.58	14.47	7.91
Histidine	1.25	2.47	2.44	2.91
Ammonia	1.69	1.13	1.15	1.28
Arginine	2.19	10.00	7.81	8.17
Aspartic acid	10.70	7.18	7.66	9.44
Glutamic acid	14.65	13.48	12.78	14.79
Threonine	5.48	5.25	5.29	4.42
Serine	5.80	5.21	6.12	5.32
Proline	5.23	4.55	6.55	4.80
Glycine	5.60	5.46	5.44	5.03
Alanine	7.68	6.28	7.15	4.48
1/2 Cysteine	0.81	0.00	0.00	0.53
Valine	7.21	5.66	5.55	5.97
Methionine	0.35	0.15	0.00	1.01
Isoleucine	5.56	5.04	4.31	4.90
Leucine	10.57	9.31	7.29	8.75
Tyrosine	3.97	3.25	2.74	3.88
Phenylalanine	6.06	3.96	3.20	5.18
Lys.:Arg.	—	1.00	1.85	—
Basic-to-acid				
Amino acids	—	1.1	1.2	—

*Amino acids expressed as % of amino acid residue per 100 g of protein.

other nuclear proteins are presented in Table 1 and Figure 2. From this table it can be seen that the histone fractions do not contain cysteine. The P-histone fraction has a ratio of lysine to arginine of 1, and a ratio of basic to acid amino acids of 1.1. This last ratio indicates that the basicity of P-histone is probably due to the presence of a considerable amount of the amide forms of glutamic and aspartic acids, as previously suspected by Monty and Dounce [1].

The minimum molecular weight of P-histone calculated on the basis of its methionine content, which is the lowest of any amino acid, was about 98,000.

Qualitative determination of the N-terminal amino acids of P-histone

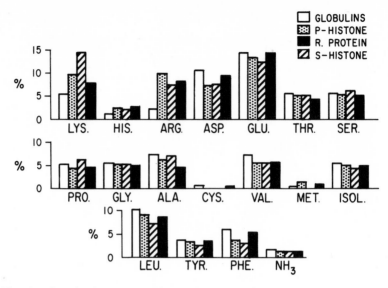

Fig. 2.—Graph of amino acid patterns of nuclear proteins. Ordinate shows percentage of each amino acid based on the total amount recovered from the Moore and Stein columns.

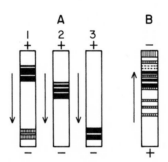

Fig. 3.—Electrophoretic pattern of nuclear proteins in acrylamide gels.
A1 = 0.1N HCl extract after removal of globulin; gel pH = 2.3
A2 = P–histone, gel pH = 2.3
A3 = S–histone, gel pH = 2.3
B = globulin fraction, gel pH = 9.0

showed that proline and alanine constitute most of the N-terminal amino acids of this fraction. A third amino acid, present in very small amounts, was tentatively identified as phenylalanine.

The results of electrophoresis of the P–histone is presented in Figure

3. This fraction contained two main components and one minor component. Electrophoresis of the HCl extract (containing only the histones) showed the same number of bands. The absence of any bands corresponding to soluble histone was due to migration of this protein out of the column, owing to its small molecular weight and the length of time used for the electrophoretic separation (see below).

It has already been shown [8] that HCl extracts containing the total histone fraction present relatively high proteolytic activity at pH 3.8. After incubation of an aliquot of an HCl extract adjusted to pH 3.8 at room temperature for 2 hours, electrophoresis of the solution showed the disappearance of the minor component and an appreciable reduction in the amount of protein contained in the two major components. These changes probably can be ascribed to proteolytic degradation of the histones during the time of incubation at pH 3.8.

When P-histone, which previously had been isoelectrically precipitated and washed four times with 95% ethanol at 0 C, was solubilized in 0.1 N HCl and incubated at room temperature at pH 3.8 for two hours, subsequent electrophoresis showed no change in the number of bands, and there was no detectable change in the amount of protein in the bands. This presumably indicates that the enzyme (or enzymes) responsible for the activity at pH 3.8 is denatured by precipitating the histone at pH 10.5 and subsequently washing it with alcohol, so that after this treatment the P-histone is stable.

It should be noted that the total number of bands found on electrophoresis of P-histone (three) is the same as the total number of N-terminal amino acids found in this fraction (three). In both cases one component is, however, very small.

Soluble histone. This histone fraction constitutes about 6% of the dry weight of the nuclei and about 10-20% of the total histone of the nucleus.

The soluble histone fraction is readily soluble in water, dilute acid, and cold or hot Mirsky's reagent (after being dissolved in dilute HCl). This histone fraction does not, however, precipitate at pH 10.5, but (as previously stated) can be precipitated from the supernatant of the P-histone by adding 3 volumes of 95% ethanol. One additional observation of interest concerning this histone is that, under conditions in which proteolytic degradation can occur, the amount of the fraction appears to increase substantially [6].

The ultraviolet spectrum of the S-histone is presented in Figure 4. An absorption maximum was found at 277 mμ but there is no well-defined minimum. The extinction coefficient at 277 mμ is 11.0.

Paper chromatograms of acid hydrolysates of S-histone disclosed no appreciable differences from chromatograms of the other nuclear proteins, except for the presence of cystine in the globulin and residual protein fraction.

The quantitative amino acid analysis of S-histone (Table 1) shows the absence of cysteine and methionine. The ratio of lysine to arginine is 1.85, which classified this fraction as lysine rich. The ratio of basic to acid amino acids is 1.2. The presence of a considerable amount of the

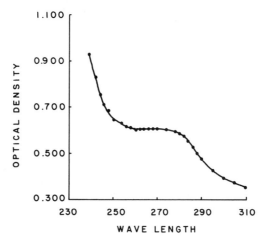

Fig. 4.—Ultraviolet spectrum of S-histone in water at pH 3.0.

amide forms of glutamic and aspartic acids presumably accounts for the basicity of the fraction, as is apparently the case with the P-histone fraction.

The minimum molecular weight of S-histone, calculated on the basis of its histidine content, was found to be 6,500.

No qualitative determination of the N-terminal amino acids of this fraction was attempted, because only very small amounts of this histone could be isolated from the nuclei in a reasonable length of time.

Electrophoresis of the S-histone in acrylamide gels showed two components migrating very close to each other (Figure 3). These components migrate very fast, needing only 10-15 minutes to reach the lower end of the column, in contrast to the 45-60 minutes needed for the P-histone components to migrate to the middle of the column. This finding explains the absence of soluble histone bands in the first electrophoretic runs of the total HCl extract, which usually were run for about 1 hour. It has been possible subsequently to show the presence of the S-histone bands in HCl extracts containing only histones by shortening the time of electrophoresis. The rapid migration of the soluble histone fraction indicates that the two components of the soluble histones not only have high positive charges, but also that they probably have small molecular weights, since the separation in acrylamide gels is based to a considerable degree on the molecular sieving effect of the gel.

For the purpose of comparison, the electrophoretic separation of the globulin fraction in acrylamide gels of pH 9.0 is also presented in Figure 3. This figure, together with the amino acid composition of the same fraction which is presented in Table 1, clearly indicate that the nuclear globulins are quite distinct from the histones and from residual protein.

Discussion

Two major problems arise in the isolation and characterization of histones. One is the susceptibility of these proteins to enzymatic degradation and the other is their tendency to aggregate at pH values above 4.5 [21-24].

The enzymatic degradation of the histones studied in this paper has been greatly minimized by homogenizing the livers within 1 minute after the death of the animal, by isolating the nuclei at pH 5.8 in 0.44 M sucrose with a ball-type homogenizer [6], and by extracting the globulin fractions at pH 5.8 instead of pH 7.0. Aggregation of the histones has been avoided by keeping the pH as low as possible, usually no higher than 2.3, during extraction and electrophoresis.

The total histone fraction contained in the HCl extract obtained after the extraction of the globulin fraction appears to be essentially free of nonhistone contaminants, as judged by solubility, reaction with the Mirsky reagent, and reaction with the Hopkins and Cole reagent, already explained.

The same conclusion can be drawn from the absence of cysteine in the qualitative and quantitative amino acid analysis of the histone fractions.

The properties of the P-histone fraction correspond fairly well to those of the arginine-rich histone of Mirsky et al. [25, 26]. Nevertheless, the amino acid composition of the P-histone fraction described in this paper is different from that shown by any of the other analyses presented in the literature. (It should also be noted that analyses of histones presented in the literature by various authors [26-30] are not concordant, either.) This discrepancy can possibly be explained on the basis of varying extents of proteolytic degradation of the nuclear proteins in different histone preparations, which no doubt would cause increases or decreases in percentages of certain amino acids, depending on the type of enzyme causing the degradation.

The number of principal fractions obtained from the P-histone was two and the number of principal N-terminal amino acids of this fraction was also two (proline and alanine). Whether the third electrophoretic fraction and the third N-terminal amino acid are of significance is not certain. In any case we do not obtain large numbers of components in the P-histone fractions, and in this respect our results are similar to those of Cruft [31].

The properties of the S-histone correspond fairly well with those described by other authors for lysine-rich histones [25, 32, 33]. Again, however, as in the case of the P-histone, the amino acid composition of the S-histone described in this paper deviates markedly from the composition of the lysine-rich histone of other authors.

The variable content of S-histone of preparations of nuclei isolated under conditions that allow different degrees of proteolytic activity and the interconversion of the P-histone into S-histone at neutral pH values [14], raise the question of whether this fraction is a true histone or results from proteolytic degradation of other nuclear proteins. This question cannot be easily answered at present, since even under the controlled conditions we used for isolating nuclei and extracting histones, it cannot be guaranteed that no enzymatic degradation occurs at any point in the procedure. The absence of cysteine, tryptophan, and methionine in the S-histone fraction suggests that this fraction is not derived from globulins or residual protein, since otherwise one might expect these amino acids to be present. However, the possibility that the S-histone fraction is a degradation product from the P-histone fraction cannot be disregarded on the basis of the amino acid composition, because the P-histone itself contains no cysteine or tryptophan and only a low concentration of methionine.

The amino acid composition and electrophoretic pattern of the globulin and residual protein fractions clearly indicate that these proteins are distinct entities of the cell nucleus. It should be emphasized that the extractability of the globulin fraction in 0.1 N HCl, as well as the possibility of coprecipitation of this fraction or a part of it with histones, makes globulin a more likely contaminant of histones than residual protein.

II.   THE RATIO OF TOTAL HISTONE TO DNA IN DIVIDING AND INTERPHASE CELLS

The principal object of the work reported in this section has been to measure the ratio of total histone to DNA in various types of cell nuclei, in an attempt to arrive at an idea of the most probable time of histone synthesis in relation to the mitotic cycle. Work of this nature would furnish a desirable independent check on cytochemical investigations of histone-DNA ratios at different times in the mitotic cycle [34-36], since it seems possible that at least some histone may have been lost in the cytochemical experiments. Nuclei from different tissues have been isolated and extracted under carefully controlled conditions, to avoid protein losses through enzymatic degradation [6, 8] as far as possible, and the ratio of total histone to DNA has been determined. Two main groups of tissues were investigated. The first comprised tissues in which most of the cells are found in interphase (liver, pancreas, and kidney), and the nuclei isolated from these tissues will be referred to as interphase nuclei. The second group is formed by tissues in which a large number of cells are found in division (regenerating rat liver, rat Walker carcinoma, ascites mouse tumor, and thymus), and the nuclei isolated from these tissues will be referred to as dividing cell nuclei. Studies on the composition of rat liver nuclei isolated from starved rats were also carried out in an attempt to induce changes in the histone-DNA ratio.

Methods

The nuclei from calf pancreas, calf and lamb kidney, and calf thymus were isolated in dilute citric acid at pH 3.6, according to the method of Dounce [37]. The nuclei from calf liver were isolated by the same method but at pH 3.8. The nuclei from livers of normal, starved, and partially hepatectomized rats were isolated in 0.44 M sucrose at pH 5.8 by the method of Dounce et al. [9] as modified by Umaña [6]. The nuclei from Walker carcinoma were isolated as described by Dounce [9], except that a Chauveau [10] centrifugation in 2.2 M sucrose was included as described elsewhere [6], and the nuclei from the mouse ascites tumor were isolated in 0.25 M sucrose at pH 5.8 as described by Sauer, Martin, and Stotz [38], and a Chauveau centrifugation step was also included.

Proteins were extracted as previously described by Monty and Dounce [1], except that the globulin fraction was extracted at pH 5.8 instead of pH 7.0. The DNA content of the nuclei was determined by the diphenylamine reaction of Dische, with the technique of Schneider to free the nucleic acids from proteins [39]. Each fraction was expressed as per cent of constituent with respect to the total dry weight of the nuclei.

Results

Analysis of interphase nuclei. The results of the analysis of inter-phase nuclei are presented in Table 2. The total histone and DNA content and the ratio of total histone to DNA in rat and calf liver nuclei, calf pancreas nuclei, and calf and lamb kidney are shown. The histone-DNA ratios are higher than 2 in all these types of nuclei except the pancreas nuclei. The slightly lower values in pancreas nuclei are not well under-stood; one possible explanation is that histone is lost during isolation and extraction of the nuclei because of protease action.

Analysis of the dividing cell nuclei. The results of the analysis of the dividing cell nuclei are presented in Table 3. The histone-DNA ratio was 0.85 for the mouse ascites tumor and 1.05 for the Walker carcinoma. The nuclei from regenerating liver were isolated 12, 27, and 33 hours after

TABLE 2

Composition of nuclei isolated from tissues in which
most of the cells are in interphase

Tissue	H_t*	DNA	H_t:DNA
Rat liver	31.2	12.3	2.64
Calf liver	28.9	12.9	2.24
Calf pancreas	15.1	8.4	1.80
Calf kidney	12.9	5.7	2.26
Lamb kidney	17.2	8.2	2.12

*Total histone.

TABLE 3

Composition of nuclei isolated from tissue
in which most of the cells are in mitosis

Tissue	H_t*	DNA	H_t/DNA
Walker carcinoma 256	11.24	13.3	0.85
Ascites mouse tumor	14.1	13.4	1.05
Calf thymus	9.6	20.2	0.48
Regenerating liver			
12 hours	22.9	17.0	1.35
27 hours	24.9	13.8	1.80
33 hours	26.3	12.3	2.14

*Total histone.

the performance of partial hepatectomies in which 60-70% of the liver had
been removed. The ratio of histone to DNA varied with time from 1.35
at 12 hours to 2.14 at 33 hours. The value obtained for normal rat liver
under the same conditions was 2.64.

Calf thymus nuclei have been isolated in aqueous citric acid at pH
values ranging from 3.0 to 3.8 [6]. The ratio of histone to DNA in nuclei
isolated at any pH value within this range, except for the value at 3.8,
has been very close to 0.5. At pH 3.8, where a peak of proteolytic activity
exists [40], the results have been inconsistent.

The low histone content of thymus nuclei is not completely understood,
although two factors may be considered. First, proteolytic degradation of
the proteins may possibly occur before and during the isolation, as well
as during the extraction procedures. Second, it is possible that part of
the histone may be extracted because of the low pH used in the isolation
procedure. It is possible that under better conditions of isolation the
ratio of 0.5 would become closer to 1.0, since the ratio in calf thymus
chromosomes is approximately 1.0 [2-4].

Effect of starvation on the histone-DNA ratio of rat liver nuclei. The
rats used in this experiment were deprived of food for various periods
of time, but were allowed unlimited access to water. After a particular
period of food deprivation, the animals were sacrificed, and the nuclei
were isolated from the livers at pH 5.8, following the procedure already
described. The results are presented in Figures 5 and 6. Figure 5 shows
the change of the total histone-DNA ratio with respect to time of starvation
of the animals. Because of the scattering of points in this graph, it is
difficult to draw the best-fitting line. The line presented, which represents our intrepretation, is based mainly on the fact that the point cor-

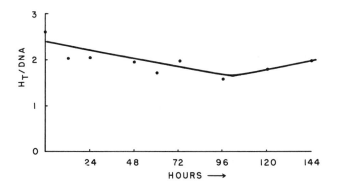

Fig. 5.—Change of total histone-to-DNA ratio during starvation. Each point represents at least one analysis on nuclei from 3 pooled livers.

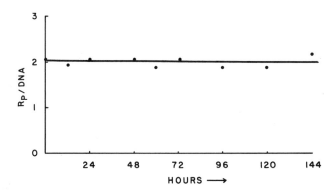

Fig. 6.—Change of residual protein-to-DNA ratio during starvation. Each point represents at least one analysis on nuclei from 3 pooled livers.

responding to the ratios obtained from normal animals (at 0 time) corresponds to an average of 5 values (each value corresponding to pooled livers from three animals), and those obtained from animals after 12 and 24 hours of food deprivation are the averages of three different determinations. This establishes the points corresponding to the initial part of the curve with considerable security. The rest of the points up to the value at 96 hours follow the initial slope reasonably well. The last two points (corresponding to 120 and 140 hours) seem to determine a line with a completely different slope, but the animals in question were moribund, and not enough data is available for proper interpretation. It is necessary to emphasize that the graph probably does not give a complete picture of the changes in the histone-DNA ratio during starvation but at least does show the general trend of the changes during prolonged fasting. The overall trend during 100 hours of starvation seems to be a mild depletion of the histone content of the nuclei, which is reflected in a decrease of the histone-DNA ratio from a normal of 2.64 to about 1.65 at 100 hours of food deprivation.

Figure 6 represents values for the ratio of residual protein to DNA. It is interesting to note the constancy of this protein fraction during the whole period of starvation.

Discussion

It will be noted that our values for the total histone content of isolated liver cell nuclei are somewhat higher than those in a previous publication [6], and the values for residual protein are lower. We attribute this difference to a decrease in the time taken for isolation of the nuclei and extraction of the protein fractions. It has already been found that if the nuclei stand before proteins are extracted, the amount of the residual protein increases [6], and therefore it seems quite possible that shortening the time of preparation would have the opposite effect. It may be that on standing, part of the globulin and histone fractions are converted into insoluble protein, which appears with the residual protein when the nuclear proteins are fractionated.

The results show that nuclei isolated from tissues in which a great number of cells are in interphase have a histone-DNA ratio close to 2 or somewhat higher, while in nuclei isolated from tissues in which a large number of cells are in the dividing state, this ratio is close to 1.0.

Studies by Wilkins [41, 42] and Zubay and Doty [43] seem to indicate that histones are linear proteins wrapped around the DNA, occupying the large groove formed by the helical structure of this molecule. Therefore, any histone in excess of that necessary to fill the major groove of the DNA would increase the histone-DNA ratio above a minimal value corresponding to a structure in which only enough histone was present to fill the large groove of the DNA molecule.

Analyses of isolated liver and calf thymus chromosomes [2-4] have shown that the histone-DNA ratio in both is about 1.0. In our experience, values lower than 1.0 are usually found in nuclei that have been subjected to conditions in which part of the histone could have been lost by extraction or by enzymatic degradation. If the value of 1.0 is taken as indicating roughly the histone-DNA ratio when the major groove of the DNA double helix is filled with histone, it would be safe to assume that the entire histone content of isolated chromosomes is wrapped around the DNA molecules in the major groove.

Nuclei isolated from tissues in which rapidly dividing cells predominate generally present a histone-DNA ratio close to 1.0, similar to that found in isolated chromosomes and presumably indicating that all the histones present in the nuclei occupy the large grooves of the DNA helices. On the other hand, considerably more histone seems to be present in nuclei isolated from tissues in which cells are predominantly in interphase than is required to fill the large grooves of the DNA double helices. If this interpretation is correct, there are at least two possible types of associ-

ation between DNA and histones within the nucleus of cells in interphase—
one in which the histones are intimately bound to DNA and probably occupy
the large groove of this molecule, and the other in which histones are more
loosely bound to DNA. In the latter association, the chief binding force
would probably be electrostatic.

One might expect the metabolism of these two hypothetical classes of
histone to be different, because any reaction involving the histones directly
would presumably be more sterically hindered and therefore slower with
the intimately bound than with the more loosely bound histone.

To look for metabolic differences between the firmly bound and loosely
bound histones, changes in the ratio of histone to DNA were measured
in rat liver nuclei isolated from animals that had been subjected to various
periods of fasting, with the assumption that the loosely bound histone would
tend to be more labile than the more firmly bound histone under conditions
of considerable protein breakdown, and that this lability might be reflected
in a lowering of the histone-DNA ratio.

Figure 5 shows a constantly declining trend in the histone-DNA ratio
up to the point corresponding to 100 hours of food deprivation, although
the ratio never falls below 1.5. These findings are compatible with the
idea that part of the histone is more labile than that which is wrapped
around the DNA double helix, although they do not prove it.

Another conclusion to be derived from the results presented in this
study concerns the time of synthesis of histones with respect to the synthesis of DNA. Some authors have claimed that histones are normally
synthesized immediately before mitosis, concomitantly with DNA synthesis
[34-36]. If the histones were synthesized at the same time that DNA is
synthesized, the ratio of histone to DNA should not show any changes
during either interphase or mitosis. On the other hand, if the histones
were not synthesized at the time of DNA synthesis, variations with time
in the ratio of histone to DNA would be expected; these would depend on
the time when the nuclei were isolated relative to mitosis.

Nuclei isolated from cells with a long interphase (normal liver, pancreas, and kidney) had a ratio of histone to DNA of 2 or somewhat higher
(Table 2), whereas cells with a short interphase (regenerating liver and
tumors) had a ratio of about 1.0. This indicates that histones may be
synthesized before DNA is synthesized, perhaps just following mitosis,
since this seems to be the only way in which the amount of newly synthesized histone could exceed the amount of DNA present. Such accumulation
of histone would be reflected in the high histone-DNA ratio presented by
nuclei in interphase.

A final word of caution may be added concerning the interpretation
offered in this discussion. It has been assumed that all of the HCl-ex-
tracted protein of cell nuclei that is soluble in the Mirsky reagent at 60 C
nuclei is true histone, i.e., basic protein associated with DNA. However,
it is necessary to consider the possibility that protein from nuclear
ribosomes might contaminate the histone and cause confusion. A basic
protein is said to exist in ribosomes [44-47], and Allfrey has claimed
the existence of ribosomes in the nucleus [48]. However, Allfrey (personal

communication) has stated that the protein of nuclear ribosomes is not soluble in the Mirsky reagent at 60 C. Moreover, the RNA content of nuclei isolated by our procedures is too low to permit one to assume sufficient contamination of our histone fraction with ribosomal protein to materially alter our histone-DNA ratios.

A second possible source of error that cannot be ruled out so easily is that an acidic protein might contaminate the histone fraction. If such a contaminant varied with the mitotic stage of the cell, it might conceivably cause the apparent changes in the ratio of histone to DNA reported by us.

We have no evidence for contamination of our histone fraction by important quantities of such an acidic protein and do not see how the relatively sharp precipitation of the precipitable histone fraction with ammonia could occur in the presence of appreciable quantities of acidic protein, but the point must nevertheless remain in question until the histone fraction is purified. Our histone fraction does contain a small quantity of nucleotide material, as can be seen from the spectrum shown in Figure 1. This nucleotide material, which has subsequently been demonstrated directly by spectroscopy after being separated from the histone through the use of hot trichloroacetic acid,* may account for the tendency of the histones to undergo aggregation under certain conditions, and it accounts for a small amount of insoluble material that remains after dissolving the ammonia-precipitated histone fraction in 0.1 N HCl. Such nucleotide material might possibly be confused with an acidic protein fraction. Too small a quantity of the nucleotide material is present, however, to alter our histone-DNA ratios significantly.

III. INCORPORATION OF L-LEUCINE-1-C^{14} IN VIVO INTO THE HISTONES OF NORMAL AND REGENERATING RAT LIVER

In Section II it was shown that the ratio of total histone to DNA varies from values between 2 and 3 in interphase nuclei to values close to 1 in nuclei isolated from tissues in which a considerable number of cells are in or near to the dividing state. These findings appear incompatible with the idea of a synchronous synthesis of histone and DNA. To investigate this point further, it was decided to make a study of the incorporation of L-leucine-1-C^{14} into the nuclear histones (as well as into other nuclear proteins). It was hoped that such a study would yield more direct evidence on the time of synthesis of the histones relative to the time of mitosis. In this work, the incorporation of L-leucine-1-C^{14} into the nuclear proteins of normal and regenerating liver was studied, and the peaks of incorpora-

---

*Before determining the spectrum of the nucleotide material in the trichloroacetic acid fraction, the trichloroacetic acid was removed by ether extraction.

tion were compared with the well-established first peak of incorporation of thymindine or phosphate into the DNA [49-51].

Methods

Incorporation of L-leucine-1-C^{14} into normal rat liver. Albino male rats weighing between 200 and 250 grams were anesthetized, and approximately 1 microcurie of carrier-free L-leucine-1-C^{14}* per gram of liver was injected into a mesenteric vein, with the tip of the needle extending into the portal vein, so that the radioactive material was injected almost completely into the liver. The mesenteric vein used for the injection was ligated to prevent leakage. Following their injection, the rats were kept anesthetized for the required period of time, and the livers were excised and immediately homogenized with a ball-type homogenizer in a solution of 0.44 M sucrose containing enough citric acid to adjust the pH of the homogenate close to 5.8. The nuclei were isolated by the method of Dounce et al. [9] as slightly modified by Umaña [6]. The nuclear proteins were extracted and fractionated as described by Monty and Dounce [1].

Incorporation of L-leucine-1-C^{14} into regenerating rat liver. For the studies on regenerating livers, rats of the same strain and weight as those in the control experiment were used. The operation removed 60-70% of the livers. After operation, the rats were returned to their cages and fed ad libitum for various periods. At the end of the desired time, the animals were anesthetized again, and labeled L-leucine was injected as previously described. The nuclei were isolated and the nuclear proteins extracted and fractionated as in the control experiment.

The protein fractions were carefully washed, and the histones were dissolved in water plus a few drops of 0.1 N HCl, as needed to cause their solution. Because residual protein and denatured globulins are insoluble in water, fine and homogeneous suspensions of them were prepared by a ball-type homogenizer. The protein content was obtained for each solution or suspension on a dry weight basis, and a suitable volume was plated and counted at infinite thinness in an automatic gas flow counter with micromil window, efficiency roughly 35% (Nuclear Chicago Corporation). The activity of each sample was expressed as counts per minute per milligram (dry weight basis) of the protein in question.

DNA was determined by the diphenylamine reaction of Dische according to the procedure of Schneider, as previously described [39].

Results

Incorporation of L-leucine-1-C^{14} into the nuclear proteins of the normal rat liver. The results of the incorporation of labeled amino acid

---

*L-leucine-1-C^{14} (specific activity 31.4 μc per mg) was obtained from Dr. L. L. Miller of the Atomic Energy Project (in the School of Medicine and Dentistry of the University of Rochester).

into the different proteins of the nucleus are presented in Figure 7. The
maximum incorporation occurs between 16 and 20 minutes after the injection of the amino acid into the portal vein. Amino acid is incorporated into
the histone and globulin fractions at approximately the same rate, but into
the residual protein at a faster rate, judging by the greater slope of the
initial part of the curve. This rapid incorporation of amino acids into the
residual protein agrees with the report of Mirsky et al. [52, 53], who found
a very rapid incorporation of glycine-N^{15} into this protein fraction.

From the data obtained in this experiment, the half-lives of the different protein fractions as well as the turnover times were calculated.
The results are presented in Table 4. As shown in this table the half-
lives and turnover times of the histones and globulins are approximately
the same, while the half-lives and turnover time of the residual protein
are somewhat shorter.

Incorporation of L-leucine-1-C^{14} into the nuclear proteins of regenerating rat liver. The same procedure was used in this experiment
as in the previous one. The livers of the previously hepatectomized rats
were removed 20 minutes after the injection of labeled amino acid, assuming that maximum incorporation would occur at the same time after injection as in nonhepatectomized animals.

The rates of incorporation of the labeled amino acid into the different
protein fractions extracted from the isolated nuclei, expressed as counts

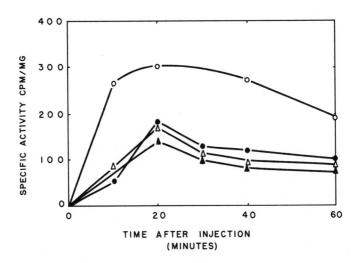

Fig. 7.—Incorporation of L-leucine-1-C^{14} into the nuclear proteins of normal
rat livers. Each point represents one determination on a given protein fraction from
nuclei obtained from a pooled liver homogenate corresponding to three animals.

   o = residual protein
   ● = precipitable histone (H_p)
   △ = globulins
   ▲ = soluble histone (H_s)

TABLE 4

Half-lives and turnover time of the
nuclear proteins

Protein Fraction	Half-life	Turnover Time
Globulins	160 min.	232 min.
P-histone	163 min.	236 min.
S-histone	160 min.	232 min.
Residual protein	135 min.	196 min.

per minute per milligram of protein (dry weight basis) at different times
after the partial hepatectomy are presented in Figure 8. In Figure 9 the
corresponding changes in the total histone-DNA ratio are presented. The
curve shows that during the first 12 hours after the operation only a very
small amount of labeled amino acid is incorporated into all the proteins
studied, and that concomitantly with this low incorporation, the value of
the histone-DNA ratio decreases from 2.7 to about 1.0. After this period
of low amino acid incorporation, the activities of all the proteins increase,
attaining a maximum 19 hours after the operation. The histone-DNA
ratio as shown in Figure 2 follows the same pattern, increasing from
the low value of about 1.0 to about 3.0, 19 hours after the operation. From
19 hours on, the incorporation curves and the curve showing the histone-
DNA ratio undulate, with a close correlation between the peaks and the
valleys of both curves. For example, the second peak of incorporation
occurred 28 hours after the operation and the second peak in the histone-
DNA ratio at about 30 hours after operation.

Section I showed that the analytical value for leucine in all the protein
fractions obtained by our method is nearly the same. It is interesting
that the globulin fraction, the two histone fractions, and the residual protein incorporate approximately the same amounts at the peaks of the
curves. However, the globulin fraction incorporates a considerably lower
total amount than the histone and residual protein fractions.

Discussion

Based on the pattern of isotope incorporation into the nuclear proteins
presented in Figure 2, it is possible to divide the period after partial
hepatectomy into two parts. The first part from the time of the operation
to about 12 hours afterwards is characterized by a low isotope incorporation into all of the proteins studied. Concomitantly with this low incorporation, the ratio of total histone to DNA decreases from 2.8 to a minimum
value of about 1.0, indicating a diminution in the histone content of the

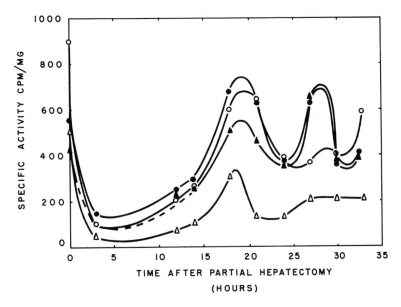

Fig. 8.—Incorporation of L-leucine-1-C[14] into the nuclear proteins of regenerating liver. Each point represents one determination on a given protein fraction from nuclei obtained from a pooled liver homogenate corresponding to three animals.

O = residual protein   △ = globulins
● = precipitable histone (H_p)   ▲ = soluble histone (H_S)

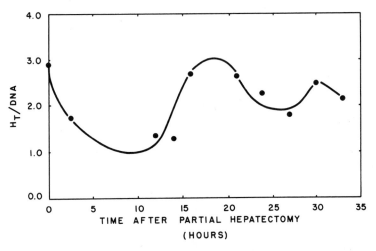

Fig. 9.—Change in the ratio of total histone to DNA during liver regeneration after partial hepatectomy. Each point represents one determination on a given protein fraction from nuclei obtained from a pooled liver homogenate corresponding to three animals.

nucleus. Therefore it seems safe to say that during the first 12 hours after the partial hepatectomy, protein catabolism is increased at the same time that there is a lowered incorporation of labeled amino acid into the proteins.

The second period begins at about 15 hours and is characterized by an active incorporation of isotope into the different protein fractions, with a concomitant rise in the histone-DNA ratio, indicating a rapid synthesis of nuclear protein. The pattern of isotope incorporation into the protein is wavelike, the first peak being attained 18 hours after the operation and the second approximately 28 hours after. Other peaks may occur subsequently, but because of a progressive increase in the percentage of mitotic cells, such peaks, if they exist, are difficult to verify. The ratio of histone to DNA follows very closely the same pattern, with peaks corresponding closely to those of the isotope incorporation. The specific activities of the histones and residual protein increase after the catabolic period to values very close to the initial values, indicating the likelihood that the protein lost during the catabolic period must be replaced before the cell can divide. This interpretation is supported by the increase of the histone-DNA ratio from the low value of 1.0 to the normal value of 2.8. Figure 2 shows that all of the nuclear proteins except the globulin fraction incorporate at similar rates and approximately to the same extent. The heterogeneous globulin fraction (see Section I) incorporates at a similar rate but to a much lower extent, judging by the slopes and the height of the peaks. The meaning of this is not clear at the present time.

The wavelike pattern of incorporation of the labeled amino acid more or less coincides with a similar undulant pattern described in the literature [54] for the number of cells undergoing mitosis. However, since counts of mitotic figures were not made in this work, it is not possible to claim exact coincidence of the peaks of protein synthesis with peaks of mitotic counts.

Another finding worth emphasizing is the cyclic changes in the histone-DNA ratio. This finding and the data presented in Section II give considerable support to the previously stated hypothesis that there are two metabolic classes of histones—histone that is metabolically stable (and presumably wound around the major groove of the DNA double helix) and histone that is metabolically labile (and presumably more loosely associated with the DNA molecule).

The work of several authors [49-51] has established that thymidine and phosphate begin to be incorporated into DNA about 18 hours after partial hepatectomy. In other words, the synthesis of DNA begins about 18 hours after the operation and reaches its maximum at about 25 hours [49, 50, 55]. This being so, it seems clear that synthesis of all of the nuclear proteins goes on just before the synthesis of DNA, which ushers in the first mitotic wave in regenerating liver, since the peak of incorporation of L-leucine-1-C^{14} and the highest histone-DNA ratio are attained at 18 hours after hepatectomy, the time when DNA synthesis begins. This finding would make it probable that the histone-DNA ratio must attain a certain value before the synthesis of DNA can begin, and this value is very close to the normal value of 2.8. Subsequently, the synthesis of DNA should lower the histone-DNA ratio temporarily to a value close to 1.0, but this ratio could not generally be observed in cells having a relatively long period of interphase if histone synthesis ordinarily occurred just subsequent to mitosis, as is being postulated.

It should be emphasized that we consider that the histone synthesis that occurs before DNA synthesis, near the first mitotic wave, in regenerating liver depends on the abrupt fall in the quantity of histone present in the nucleus of the liver cell that took place immediately following the partial hepatectomy, and that such synthesis is therefore in a sense an abnormality. The second peak of incorporation of L-leucine-1-C^{14} by histone, which occurs just subsequent to the first wave of mitosis (which probably takes place between 25 and 30 hours after hepatectomy), we interpret as representing the normal time of histone synthesis relative to the mitotic cycle.

Regarding the discrepancy between the conclusions from cytochemical studies [34-36] and from our chemical studies as to the time of histone synthesis in the cell, it may be noted that the cytochemical work often gives ratios of histone to DNA of about 0.5 to 0.6 [35], which are lower than the values obtained by the chemical procedures in all cases except one. These different ratios may indicate that part of the histone is lost or not accounted for in the cytochemical procedure. If there is any loss of histone, one would expect the loosely bound histone to be lost more easily than the firmly bound histone, assuming that these two classes of histones exist. Loss of the loosely bound histone would maintain the apparent histone-DNA ratio at a constant level, regardless of the state of the cell in relation to mitosis. This explanation may or may not be correct, but it indicates that more experiments with the cytochemical procedure are probably necessary before this procedure can be considered as reliable.

IV. SPECULATIONS ON THE ORIGIN, FUNCTION,
AND FATE OF THE HISTONES

If we have correctly interpreted the findings reported in previous sections of this paper, only part of the histone of the liver cell should be regarded as metabolically inert, the rest being subject to synthesis and degradation during interphase. If this idea is correct, we should expect synthesis of histone by a mechanism similar to or identical with the usual mechanism of protein synthesis, involving RNA templates, and so forth. In the absence of information indicating the presence of histone in the cytoplasm, one would, as a first approximation, assume that histone synthesis occurred within the nucleus.

However, there are certain possible complications to consider. Considerable evidence points to the passage of macromolecules through the pores in the nuclear membrane, and even colloidal gold particles coated with polyvinyl pyrrolidone can pass through the pores [56, 57]. Hence one might bring up the possibility that histone could be synthesized in the cytoplasm and later migrate into the nucleus. At the present, this idea appears somewhat improbable, but it cannot be excluded. Looking at the matter in a different way, one might ask what prevents the escape of the loosely bound, metabolically labile histone from the nucleus into the cytoplasm. No answer can be given to this question except to hypothesize that perhaps there is enough unneutralized charge on DNA to hold this type of histone within the nucleus. We cannot even say that such escape does not occur. However, if it does occur, one would expect to find at least some histone in the cytoplasm. There is said to be a basic protein in ribosomes [45-47], which conceivably could represent histone that had leaked out of the nucleus and diffused into the ribosomes, although this seems improbable. In any case, it would seem essential to make a very careful comparison between nuclear histone and the basic protein of ribosomes.

Turning to the function of the histones, the results reported in the previous sections of this paper would seem to point to a fairly general type of function (or functions), contrary to what would be expected if there were a great number of histone components. This conclusion depends on the still controversial finding that there are, at most, only a few types of histone in a given cell type. One possible function of histone might be to neutralize charge on RNA that passes from the nucleus into the cytoplasm. If a part of the histone escapes from the nucleus into the cytoplasm, possibly it could do so while complexed with RNA. Charge on RNA could thus be neutralized without the necessity of using Na^+ or K^+. As has been stated, ribosomal RNA does appear to be combined with basic protein, and ribosomes may well come from the nucleus, so that the loosely bound histone fraction of the nucleus might play a role in the transport of ribosomal RNA. (Such a role would seem less probable for soluble RNA and messenger RNA.) However, even if part of the histone should act in the transport of RNA as just suggested, this role should not exclude the use of the loosely bound histone as a reservoir of histone that is to occupy the major groove of newly synthesized DNA, as suggested in Sections II and III. It seems obvious that a detailed investigation of the basic protein of ribosomes will be required before sound conclusions can be drawn concerning the possible role of histone in RNA transport.

We already have at hand at least two proposals for a general function of that part of the histone which is thought to be wrapped around the DNA double helix in the major groove. One is the idea of the Stedmans that histone may act as a gene inhibitor and thus play a vital role in cell differentiation [58]. A second idea is one proposed by the senior author, namely that histone might block off one of the two strands of the DNA double helix so that only a single strand would function in RNA synthesis [59]. It has been proposed by others that only one strand of the DNA double helix may function as a template in RNA synthesis (Champe and Benzer [60], for example). Reports that histone diminishes the rate of RNA synthesis on a DNA template [61, 62] could be compatible with either of the two proposals above.

One difficulty with the gene-inhibitor idea is how to make the histone select the proper genes to inhibit. Even if one discards the idea that there are only a few histones, and assumes a specific histone for every gene inhibited, it is difficult to imagine a process that could select what histones should be synthesized for the purposes of gene inhibition. Another difficulty is that there seems to be more than enough histone present in most cells to complex with all of the DNA of the nucleus, so that there would be no free DNA left over to act as functional gene material.

A possible additional role of the firmly bound histone is that of serving to stabilize the DNA double helix and therefore the gene material. This idea is compatible with results obtained by Bonner, Haung, and Murray [62] on the stabilization of DNA toward heat denaturation by histone, and with results obtained in the laboratory of the senior author [63] on the stabilization of DNA toward low pH by histone and by residual protein.

In general terms, it seems safe to conclude that histone acts in some manner to modify or regulate DNA function, rather than being an obligate component in the basic mechanisms that operate in the functioning of DNA as template material. This conclusion is based on the observation that histone does not appear to be necessary in the system of Lehman et al. [64, 65] for synthesizing DNA, or in the system of Hurwitz [66-68] for synthesizing RNA with DNA as template, and is in fact inhibitory in the latter system. The only obvious way to avoid this conclusion would be to consider histone as an enzymatic component of one or both of the above systems, but such a possibility seems extremely remote.

Considerably more investigation will be needed to demonstrate unequivocally the role of histone. One experiment might be an attempt to use the nucleohistone of Doty and Zubay [69] in the DNA-dependent RNA-synthesis system [66-68] and then investigate the synthesized RNA to see whether it mimicked double-stranded DNA in regard to base ratios. DNA of the same type, but free of histone, would be used as a control. The latter should yield RNA with base ratios resembling double-stranded DNA. This experiment was once attempted in the author's laboratory, but it failed for technical reasons. There seems to be no fundamental reason, however, why it might not be made to work.

In regard to the fate of histone, we should probably consider separately the histone that is supposed to be wrapped around the major groove of the DNA double helix and the alleged loosely bound histone. If our interpretation is correct, the loosely bound histone can be synthesized and, if necessary, degraded in the interphase cell, so that its formation and fate is presumably similar to that of other cell proteins, as long as it does not become wrapped around newly formed DNA, which, according to our theory, it does just before mitosis and after the synthesis of new DNA.

Once installed in the major groove of the DNA, the fate of the histone, now of the more firmly bound variety, would probably depend on the mechanism of replication of DNA. If the double helix is unwound before or during replication, this histone might be set free to mix with the loosely bound histone fraction in the short period before resynthesis of new double helices. On the other hand, if the double helices do not unwind, as suggested by the work of Cavalieri and Rosenberg [70] and by a hypothesis proposed by the senior author [71], histone wound around the major groove of the double helix might persist indefinitely, subject only to possible piecemeal replacement because of degradation due to wear and tear.

Work on the histones is still more or less exploratory, and the ideas expressed above as to the possible role of these proteins should not be considered as anything more than tentative proposals. Nevertheless, it is hoped that the discussion may be of some value in pointing the way to meaningful experiments.

Comment: J. A. V. Butler

In our laboratory we have also investigated the temporal relations of the synthesis of histone and other proteins in regenerating rat liver. These relations are summarized in Figure 10. DNA synthesis begins in our experiments about 18 hours after partial hepatectomy. Histone synthesis, on the contrary, is less rapid than the average of all protein

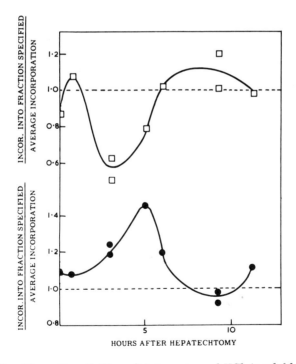

Fig. 10.—Specific radioactivities of histone, □, and HCl–insoluble protein, ●, from nuclei of regenerating rat liver. (From Butler, J. A. V., and Cohn, P., Biochem. J., 87, 330, 1963.)

synthesis, during the first 10 hours after hepatectomy, reaching a minimum at 5 hours. Histone synthesis increases in rate after 5 hours, reaching a maximum at about 18 hours. The acid-insoluble proteins of the nucleus behave differently, reaching a minimum in rate of synthesis about 15 hours after partial hepatectomy. The histone curve is similar to that given by Dounce up to about 17 hours. We have not, however, observed a second peak in rate of synthesis at about 20 hours. The time of DNA synthesis varies with different strains of rats and the time scales for our and Dounce's curves may not be strictly comparable.

Acknowledgments

Support of the United States Public Health Service, National Cancer Institute, and Grant No. C-994-C12 (1962) C-994-14 (1963) is gratefully acknowledged.

REFERENCES

1.   Monty, K. J., and Dounce, A. L., J. Cellular Comp. Physiol., 53, 377, 1959.

2.   Mirsky, A. E., and Ris, H., J. Gen. Physiol., 31, 7, 1947-48.

3.   Mirsky, A. E., and Ris, H., J. Gen. Physiol., 34, 475, 1951.

4.   Mirsky, A. E., and Ris, H., Nature, 163, 666, 1949.

5.   Umaña, R., and Dounce, A. L., Fed. Proc., 20 (no. 1, pt. IA), 147, 1961.

6.   Dounce, A. L., and Umaña, R., Biochemistry, 1, 811, 1962.

7.   Umaña, R., Updike, S., and Dounce, A. L., Fed. Proc., 21, (no. 2, A), 156, 1962.

8.   Umaña, R., Ph. D. Thesis, Univ. Rochester Biochemistry Dept., 1963.

9.   Dounce, A. L., Witter, R. F., Monty, K. J., Pate, S., and Cottone, M. A., J. Biophys. Biochem. Cytol., 1, 139, 1955.

10. Chauveau, J., Moulé, Y., and Rouiller, Ch., Exptl. Cell Res., 11, 317, 1956.

11. Mirsky, A. E., and Pollister, A. W., J. Gen. Physiol., 30, 117, 1946.

12. Hawk, P. B., Oser, B. L., and Summerson, W. H., In Practical Physiological Chemistry (Toronto: Blakiston Co., 1947).

13. Hirs, C. H. W., Stein, W. H., and Moore, S., J. Biol. Chem., 211, 941, 1954.

14. Redfield, R. R., Biochim. Biophys. Acta, 10, 344, 1953.

15. Hardy, T. L., Holland, D. O., and Nayler, J. H. C., Anal. Chem., 27, 971, 1955.

16. Moore, S., and Stein, W. H., J. Biol. Chem., 211, 893, 1954.

17. Sanger, F., Biochem. J., 39, 507, 1945.

18. Biserte, G., Holleman, J. W., Holleman-Dehove, J., and Sautière, P., J. Chromatog., 2, 225, 1959.

19. Pairent, F. W., J. Chromatog., 4, 80, 1960.

20. Ornstein, L., and Davis, B. J., In Disk-electrophoresis (Distillation Products Industries, Division of Eastman Kodak Company).

21. Moore, S., In R. Stoope (ed.), Nucleoproteins (New York: Interscience Publishers, Inc., 1959), p. 77.

22. Davison, P. F., James, D. W. F., Shooter, K. V., and Butler, J. A. V., Biochim. Biophys. Acta, 15, 415, 1954.

23. Butler, J. A. V., and Davison, P. F., Adv. Enzymol., 18, 170, 1957.

24. Cruft, H. J., Mauritzen, C. M., and Stedman, E., Nature, 174, 580, 1954.

25.   Daly, M. M., and Mirsky, A. E., J. Gen. Physiol., 38, 405, 1955.

26.   Daly, M. M., Mirsky, A. E., and Ris, H., J. Gen Physiol., 34, 439, 1951.

27.   Crampton, C. F., Stein, W. H., and Moore, S., J. Biol. Chem., 225, 363, 1957.

28.   Davison, P. F., and Butler, J. A. V., Biochim. Biophys. Acta, 15, 439, 1954.

29.   Rasmussen, P. S., Murray, K., and Luck, J. M., Biochemistry, 1, 79, 1962.

30.   Phillips, D. M. P., and Johns, E. W., Biochem. J., 72, 538, 1959.

31.   Cruft, H. J., Biochim. Biophys. Acta, 54, 611, 1961.

32.   Davison, P. F., and Butler, J. A. V., Biochim. Biophys. Acta, 15, 439, 1954.

33.   Luck, J. M., Rasmussen, S., Satake, K., and Tsvetikov, A. N., J. Biol. Chem., 233, 1407, 1958.

34.   Ansley, H. R., Chromosoma, 8, 380, 1957.

35.   Bloch, D. P., and Godman, G. C., J. Biophys. Biochem. Cytol., 1, 17, 1955.

36.   Seed, J., Proc. Roy. Soc. (London), Ser. B., 156, 41, 1962.

37.   Dounce, A. L., In E. Chargaff and J. N. Davison (eds.), The Nucleic Acids (New York: Academic Press, Inc., 1955), p. 93.

38.   Sauer, L. A., Martin, A. P., and Stotz, E., Cancer Res., 20, 251, 1960.

39.   Schneider, W. C., J. Biol. Chem., 161, 293, 1945.

40.   Sarkar, N. K., and Dounce, A. L., Arch. Biochem. Biophys., 92, 321, 1961.

41.   Wilkins, M. H. F., Zubay, G., and Wilson, H. R., J. Mol. Biol., 1, 179, 1959.

42.   Wilkins, M. H. F., In R. Stoop (ed.), Nucleoproteins (New York: Interscience Publishers, Inc.), p. 45.

43.   Zubay, G., and Doty, P., J. Mol. Biol., 1, 1, 1959.

44.   Crampton, C. F., and Petermann, M. L., J. Biol. Chem., 234, 2642, 1959.

45.   Butler, J. A. V., Cohn, P., and Simson, P., Biochim. Biophys. Acta, 38, 386, 1960.

46.   Waller, J. P., and Harris, J. I., Proc. Natl. Acad. Sci. U. S. A., 47, 18, 1961.

47.   Leslie, I., Nature, 189, 260, 1961.

48.   Frenster, J. H., Allfrey, V. G., and Mirsky, A. E., Proc. Natl. Acad. Sci. U. S. A., 46, 432, 1960.

49.   Hecht, L. I., and Potter, V. R., Cancer Res., 18, 186, 1958.

50.   Nygaard, O., and Rusch, H. P., Cancer Res., 15, 240, 1955.

51.   Bollum, F. J., and Potter, V. R., J. Am. Chem. Soc., 79, 3603, 1957.

52. Allfrey, V. G., Daly, M. M., and Mirsky, A. E., J. Gen Physiol., 38, 415, 1954-55.

53. Daly, M. M., Allfrey, V. G., and Mirsky, A. E., J. Gen. Physiol., 36, 173, 1952-53.

54. Evans, J. H., Holbrook, D. J., Jr., and Irvin, J. L., Fed. Proc., 20, 148, 1961.

55. Bucher, N. L. R., and Swaffield, M. N., Fed. Proc., 21, 300, 1962.

56. Feldherr, C. M., and Marshall, J. M., J. Cell Biol., 12, 640, 1962.

57. Feldherr, C. M., J. Cell Biol., 14, 65, 1962.

58. Stedman, E., and Stedman, E., Nature, 166, 780, 1950.

59. Dounce, A. L., Ann. N. Y. Acad. Sci., 81, 794, 1959.

60. Champe, S. P., and Benzer, S., Proc. Natl. Acad. Sci. U. S. A., 48, 532, 1962.

61. Allfrey, V. G., and Mirsky, A. E., Proc. Natl. Acad. Sci. U. S. A., 48, 1590, 1962.

62. Bonner, J., Huang, R. C., and Murray, K., Fed. Proc., 22, (no. 2, pt. 1), 353, 1963.

63. Dounce, A. L. and Sarkar, N. K., In J. S. Mitchell (ed.), The Cell Nucleus (New York: Academic Press, Inc., 1960), p. 206.

64. Lehman, I. R., Bessman, M. J., Simms, E. S., and Kornberg, A., J. Biol. Chem., 233, 163, 1958.

65. Lehman, I. R., Ann. N. Y. Acad. Sci., 81, 745, 1959.

66. Furth, J. J., Hurwitz, J., and Goldmann, M., Fed Proc., 20, 363, 1961.

67. Weiss, S. B., Proc. Natl. Acad. Sci. U. S. A., 46, 1020, 1960.

68. Chamberlin, M., and Berg, P., Proc. Natl. Acad. Sci. U. S. A., 48, 81, 1962.

69. Doty, P., and Zubay, G., J. Am. Chem. Soc., 78, 6207, 1956.

70. Cavalieri, L. F., and Rosenberg, B. H., Ann. Rev. Biochem., 31, 247, 1962.

71. Dounce, A. L., J. Theoret. Biol., 2, 152, 1962.

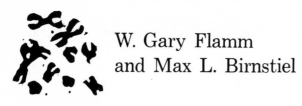

W. Gary Flamm
and Max L. Birnstiel

STUDIES ON THE METABOLISM OF NUCLEAR BASIC PROTEINS

INTRODUCTION

The synthesis of nuclear proteins has been extensively investigated in animal [1-7] and in plant tissue [8-11] and has been comprehensively reviewed by Allfrey and Mirsky [12] and by Sirlin [13]. The more specific problem of histone biosynthesis and metabolism also has received considerable attention [14-20]. These studies have suggested that histones are relatively stable proteins, intermediate in stability between DNA and the metabolic proteins of the cell [15, 16-18], and that histone synthesis may be inextricably coupled to DNA synthesis [19]. In vitro studies involving the incubation of isolated nuclei with labeled amino acid have invariably indicated the inertness of histones [1, 11, 20].

Our initial attempts to study the synthesis of histones were with isolated nuclei. We found, in agreement with others, that incorporation of C^{14}-lysine into the histone fraction is much slower than its incorporation into the residual (nonhistone) fraction. However, when whole cells were incubated in C^{14}-lysine the histones of the subsequently isolated nuclei were found to be highly labeled, in fact as much so as the residual proteins. This paper deals exclusively with the in vivo system and is primarily concerned with the kinetics of histone synthesis, the interrelationship between histone and DNA synthesis, and the nuclear site of histone synthesis.

MATERIALS AND METHODS

Tobacco cells, derived from the stem of Nicotiana tabacum var. Xanthi, were grown in a liquid medium under conditions which elicit exponential growth (generation time 36 hours) [21]. The cells grow to high titers, reaching concentrations of 2×10^5 cells per ml (60 mg/ml fresh weight or 3 mg/ml dry weight). With but one exception (Fig. 1), log phase cells were used. These were collected and used 4 days after their inoculation into fresh medium.

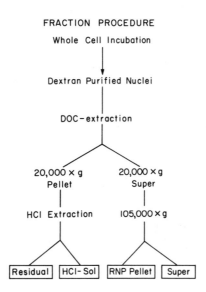

FRACTION PROCEDURE

Whole Cell Incubation

Dextran Purified Nuclei

DOC-extraction

| 20,000 × g | 20,000 × g |
| Pellet | Super |

| HCl Extraction | 105,000 × g |

| Residual | HCl-Sol | RNP Pellet | Super |

Fig. 1.—Flow sheet for fractionation of subnuclear constituents.

For each incubation, 30-40 g of cells (wet weight) collected by filtration through Miracloth were incubated in 30 ml of growth medium. Either 100 μc of C^{14} algal protein hydrolysate, 20 μc of D,L-lysine-1-C^{14}, 20 μc of D,L-arginine-C^{14}, or 5 μc of orotic acid-2-C^{14} was added to the cell suspension, which was then incubated at 27 C with shaking. Reaction was stopped by the addition of 10 volumes of ice-cold grinding medium (0.25 sucrose and 0.01 M tris-HCl, pH 7.5) and by immediate filtration of the cells. With the exception of the orotic acid experiments, nuclei were next isolated and purified as earlier described [22]. The nuclear pellets were resuspended and fractionated according to the scheme shown in Figure 1. The deoxycholate fractionation has been described by Birnstiel, Chipchase, and Hyde [23]. The resulting 20,000 x g pellet was incubated for 30 minutes at 90 C in 0.2 N HCl to extract the acid-soluble proteins [24, 25]. All fractions were washed in TCA and ethanol-ether, dissolved in formic acid, and counted in a Nuclear Chicago D181 gas flow counter, as previously reported [22]. Protein content was determined by the Lowry method [26], and RNA and DNA were measured by the method of Ogur and Rosen [27]. The diphenylamine procedure for the determination of DNA levels was also used [28].

Total cellular RNA and DNA were extracted from cells incubated in labeled orotic acid. The cells were exhaustively ground in a tight fitting glass-teflon homogenizer by high speed homogenization. The suspension was filtered through Miracloth to remove cell walls, and the filtrate was treated with an equal volume of ice-cold TCA (40%). The resulting precipitates were washed four times in 100% ethanol, twice in ether:ethanol (1:1), and suspended in distilled water. This suspension was dialyzed for ten hours against distilled water and was then precipitated by the addition of 10 volumes of 100% ethanol. All operations were carried out at 4 C or below. RNA was extracted with 0.3 M KOH as described by Schmidt and Thannhauser [29] to give a DNA-containing pellet. Radioactivities of the fractions were determined as described above. Radioactivity of RNA was taken as the difference between total counts (RNA + DNA) and the counts left after RNA extraction. In all experiments reported, the counts associated with zero time controls were essentially equivalent to the counting background.

RESULTS

The chemical composition of tobacco nuclei and of the nuclear fractions illustrated in Figure 1 are shown in Table 1. The high nucleic acid content of these nuclei (30%) is probably the result of the isolation procedure, in which much of the soluble protein appears to be lost. The

TABLE 1

Composition of tobacco nuclei and chemically
extracted constituents

Fraction	mg Protein	mg DNA	mg RNA	% dry weight*	
				DNA	RNA
Whole nuclei	2.0	0.25	0.50	9.1	18.1
Nuclear constituents					
Residual	1.5	0.17	0.18	9.2	9.7
HCl-extracted [†]	0.20	---	---	---	---
DOC-extracted	0.26	0.01	0.17	2.2	38.8
Supernatant	0.04	0.00	0.003	0	6.9

*The sum of RNA, DNA, and protein is taken as a measure of the dry weight.
[†]Ratio of HCl-extractable protein to total DNA is approximately 1.0.

ratio of RNA to DNA is somewhat higher than that reported for other nuclei [30], but this is because the nuclei in our studies were derived from exponentially growing cells, which have a higher RNA content than non-dividing cells [31]. The RNA-protein ratio of the DOC-extracted RNP is 0.65, in good agreement with the ratio obtained for ribosomal particles from pea cytoplasm [32], pea nuclei [23], and animal nuclei [33]. The ratio of HCl-extractable protein (histone) to DNA is approximately 1, as is the ratio of histone to DNA in purified chromatin derived from pea seedlings [34].

Table 2 compares the incorporation of various amino acids into the HCl-soluble fraction and into residual protein fractions during a 60-minute incubation. The newly synthesized HCl-soluble protein is relatively lysine

TABLE 2

Relative uptake of amino acids into newly
synthesized nuclear protein

Nuclear fraction	cpm incorporated/mg protein		
	C^{14} arginine	C^{14} lysine	C^{14} amino acids
HCl-extracted	1,800	3,250	38,000
Residual	2,250	2,112	33,000
Ratio of:			
HCl-extractable Residual	0.80	1.55	1.14

rich and arginine poor (Table 2). The possibility that this fraction either represents histone or is predominantly histone is suggested by the fact that its rate of synthesis is directly related to culture age and hence to the number of dividing cells in the culture (Fig. 2). This observation is in good agreement with the findings of others that the rate of histone synthesis depends largely on the rate of cell division [15, 19]. Also in agreement with findings relative to histone synthesis [1, 11, 20] is the observation that HCl-soluble nuclear proteins do not become highly labeled during incubation of isolated nuclei, but that the residual proteins of such nuclei become highly labeled (up to 1 mμmole of C^{14}-lysine). These observations, then, support the view that the present basic proteins are biologically distinct from the other nuclear proteins and may, in fact, be histones.

The kinetics of amino acid incorporation into four nuclear fractions is shown in Figure 3. Residual proteins are labeled most rapidly, RNP particles least rapidly, and histone-like proteins at a rate intermediate between these two.

RELATIVE RATE OF "HISTONE" SYNTHESIS
AS A FUNCTION OF CULTURE AGE

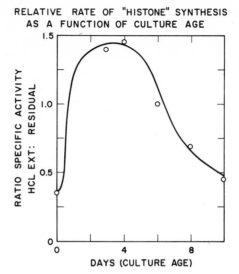

Fig. 2.—Cells of various ages were incubated in D,L–lysine–1–C^{14} as described in text. Four or five days after the inoculation of cells, they cease growing at exponential rate and the number of dividing cells per culture falls by a factor of 2 or 3.

As shown in Figure 4, concentrations of 5–FDU (5–fluorodeoxyuridine) of 10^{-7}–10^{-6} M result in nearly complete inhibition of DNA synthesis by tobacco cells without affecting the rate of RNA synthesis. The data represent results after a 2–hour pretreatment with 5–FDU, but later studies gave a similar pattern for pretreatment times ranging from 0 to 18 hours. Microscopic examination of cells incubated in 5–FDU under growth conditions for 18 hours revealed no mitotic figures, although evidence of mitosis was readily observable in cells not treated with 5–FDU.

The effect of 10^{-7} M 5–FDU on the incorporation of amino acids into nuclear proteins is shown in Table 3. It is clear that there is no significant inhibition of such incorporation. That amino acid incorporation into these fractions reflects the rate at which they are synthesized and not simply differences in turnover has been indicated by pulse–chase experiments. Cells pretreated with 5–FDU (18 hours, 10^{-7} M) together with untreated control cells were incubated in labeled amino acids for one hour. The 5–FDU concentration was maintained during the incubation of the pretreated cells. The cells were filtered and transferred to non–isotopic medium so that the label was diluted 1,000 fold. The changes in radioactivity of the previously labeled proteins were then followed for 6 hours. With the exception of the RNP fraction, no loss of radioactivity could be detected in either the treated or control cells.

The distribution of radioactivity in subnuclear fractions after incubation for very short or for longer times is shown in Table 4. After a 20–second incubation the specific activity of the nucleoli–rich fraction

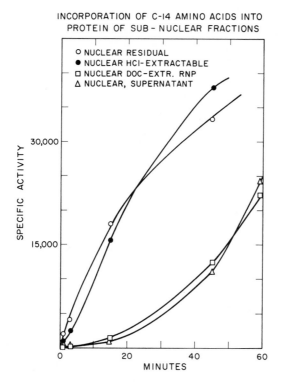

INCORPORATION OF C-14 AMINO ACIDS INTO
PROTEIN OF SUB-NUCLEAR FRACTIONS

Fig. 3.—Tobacco cells were incubated with C^{14} algal protein hydrolysate, and the nuclei were isolated and purified. The fractionation was carried out as described in the test.

is twice that of the chromatin. With longer incubation times, the fractions become equally labeled. It appears, therefore, that the initial seat of synthesis of HCl-soluble protein is the nucleolus.

Table 5 presents results obtained by incubation of subnuclear preparations of isolated pea nuclei in media containing labeled amino acid. The nucleolar preparation appears to be significantly more active in synthesis of HCl-soluble protein, as well as in other protein fractions, than the chromatin.

Discussion

Several lines of evidence suggest that the HCl-extractable protein of deoxycholate nondispersable fraction of nuclear pellets is either histone

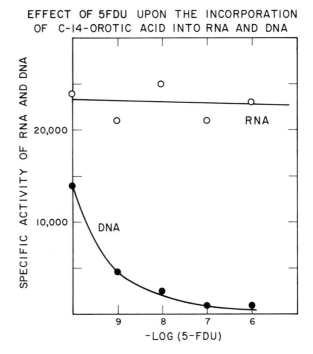

EFFECT OF 5FDU UPON THE INCORPORATION
OF C-14-OROTIC ACID INTO RNA AND DNA

Fig. 4.—Tobacco cells were pretreated for 2 hours with 5–FDU under growth conditions. The cells were collected and incubated with C^{14} orotic acid as described in text. Extraction procedure and analyses were as specified under Methods.

TABLE 3

Effect of 5–FDU upon nuclear protein synthesis*

Fraction	Specific Activity as % of Control			
Hours pretreatment with 5–FDU	0.5	3	6	18
Residual	96	89	110	134
HC1-extractable	105	75	104	140
DOC-extractable	89	86	109	115
Supernatant	112	109	99	110

*Tobacco cells were pre-treated with 10^{-7} M 5–FDU under growth conditions for various times. The cells were collected and incubated for 1 hour in 20 ml of growth medium containing 100 μc C^{14} algal protein hydrolysate and 10^{-7} M 5–FDU.

TABLE 4

Distribution of radioactivity in subnuclear fractions
following incubation with C^{14} amino acid mixture*

Nuclear Fraction	Specific activity (cpm/mg protein)	
	20 seconds	60 minutes
Nucleolar rich		
residual	350	38,000
HCl-extractable	350	40,000
total	350	38,500
Chromatin rich		
residual	280	39,000
HCl-extractable	25	37,000
total	165	38,000

*Whole cells were incubated with 100 μc of C^{14} algal protein hydrolysate. Nuclei
were fractionated in 2.2 M sucrose as described by Birnstiel el al. [35].

TABLE 5

In vitro incorporation of L-leucine-C^{14}
into subnuclear fractions of pea nuclei*

Preparation	Protein fraction	$\mu\mu$moles incorporated/ mg protein
Nucleoli	weak saline-extractable	9.2
	HCl-extractable	7.2
	residual	14.0
Chromatin	weak saline-extractable	5.2
	HCl-extractable	1.8
	residual	11.2

*Nuclear fractions were prepared as previously described [11] and incubated
at 37 C for 20 minutes in the presence of a complete amino acid mixture, an energy-
generating system, and 9.6 μc L-leucine-C^{14} (24 $\mu c/\mu$mole).

or is predominantly histone. The ratio of HCl-extractable protein to DNA is approximately 1, in accordance with the histone-DNA ratio of pea chromatin [34]. The newly synthesized protein of this fraction is relatively lysine rich, as expected for a histone fraction. The inactivity of the acid-soluble protein in vitro and the relationship between the rate of its in vivo synthesis and the metabolic activity of the cell (culture age) are in agreement with the findings of others concerning histone synthesis [1, 11, 15, 19, 20].

The kinetics of C^{14} amino acid incorporation into the four nuclear fractions (Fig. 2) have shown that for brief incubations the deoxycholate-extractable RNP fraction has a lower specific activity than either the residual or the HCl-extractable proteins. In fact, both the residual and the histone proteins are highly labeled at a time when essentially no activity is associated with the RNP fraction. These findings are consistent with the in vitro studies of Rendi [36] and of Birnstiel and Hyde [37] and suggest that the deoxycholate-extractable RNP fraction is not the site of nuclear protein synthesis. The possibility that active ribosomes exist in the nucleus and are responsible for synthesis of nuclear proteins [20, 33] has certainly not been excluded by our findings, since the most rapidly labeled fraction (residual) contains an appreciable amount of RNA. It is tempting to speculate as to the nature of this RNA and the possibility that it may sediment with the heavy material of the nucleus because it is a ribosomal complex of the polysome type [38, 39].

Tobacco cells have been treated with various concentrations of 5-fluorodeoxyuridine, which is a highly active inhibitor of the enzyme thymidylate synthestase [40]. Since thymidylate functions primarily as a precursor in DNA synthesis, the inhibition is generally well restricted in its effects on cellular metabolism [41, 42], as was found in our studies. DNA synthesis and mitosis were blocked, but rate of RNA synthesis and the synthesis of nuclear protein, including the histone fraction, were essentially unchanged. Assuming the HCl-extractable protein does represent histone, the possibility that histone synthesis depends on the simultaneous synthesis of DNA, as has been suggested [19], is excluded. It also follows that mitosis or cell division is not an obligatory feature of histone synthesis.

Preliminary studies involving in vivo incubations of tobacco cells in addition to the in vitro studies with isolated pea chromatin and nucleolar fractions suggest that the nucleolus is the most active site of nuclear protein synthesis. An interference concerning the site of histone synthesis within the nucleus is provided by the finding that there is essentially no synthesis of acid-extractable protein by chromatin either in vitro or in short-term in vivo incubations. The synthesis of HCl-extractable protein, possibly histone, is however, associated with the nucleolus in both systems.

Acknowledgments

We are grateful to Professor J. Bonner for his support and advice and to Margaret I. H. Chipchase for her interest and appraisals. One of us (W.G.F.) is a Postdoctoral Research Fellow of the United States Public Health Service. This investigation was supported by a grant (GM-03977) from the National Institutes of Health, United States Public Health Service.

D,L-lysine-1-C^{14} (4.2 mc/mm) and C^{14} algal protein hydrolysate (0.6 mg/mc) were obtained from New England Nuclear Corporation; orotic acid-2-C^{14} (4.2 mc/mm) and D,L-arginine, guanido-C^{14} (5.4 mc/mm) were purchased from CalBiochem; dextran (60,000 to 90,000 GMW) from Nutritional Biochemical Corporation. 5-Fluorodeoxyuridine was generously given to us by Dr. W. E. Scott of Hoffmann-LaRoche, Inc.

REFERENCES

1.   Allfrey, V. G., Mirsky, A. E., and Osawa, S., J. Gen. Physiol., 40, 451, 1957.

2.   Allfrey, V. G., Proc. Natl. Acad. Sci. U. S. A., 40, 881, 1954.

3.   Allfrey, V. G., and Mirsky, A. E., Proc. Natl. Acad. Sci. U. S. A., 44, 981, 1958.

4.   Frenster, J. H., Allfrey, V. G., and Mirsky, A. E., Biochim. Biophys. Acta, 47, 130, 1961.

5.   Frenster, J. H., Allfrey, V. G., and Mirsky, A. E., Proc. Natl. Acad. Sci. U. S. A., 46, 432, 1960.

6.   Rees, K. R., and Rowland, G. F., Biochem. J., 78, 89, 1961.

7.   Logan, R., Ficq, H., and Errera, M., Biochim. Biophys. Acta, 31, 402, 1959.

8.   Rho, J., Birnstiel, M. L., Chipchase, M. I. H., and Bonner, J., Fed. Proc. 20, 147, 1961.

9.   Birnstiel, M. L., Chipchase, M., and Bonner, J., Biochem. Biophys. Res. Commun., 6, 161, 1961.

10.   Birnstiel, M. L., Chipchase, M. I. H., and Hayes, R. J., Biochim. Biophys. Acta, 55, 728, 1962.

11.   Birnstiel, M. L., Chipchase, M. I. H., and Hyde, B. B., J. Cell Biol., in press, 1963.

12.   Allfrey, V. G., and Mirsky, A. E., Symp. on Protein Synthesis (London: Academic Press, Inc., 1961), p. 49.

13. Sirlin, J.L ., The Cell Nucleus (New York: Academic Press, 1960), p. 35.

14. Alfert, M., and Geschwind, I. I., Proc. Natl. Acad. Sci. U. S. A., 39, 991, 1953.

15. Daly, M. M., Allfrey, V. G., and Mirsky, A. E., J. Gen. Physiol., 36, 173, 1952.

16. Vendrely, R., and Vendrely, C., Nature, 172, 30, 1953.

17. Hoberman, H. D., and Peralta, P. H., Fed. Proc., 11, 231, 1952.

18. Mirsky, A. E., and Ris, H., Nature, 163, 666, 1949.

19. Bloch, D. P., and Godman, G. C., J. Biophys. Biochem. Cytol., 1, 17, 1955.

20. Wang, T. Y., Biochim. Biophys. Acta, 68, 52, 1963.

21. Filner, P., Unpublished data.

22. Flamm, W. G., Birnstiel, M. L., Filner, P., Biochim. Biophys. Acta, 76, 110, 1963.

23. Birnstiel, M. L., Chipchase, M. I. H., Hyde, B. B., Biochim. Biophys. Acta, 76, 454, 1963.

24. Bonner, J., and Huang, R. C., J. Mol. Biol., 6, 169, 1963.

25. Sporn, M. B., and Dingman, C. W., Science, 140, 316, 1963.

26. Lowry, O. H., Rosebrough, N. J., Farr, A. L., and Randall, R. J., J. Biol. Chem., 193, 265, 1951.

27. Ogur, M., and Rosen, G., Arch. Biochem., 25, 262, 1950.

28. Burton, K., Biochem. J., 62, 315, 1956.

29. Schmidt, G., and Thannhauser, S. J., J. Biol. Chem., 161, 83, 1945.

30. Vincent, W. S., Proc. Natl. Acad. Sci. U. S. A., 38, 139, 1952.

31. Flamm, W. G., Unpublished data.

32. Ts'o, P. O. P., Bonner, J., Vinograd, J., Biochim. Biophys. Acta, 30, 582, 1958.

33. Pogo, A. O., Pogo, B. G., Littau, V. C., Allfrey, V. G., and Mirsky, A. E., Biochim. Biophys. Acta, 55, 849, 1962.

34. Huang, R. C., and Bonner, J., Proc. Natl. Acad. Sci. U. S. A., 48, 1216, 1962.

35. Birnstiel, M. L., Rho, J. H., and Chipchase, M. I. H., Biochim. Biophys. Acta, 55, 734, 1962.

36. Rendi, R., Exptl. Cell Res., 19, 489, 1960.

37. Birnstiel, M. L., and Hyde, B. B., J. Cell Biol., 18, 41, 1963.

38. Warner, J. R., Rich, A., Hall, C. E., Science, 138, 1399, 1962.

39. Watson, J. D., Science, 140, 17, 1963.

40. Cohen, S. S., Flaks, J. G., Barner, H. D., Loeb, M. R., and Lichtenstein, J. Proc. Natl. Acad. Sci. U. S. A., 44, 1004, 1958.

41. Taylor, J. H., Haut, W. F., and Tung, J., Proc. Natl. Acad. Sci. U. S. A., 48, 109, 1962.

42. Harbers, E., Chaudhuri, N. K., and Heidelberger, C., J. Biol. Chem., 234, 1255, 1959.

Harris Busch, William J. Steele,
Lubomir S. Hnilica, and Charles Taylor

METABOLISM OF HISTONES

Labeling of histones. To determine the incorporation of labeled amino acids into proteins of the various subfractions of liver cells and tumor cells, labeled amino acids were injected into tumor-bearing rats [1]. A very large amount of the isotope went to the microsome fraction of the liver. About one-fourth was incorporated into nuclear proteins [2, 3]. In the Walker tumor, a much larger proportion of the isotope was incorporated into the nuclear proteins and a correspondingly smaller proportion went into the microsome proteins.

Figure 1 shows the specific activity in counts per minute per milligram of protein of some protein fractions. The black bars show the average for the Walker tumor and indicate that the specific activity of the whole histone fraction was greater than that of the other nuclear proteins. All of the other proteins are acidic proteins.

The data for the liver have been doubled to make a rough equivalence of most fractions to those of the Walker tumor. In the liver, the acidic proteins are relatively more labeled than the histones. Thus there would appear to be excess synthesis of histones in the tumor, which would be expected because of the increased growth rate of the tumor. The higher labeling of the acidic nuclear protein in non-tumor tissues has been reported [4, 5].

In studies of labeling of the histones in a variety of tumors, specific activities were uniformly high in the tumors and low in the other tissues [6]. When compared with the labeling of proteins of other cellular fractions, the labeling of the histones in the Walker tumor was high. In other tissues, the labeling of the histones was lower than that of the other cellular fractions.

These data suggested that the amino acid pool was being utilized for different purposes in individual tissues and that there was an emphasis on synthesis of nuclear proteins in the tumors.

Labeling of individual histone fractions. The labeling of various fractions of the histones in one hour is presented in Table 1. In the Walker tumor, the labeling of the most lysine-rich fraction is higher than that of the other fractions on the basis of counts per minute per milligram of protein, but in one hour, other fractions were more highly labeled on the basis of counts per minute per μmole of lysine. The chief point, however, of these data is that the specific activity differs for the different histones in the Walker tumor.

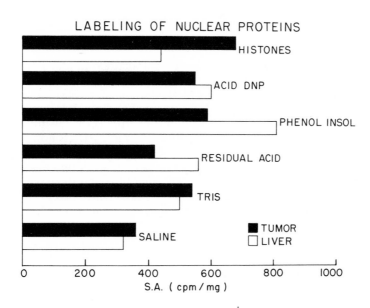

Fig. 1.—Labeling of acidic nuclear proteins and histones 1 hour after intraperitoneal injection of 10 μc of L-lysine-U-C^{14}, as cpm per mg protein.

TABLE 1

Specific activities of various histone subfractions 1 hour after injection of 5 μc of L-lysine into tumor-bearing rats

Fraction	Walker Tumor		Rat Liver	
	cpm/mg	cpm/μmole lys.	cpm/mg	cpm/μmole lys.
F1	830	360	90	40
F2a	400	540	50	70
F2b	540	470	80	70
F3	460	700	50	80

What is particularly interesting is the data for the rat liver. These show that there is also labeling of these various fractions in the rat liver. In Fraction 3, labeling was about twice that of the other fraction on the basis of counts per minute per milligram. The intriguing point is that in a tissue such as liver, in which DNA synthesis is very small (the rats weighed 200-250 g), the turnover of histones, at least as measured on the basis of specific activity, was approximately one-tenth that of the Walker tumor, a rapidly growing tissue. Although labeling is just one measure of biosynthesis, it must also reflect loss of histone, since the amount of histone is relatively constant in this tissue.

Histone-DNA dissociation. These data suggested that histones dissociate from DNA complexes and, moreover, that there may be specific dissociation constants for the individual histone fractions. It is possible that histones are associating in nuclei with acidic proteins and are thereby being made unavailable for reassociation with DNA. If this is so, the histones would have alternative pathways—one to DNP complexes and the other to complexes with acidic protein.

Histone turnover. Calculating minimal turnovers and assuming that the radioactive lysine is not significantly diluted in the tissues, about 50% of the histones in the tumor would be synthesized every 24 hours. In the liver, about 3-6% of the histones would be turning over or being resynthesized every 24 hours.

The question is, why should there be a histone turnover in an essentially resting tissue like the interphase liver cell? If one considers that in a liver cell there are approximately three-fourths of a million DNA molecules, assuming an average molecular weight of 10^7, and there are about 5,000 coding units per DNA molecule, the total number of coding units is 3.7×10^9. Assuming that most proteins weigh about 50,000, this could mean that the total genomes would make about 7,000,000 proteins. The total number of histone molecules, assuming an average molecular weight of 20,000, would be about 2.5×10^8 histone molecules.

To shut off all protein synthesis, the cell would need only about 7 million "repressor molecules." If these were histones, there is a very large excess. There are not enough histones to block each coding unit on the basis of one histone per coding unit. As Phillips indicated, it is possible that a histone may cover many more than just one coding unit [7]. Assuming that histones are like stops on a musical instrument, there must be a way for a cell to get the histones off the DNA. It is possible that an equilibrium between DNA, histones, and acidic proteins might provide such a mechanism.

Synthesis of histones. We do not know how many histones there are, precisely what they do, or where they are synthesized. In the nucleus, as has just recently been found by Smetana, working in our laboratory, there is a nuclear ribonucleoprotein network with the nucleolus as one component. This RNP network is one possible place where the histones might be synthesized. Whether they are synthesized on DNA, as some have suggested, is uncertain, but it is currently believed that RNA is involved. Efforts to fractionate the components of this reticulum have been made,

and of particular interest are the nucleoli; these have recently been isolated from both Walker tumor and liver [8].

The histones might be synthesized in nucleoli even though their concentration in nucleoli is very low. We have looked for biosynthetic reactions in the isolated nucleoli. As yet, evidence for biosynthetic reactions
in the isolated nucleoli has not been obtained, but possibly further experiments will provide a biosynthetic system sufficient to answer the question
of the origin of the histones.

Acknowledgments

These studies were supported in part by grants from the Jane Coffin
Childs Fund, the United States Public Health Service, and the American
Cancer Society.

REFERENCES

1.   Busch, H., Davis, J. R., and Anderson, D. C., Cancer Res., 18, 916, 1958.

2.   Davis, J. R., and Busch, H., Cancer Res., 18, 718, 1958.

3.   Busch, H., Davis, J. R., Honig, G. R., Anderson, D. C., Nair, P. V., and
      Nyhan, W. L., Cancer Res., 19, 1030, 1959.

4.   Daly, M. M., Allfrey, V. G., and Mirsky, A. E., J. Gen. Physiol., 36, 173,
      1952.

5.   Smellie, R. M. S., McIndoe, W. M., and Davison, J. N., Biochim. Biophys.
      Acta, 11, 559, 1953.

6.   Starbuck, W. C., and Busch, H., Cancer Res., 20, 891, 1960.

7.   Phillips, D. M. P., Progr. Biophys. Biophys. Chem., 12, 211, 1961.

8.   Muramatsu, M., Smetana, K., and Busch, H., Cancer Res., 23, 510, 1963.

V. ENZYMOLOGY RELATED
TO THE NUCLEOHISTONES

 Edgar Stedman

INTRODUCTION

The title of this section, "Enzymology Related to the Nucleohistones," does not imply that histones or nucleohistones are enzymes. There is not, as far as I am aware, any evidence that this is the case. Nor, on very simple grounds, should I expect histones to possess such a function, because they are present in the cell nucleus in much greater amount than is usual with the familiar enzymes. According to the work my collaborators and I have carried out, they constitute roughly 30% of the dry weight of the cell nuclei of the higher animals, the per cent varying appreciably with the nature of the cell. But if this figure does not accord with our ordinary conception of enzymes, it certainly suggests that histones perform some very important functions. To answer this question of what these functions are is the purpose of this section. Let me briefly summarize the indirect evidence that many years ago led me to advance the hypothesis that one of the functions of histones is to act as gene inhibitors.

The existence of gene inhibitors seems necessary if we are to accept the findings of cytogeneticists that all the cells of a given organism contain identical chromosomes and hence identical genes. For if genes control the physiological functions of the cell, as we must assume they do, there must clearly be some mechanism for modifying or repressing their activity according to the type of cell in which they are contained. Otherwise all cells would be identical; that is, cell differentiation would not occur.

A clue as to the possible nature of these hypothetical inhibitors was given by a comparison of the chemical composition of different cell nuclei from the salmon, particular attention being paid to the basic proteins they contained. Of the cells examined [1-3], the sperm yielded protamine, as was known from the classical work of Miescher and Kossel. On the other hand, the mixed cells from immature testes, which contain some but not many fully formed spermatozoa, yielded a mixture of protamine and histone. Liver cells and erythrocytes yielded only histones. These conclusions are established, for example, by the arginine content of the several types of cells.

From these and other facts, it was concluded that: (1) protamines and histones are homologous proteins; (2) sperm mother cells (presumably mainly spermatogonia) contain histones; and (3) liver cells and erythrocytes contain different histone complexes. These conclusions may be summarized in the statement that the basic proteins in the cell nuclei of the salmon are cell specific. It follows that, at least in the salmon, basic proteins are suited to play the role of gene inhibitors or modifiers. Whether they function in this way or not, it is obvious that they must contribute to the different physiological properties which we must assume the nuclei of different types of cell to possess.

Attempts to extend the concepts developed for the salmon to other species resulted in the finding [4, 5] that histone, previously assumed to be a single substance, is in fact composite, a result which led to attempts to separate the individual components. Now it appears that some of the specificity resides in the β- or aggregating histones in the domestic fowl [6]. For the ox [7], this is less certain, since the β-histones examined from this source have long been known to be impure. Nevertheless, I think it is indisputable that the total histone complexes of different types of cells in the same organism do exhibit cell specificity in amino acid composition, although it is not known in all cases whether this is due to the presence of corresponding components of different amino acid composition or to identical components present in different proportions. The histone complexes of different cell types also exhibit different patterns when subjected to starch-gel electrophoresis. Neelin and Butler [8], for example, have found such differences in the domestic fowl. This is true, too, for the histone complexes from the thymocytes and liver cells of the ox. The extent and real nature of such specificity must await the isolation in pure form of the various components of the histone complex.

REFERENCES

1.   Stedman, E., and Stedman, E., Biochem. J., 38, 26, 1944.

2.   Stedman, E., and Stedman, E., Symp. Soc. Exp. Biol., 1, 232, 1947.

3.   Stedman, E., and Stedman, E., Cold Spring Harbor Symp. Quant. Biol., 12, 224, 1947.

4.   Stedman, E., and Stedman, E., Nature, 166, 780, 1950.

5.   Stedman, E., and Stedman, E., Phil. Trans. Roy. Soc. (London), Ser. B, 235, 565, 1951.

6.   Mauritzen, C. M., and Stedman, E., Proc. Roy. Soc. (London), Ser. B, 150, 299, 1959.

7.   Mauritzen, C. M., and Stedman, E., Proc. Roy. Soc. (London), Ser. B, 153, 80, 1960.

8.   Neelin, J. M., and Butler, G. C., Can. J. Biochem. Physiol., 39, 485, 1961.

James Bonner
and Ru-chih C. Huang

ROLE OF HISTONE IN CHROMOSOMAL RNA SYNTHESIS

We have already studied and reported [1-4] procedures for the isolation of chromatin from plant tissues, chromatin active in the conduct of DNA-dependent RNA synthesis. We have also reported studies on the separation and purification of the chromosomal RNA polymerase from the chromosome, as well as procedures for the preparation of the native nucleohistone component from the original chromatin. Perhaps the most provocative fact we have found is that the native nucleohistone component of chromatin is inactive in the support of DNA-dependent RNA synthesis, but becomes fully active if the histone is removed from the DNA. The native nucleohistone of pea embryo chromatin is inactive in the support of DNA-dependent RNA synthesis, not only by the chromosomal RNA polymerase, but also by the purified RNA polymerase of Escherichia coli, as is shown in Figure 1. The small residual activity in support of RNA synthesis exhibited by the native nucleohistone we attribute to some dissociation of histone from DNA that occurs in the reaction mixture of relatively high ionic strength required for the conduct of DNA-dependent RNA synthesis.

The inactivity of native nucleohistone in the support of RNA synthesis is not due to aggregation or precipitation of the nucleohistone by the components of the RNA-synthesis reaction mixture. This is shown by the data of Table 1, which concerns an experiment in which nucleohistone, the complete reaction mixture including Mg^{++} ions and the four riboside triphosphates (GTP, CTP, UTP, and C^{14}-ATP) were centrifuged for 15 minutes at 35,000 rpm, SW-39. The analytical data of Table 1 show that the DNA of the nucleohistone remains in the supernatant under these conditions. The enzymatic data of Table 1 show that the DNA of the nucleohistone cannot support DNA-dependent RNA synthesis.

DNA, when it is complexed with histone in the native nucleohistone, is altered not only in regard to its biological properties but is altered physically as well. Thus the T_m (temperature of half melting) of the DNA in the form of nucleohistone is 14° higher than that of deproteinized DNA in the same medium.

We have earlier shown that nucleohistone, inactive in the support

251

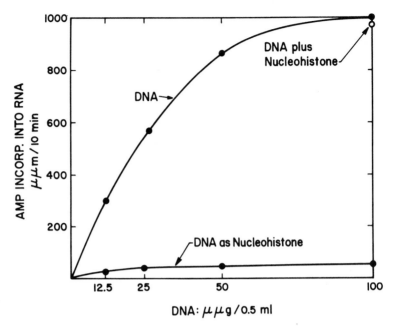

Fig. 1.—Rate of RNA synthesis by E. coli RNA polymerase as a function of DNA concentration. DNA added as deproteinized pea chromosomal DNA or as native nucleohistone. X indicates 100 mg deproteinized DNA plus 100 mg DNA as native nucleohistone.

of DNA-dependent RNA synthesis, may be reconstituted from deproteinized DNA and purified whole histone. For such reconstitution experiments, the histone and DNA are mixed in medium of high ionic strength (1.0 M NaCl) in which both are soluble, and the mixture is then slowly dialyzed to low ionic strength. Under these conditions, histone and DNA appear to associate in configurations of near maximum stability, and we have been able to prepare reconstituted nucleohistone from pea embryo DNA and pea embryo chromatin whole histone with T_m's as high as 81 C; not as high as that of the native nucleohistone, but none the less approaching it. It may be noted in passing that whole thymus histone is as effective as pea histone in suppression of the ability of pea embryo DNA to conduct DNA-dependent RNA synthesis, while whole pea histone is as effective as whole thymus histone in repressing the effectiveness of thymus DNA in the support of RNA synthesis.

The procedures outlined above open the way to the study of the biological roles of the different histone components of whole histone. It is known, as brought out earlier in this volume, that histone of calf thymus, for example, is composed of a great variety of separable components. Such separation may be done in various ways, but for our studies we have used gradient elution with guanidinium chloride from an Amber-

TABLE 1

Results showing that native nucleohistone of pea embryo chromatin is not aggregated or precipitated by the reaction mixture used to assay RNA synthesis*
and is inactive in the support of RNA synthesis.†

Fraction Assayed	DNA content μg/0.5 ml	RNA synthesized‡ μμmole/0.5 ml/10 min.
Top 1 ml	120	15
Second 1 ml	110	24
Third 1 ml	95	21
Bottom 1 ml	95	15
Average	105	19
Bottom 1 ml + 100 μg free DNA	195	2,137

†Native nucleohistone, containing 200 μg DNA/ml, centrifuged for 15 minutes at
35,000 rpm, SW-39. Analysis of DNA distribution in tube by dephenylamine
method. (After Huang, Bonner, and Murray [5].)
*Reaction mixture contained per ml; 40 μmoles tris pH 8.0, 1.0 μmole MnCl₂,
4 μmoles MgCl₂, 0.4 μmoles each ATP, GTP, CTP and UTP, 12 μmoles β-
mercaptoethanol.
‡20 μg E. Coli RNA polymerase added to each fraction after centrifugation.

lite IRC-50 column. We have further confined our attention to the four
principal histone components of calf thymus histone, all prepared by
Kenneth Murray as described in this volume (see also Huang, Bonner,
and Murray [5]). These four histone fractions form a series of increasing
arginine and decreasing lysine, content, as is shown in Table 2. Associated with the differences in arginine-lysine ratio are other differences
as well. Thus, that richest in lysine, histone Ib, is also richest in proline,
and has the lowest molecular weight, approximately 10,000. That richest
in arginine, histone IV, is lowest in proline and has the highest molecular
weight, approximately 30,000. We have reconstituted soluble nucleohistones from the four histone components of Table 2. It should be emphasized that the preparations are optically clear, and free of any aggregates.
In the reconstituted nucleohistones also, histone and DNA are present in
very close to equivalent amounts. The melting behaviors of the several
reconstituted nucleohistones are summarized in Table 2. It is clear

TABLE 2

Histone-DNA ratios and T_m's of soluble nucleohistones reconstituted
from thymus DNA and varied fractions of calf thymus histone and of the
protamine salmine.*

Histone fraction used in reconstitution	Arg-lys ratio of histone	Histone-DNA mass ratio of nucleohistone	T_m of complex in dilute saline citrate °C
None (DNA alone)	-	-	70
Fraction Ib	0.1	1.37	81
Fraction IIb	0.6	1.32	75
Fraction III	1.4	1.45	72.5
Fraction IV	1.4	1.35	71
Whole thymus histone	0.5	1.33	76
Salmine	-	-	70

*Data from Huang, Bonner, and Murray [5].

that the T_m's of the several nucleohistones increase with increasing
lysine and decreasing arginine content of the histone. Since histone IIb
is the principal component of calf thymus histone, comprising two thirds
or more of the total material, while histone Ib is next most abundant, it
is not surprising that the melting behavior of the nucleohistone of whole
calf thymus is intermediate between nucleohistones of IIb and Ib.

The activities in support of DNA-dependent RNA synthesis of the
several reconstituted nucleohistones are summarized in Table 3, both
for RNA synthesis by the pea embryo chromosomal RNA polymerase,
and in Table 4 for the purified RNA polymerase of Escherichia coli. The
data show that nucleohistone Ib is inactive, or essentially so, in the support of DNA-dependent RNA synthesis, while nucleohistone IV is moderately active in the support of such synthesis, with the other two nucleohistones being intermediate in their behaviors. Again, the properties
of the nucleohistone reconstituted from whole thymus histone resembles
those of nucleohistones Ib and IIb.

When DNA and histone are mixed in media of low ionic strength,
extensive crosslinking and aggregate formation take place immediately.

TABLE 3

Effectiveness of varied nucleohistones in support of DNA-dependent RNA synthesis.*

DNA provided as:	RNA synthesized/10 min. $\mu\mu$moles nucleotide [†]
Nucleohistone Ib	0
Nucleohistone IIb	24
Nucleohistone III	80
Nucleohistone IV	216
Whole thymus nucleohistone	0
DNA alone	320

*120 μg pea DNA per 0.5 ml reaction mixture in presence of chromosomal RNA polymerase. After Huang, Bonner, and Murray [5].
[†]Incorporation by enzyme alone subtracted.

TABLE 4

Activities of various reconstituted nucleohistones in support of RNA synthesis by Escherichia coli RNA polymerase.*

DNA (50 μg) provided as:	RNA synthesized $\mu\mu$moles nucleotide/0.5 ml/10 min. [†]
DNA (thymus) alone	8,474
Nucleohistone Ib	56
Nucleohistone IIb	140
Nucleohistone IV	4,000
Nucleoprotamine (salmine)	7,287

*After Huang, Bonner, and Murray [5].
[†]Incorporation by enzyme alone subtracted.

The activity of such aggregates in the support of DNA-dependent RNA synthesis is reported in Table 5. For these experiments, DNA was mixed with an equivalent amount of histone in the enzymatic reaction mixture appropriate for the conduct of RNA synthesis by the Escherichia coli polymerase. The data of Table 5 indicate again that the effect of lysine-rich histone Ib is to greatly depress the ability of DNA to support RNA synthesis, while the aggregate produced by histone IV is highly active in the conduct of such synthesis.

TABLE 5

Influence of varied histones on DNA-dependent RNA synthesis by Escherichia coli RNA polymerase.*

Addition to otherwise complete reaction mixture	Rate of RNA synthesis $\mu\mu$moles nucleotide/10 min.
DNA (no histone)	5,340[†]
DNA + histone Ib	450
DNA + histone IIb	850
DNA + histone III	3,290
DNA + histone IV	3,770

*Histones added directly to complete reaction mixture in amounts equivalent to the amount of DNA. 100 μg DNA per 0.5 ml reaction mixture. After Huang, Bonner, and Murray [5].
[†]Incorporation by enzyme alone (130 $\mu\mu$moles) subtracted.

The role of histones in suppression of the ability of DNA to conduct DNA-dependent RNA synthesis does not reside in their ability to cause aggregate formation, since fully soluble (not sedimented at 130,000 x g for 15 minutes) nucleohistone is inactive in support of such synthesis. Rather, histone and DNA must apparently be associated in some appropriate manner. The difference in ability of the different nucleohistones to support DNA-dependent RNA synthesis most probably resides in differences in the physical structure of the several nucleohistones. The wide differences in α-helical content of the several nucleohistones is suggested by the differences in proline content, as among the several histones. In addition, however, it is of interest to know why chromatin contains different kinds of histones. One may presume that the different histones play different roles in the chromosomal economy; particular histones, such as Ib or IIb, may have to do with the repression of genetic activity, while others, such as III and IV, perhaps may have to do with the binding of DNA molecules into the structure of the chromosome itself.

The fact that the nucleohistone component of chromatin is inactive in the support of DNA-dependent RNA synthesis, while chromatin as a whole is active in this role, suggests at once that chromatin must contain DNA, not only in the form we isolate as the native nucleohistone, but also some further form capable of supporting DNA synthesis. That chromatin does contain DNA in different forms is, in the first place, indicated by its melting behavior. The melting profiles of pea embryo DNA and of the native nucleohistone of pea embryo chromatin are shown in Figure 2a. The melting profile of whole pea embryo chromatin, shown in Figure 2b, is clearly a two-step process, the first step having a T_m corresponding to that of DNA not complexed with any stabilizing histone, and the second step corresponding to the melting temperature of the native nucleohistone component. We estimate from the hyperchromicities of the two steps that the nucleohistone component includes about 80% of the chromosomal DNA of pea embryo chromatin.

A second kind of study, which also indicates that chromatin contains DNA in somewhat different forms, is analytical investigation of the process by which native nucleohistone component of chromatin is prepared. Our procedure for the preparation of native nucleohistone is adapted from that of Zubay and Doty [6] and consists in the dispersion of chromatin in a medium, of low ionic strength, followed by shearing of the thus dispersed chromatin in a Virtis homogenizer. The sheared material is then centrifuged in a field sufficient (10,000 x g) for the removal of all unsheared chromatin. By this process, the original chromatin is separated into a supernatant, the native nucleohistone component, and a pellet. The partition of histone and of DNA between the nucleohistone and pellet fractions of pea embryo chromatin is presented in Figure 3. The histone-DNA ratio of original whole chromatin is very close to 1. The nucleohistone component, on the other hand, which makes up 70-80% of the total DNA of the original chromatin, possesses a histone-DNA ratio of 1.3-1.4, a ratio which indicates a very nearly exact equivalence between the cationic groups of histone and the anionic groups of DNA. The pellet fraction, on the other hand, making up 20-30% of the total DNA of the chromatin possesses a histone-DNA ratio of only 0.4 in the example of Figure 3. It is clear, therefore, that by the Zubay-Doty procedure, chromatin has been fractionated into a portion richer in and a portion impoverished in histone. The pellet fraction in fact does not contain, by a large factor, sufficient histone for equivalence between cationic groups of histone and anionic groups of DNA. However, various attempts to isolate the free DNA from the pellet fraction by methods other than high salt or deproteinization are so far unsuccessful.

Finally, if chromatin contains DNA not associated with histone in the manner characteristic of the native nucleohistone component, then one might expect such chromatin to support DNA-dependent RNA synthesis

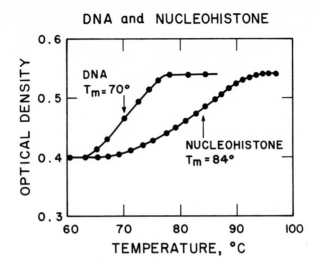

Fig. 2a.—Deproteinized DNA and native nucleohistone.

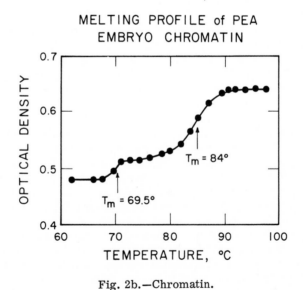

Fig. 2b.—Chromatin.

Fig. 2.—Melting profiles of pea embryo DNA in varied states. Heating carried out in dilute saline citrate, 0.016 M.

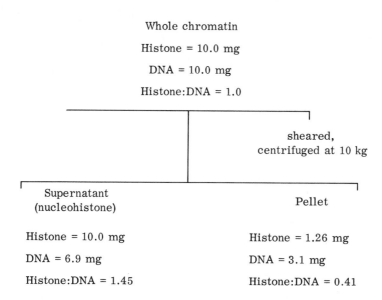

Fig. 3.—Distribution of DNA and of histone during preparation of chromosomal nucleohistone from pea embryo chromatin.

by added exogenous RNA polymerase. We have already reported [4] that chromatin heated to 60 C to inactivate the native RNA polymerase is able to support DNA-dependent RNA synthesis by added, purified chromosomal RNA polymerase, and that pea embryo chromatin is about one-fifth as effective in such support as an equivalent amount of pure, deproteinized pea embryo DNA. The data of Table 6 concern similar experiments with pea cotyledon chromatin fortified by the presence of purified Escherichia coli RNA polymerase. Although the nucleohistone component of pea coty-ledon chromatin is inactive in the support of DNA-dependent RNA syn-thesis, just as is the nucleohistone of pea embryo chromatin, yet it is clear that the whole pea cotyledon chromatin is capable of the support of DNA-dependent RNA synthesis, although less effectively than an equal amount of deproteinized DNA. Evidence adduced above then, shows, that a portion of the genome of the cells we have investigated is present in chromatin in a form capable of the support of DNA-dependent RNA syn-thesis, while another portion, in fact the greater portion, is present in the form of nucleohistone and inactive in the production of RNA.

In what physical state is the chromosomal DNA that can support RNA synthesis? Clearly it is ionically complexed, presumably by histone, into the chromosomal superstructure, because treatment of chromatin with media of high ionic strength releases all of the chromosomal DNA as molecules of sedimentation constant 18 S [3]. Clearly also, the active

TABLE 6

Activity of chromatin of developing pea cotyledons in support of RNA synthesis
by <u>Escherichia coli</u> polymerase

DNA supplied to reaction mixture as:	RNA synthesis $\mu\mu$moles nucleotide/10 min.
125 μg DNA, deproteinized	2,220*
37.5 μg DNA, deproteinized	2,030
12.5 μg DNA, deproteinized	740[†]
125 μg DNA as nucleohistone	25
125 μg DNA as whole chromatin	940

*Incorporation by enzyme alone (185 $\mu\mu$moles) subtracted.
[†]From separate saturation curve for enzyme by DNA.

chromosomal DNA is not complexed with histones of the types that yield
the highly stabilized high-melting nucleohistones and are inactive in support of RNA synthesis. The active DNA could, in principle, be associated
with histones of the types III or IV, which, as shown above, yield nucleohistones active in support of RNA synthesis or, alternatively, could be
largely histone noncomplexed. Each of these alternatives may very well
be represented.

Chromatin, then, at least of the kinds we have studied, behaves physically and enzymologically as though it consists of two parts, a nucleohistone fraction that is inactive, or very slightly active, in the support of
RNA synthesis, and a DNA fraction, structurally also a part of chromatin,
that is highly active in the support of RNA synthesis. So far as the nucleohistone component is concerned, it consists of a great variety of subcomponents in which the several kinds of histones are complexed with
DNA. Our reconstitution experiments show that the different histone
fractions, when complexed with DNA, yield soluble nucleohistones of
widely different physical and biological properties. Real understanding
of the significance of the presence in chromatin of the different histones,
and hence of different nucleohistones, must, however, await fuller understanding of the structure of chromatin and of the nucleohistone component
of chromatin. Studies of the structures and properties of the reconstituted
nucleohistones should ultimately reveal much concerning the role of
histones in chromosomal structure and in the control of genetic activity.

Comment

Butler has shown that the native nucleohistone component of thymus is inactive in the support of RNA synthesis by a polymerase prepared from <u>Bacillus megatherium</u>. The whole nuclear chromatin fraction supports RNA synthesis and contains a polymerase that is associated with the DNA of the chromatin, as is the case with pea embryo chromatin.

The histone of pea chromatin is composed of fractions that, on the whole, are richer in lysine than those of thymus histone. None the less, both pea histone complexes with thymus DNA and thymus histone with pea DNA yield reconstituted nucleohistones inactive in the support of DNA-dependent RNA synthesis. There appears to be no clear specificity with respect to histone-DNA recombination.

REFERENCES

1.   Huang, R.-c. C., Maheshwari, N., and Bonner, J., Biochem. Biophys. Res. Commun. 3, 689, 1960.

2.   Bonner, J., Huang, R.-c. C., and Maheshwari, N., Proc. Natl. Acad. Sci. U. S. A., 47, 1548, 1961.

3.   Huang, R.-c. C., and Bonner, J., Proc. Natl. Acad. Sci. U. S. A., 48, 1216, 1962.

4.   Bonner, J., and Huang, R.-c. C., J. Mol. Biol., 6, 169, 1963.

5.   Huang, R.-c. C., Bonner, J., and Murray, K., J. Mol. Biol., in press.

6.   Zubay, G., and Doty, P., J. Mol. Biol., 1, 1, 1959.

Ru-chih C. Huang
and James Bonner

ROLE OF HISTONES
IN PROTEIN SYNTHESIS

The purpose of our experiments is to study the molecular nature of the control of the genetic activity of chromosomes. Because the genetic activity of chromosomes is expressed by the synthesis of messenger RNA, we are concerned with the control in chromosomes of messenger RNA synthesis. The method we have chosen is study of the synthisis of messenger RNA by looking at the amount and nature of the proteins synthesized by a ribosomal system in response to such messenger. We acknowledge immediately that we have not yet delved deeply into the nature of the control of chromosomal genetic activity. We have, however, completed preliminary steps in the establishment of an in vitro system for the study of this matter.

To accomplish our ends, we have first set up a system for the conduct of chromosomal DNA-dependent RNA synthesis. We have then coupled this system to a messenger-RNA-dependent protein-synthesizing ribosomal system. In the complete system, protein is synthesized in response to chromosomally produced messenger RNA.

In our system, messenger RNA is synthesized by chromatin in response to exogenous Escherichia coli RNA polymerase purified according to the method od Chamberlin and Berg [1]. The addition of such polymerase increases very considerably (10 fold or more) the amount of RNA synthesized per unit time by a given amount of chromatin, indicating that chromatin as we isolate it [2] is limited by the amount of polymerase it contains. The RNA synthesized by the chromatin of developing pea cotyledons in response to added exogenous RNA polymerase is largely free—that is, does not sediment with chromatin at 10,000 x g (Table 1). It is therefore able to interact with ribosomes and thus to serve as messenger RNA. The data of Table 1 also show that rate of synthesis of RNA by chromatin is increased by pretreatment of the latter at 60 C [3]. This temperature is well below that required to cause detectable melting (as followed by optical density) of pea chromatin, and we do not in fact know exactly how the heat treatment exerts its effect.

The messenger RNA-dependent ribosomal system we have used, like the polymerase, is borrowed from Escherichia coli. It is prepared in a

TABLE 1

Chromatin of developing pea cotyledons as a primer for RNA synthesis
by Escherichia coli RNA polymerase and release of RNA from such chromatin*

Primer added as:	RNA synthesized: $\mu\mu$moles AMP incorp./10 min./0.5 ml		
	Total	In 10,000 x g supernatant	% release of RNA
Deproteinized DNA, 50 μg	2,600	2,400	92
Cotyledon chromatin, containing 50 μg DNA	430	375	85
Cotyledon chromatin, containing 50 μg DNA; heated to 60 C, 5 min.	750	610	81

*Complete reaction mixture includes 0.7 μmoles each of GTP, CTP, UTP and
C^{14}-ATP (1.5 μc/μmoles), 12 μmoles $MgCl_2$, 0.5 μmoles $MnCl_2$, 20 μmoles tris
pH 8.0, 6 μmoles β-mercaptoethanol, and E. coli RNA polymerase.

manner which largely frees it of endogenous messenger and endogenous
Escherichia coli DNA, and therefore it is highly dependent on exogenous
messenger RNA. The preparation consists of pre-incubation of the 30,000
x g supernatant of alumina powder-ground Escherichia coli in the presence
of a complete protein-synthesizing reaction mixture, a reaction mixture
including amino acids, ATP, GTP, and others, and in these respects follows the method of Nirenberg and Matthei [4]. From the pre-incubation
reaction mixture, ribosomes are pelleted, resuspended, and exhaustively
dialyzed. The supernatant from the initial ribosome pelleting is used
after dialysis as the source of the supernatant protein synthesis system enzymes, transfer RNA, etc. This supernatant fraction is freed
of Escherichia coli DNA by centrifugation for 18 hours at 40,000 rpm
in the No. 40 Spinco head. Table 2 summarizes the added dependency
conferred on the system by the pre-incubation, and also shows that protein synthesis in the pre-incubated system depends on the presence of
both DNA and RNA polymerase.

We now replace DNA in the messenger RNA-dependent system by
chromatin, selecting in the first instance, the chromatin of developing
pea cotyledons. Table 3 shows that such chromatin supports the RNA
synthesis required to support ribosomal protein synthesis. Other data

TABLE 2

Support of ribosomal protein synthesis by pea DNA
Ribosomal system and RNA polymerase from Escherichia coli

System *	Protein synthesized μμmoles leucine incorp./hr.
1. Ribosomal system pre-incubated for depletion of endogenous messenger	
a. Complete system including pea DNA and E. coli RNA polymerase	844
b. Ribosomal system without RNA generating system	88
2. Ribosomal system not pre-incubated.	
a. Complete system including pea DNA and E. coli RNA polymerase	754
b. Ribosomal system without RNA generating system	251

*Complete system includes per 0.3 ml: tris pH 8, 5 μmoles; MgAc$_2$, 2 μmoles; MnCl$_2$, 0.5 μmoles; KCl, 20 μmoles; SHEtOH, 3 μmoles; 18 amino acids each 0.02 μmoles; leucine-C^{14} (131 μc/μmoles) 0.02 μmoles; ATP(K), 1 μmole; GTP, CTP, UTP each 0.1 μmoles pea DNA, 50 μg; RNA polymerase; approximately 100 μg E. coli ribosomes and 70 μg of E. coli 105,000 x g supernatant protein.

have indicated that synthesis of approximately 20 mμmoles RNA per 100 μg ribosomes yields maximal or near maximal protein synthesis under our conditions. This amount of RNA corresponds to the synthesis of approximately one RNA molecule of molecular weight 3×10^5 per ribosome present in the reaction mixture. Table 3 also shows that the coupling of chromosomal RNA synthesis to the ribosomal system can be carried out in two stages. In the first stage, chromatin is allowed to synthesize RNA in response to added Escherichia coli RNA polymerase. The chromatin is then removed by centrifugation at 10,000 x g, and the ribosomal system is added to the supernatant. Table 3 shows that such two-stage, chromosomally supported ribosomal protein synthesis, although possible, is less effective than the simultaneous presence of all components in the reaction mixture. Table 3 shows further how the production of messenger RNA, and hence of protein, in this system is highly dependent on added

TABLE 3

Support by chromosomal RNA synthesis of messenger RNA–dependent ribosomal protein synthesis

Components of system*	Incorp. of C^{14}-leucine into protein cpm/0.3 ml/30 min.	
	All ingredients present simultaneously	RNA synthesized in step 1: ribosomes added after chromatin removal for step 2
Cotyledon chromatin, RNA polymerase, ribosomal system	721	505
Cotyledon chromatin, ribosomal system (no RNA polymerase)	87	132
Ribosomal system alone	40	40

*Complete system includes per 0.3 ml: tris pH 8, 5 μmoles; MgAc$_2$, 2 μmoles; MnCl$_2$, 0.5 μmoles; KCl, 20 μmoles; SHEtOH, 3 μmoles; 18 amino acids, each .02 μmoles; leucine-C^{14} (131 μc/μmoles), 0.02 μmoles; ATP(K), 1 μmoles; GTP, UTP, CTP, each 0.1 μmoles chromatin containing 150 μg DNA; RNA polymerase; approximately 100 μg Escherichia coli ribosomes and 70 μg Escherichia coli 105,000 x g supernatant protein.

RNA polymerase. We have, then, in this system, a tool for the study of chromosomally dependent synthesis of protein.

The methods we have used for the preparation of chromatin from pea embryonic axes and from developing pea cotyledons, appear to apply equally well to the isolation of chromatin from a variety of tissues of a variety of organisms. Thus we have prepared chromatin from the vegetative buds of pea plants, from reticulocytes, erythrocytes, and duck liver (in collaboration with Dr. Alex Miller), from calf thymus, and from liver. All of the chromatin preparations prepared by our procedures possess some ability to support RNA synthesis. In this respect, the chromatin of the nucleated erythrocytes of duck is the least active of those we have studied, a fact which correlates interestingly with the fact that erythrocytes of duck and other fowl are extraordinarily inactive in the production of RNA in vivo. We have also tested certain of the kinds of chromatin we have prepared for their ability to support protein synthesis in our ribosomal system.

The next logical step in these investigations properly should focus on specific individual genes of the genome of the creature concerned, together with the protein whose formation is determined by each gene. We propose to select particular genes and their product proteins; to isolate chromatin from cells, tissue, or organs that have the ability to synthesize that protein, as well as chromatin from cells, tissue, or organs in which the particular gene is repressed; and to determine whether the control of genetic activity as it is expressed in vivo is preserved in the in vitro isolated chromatin. If such control is, in fact, preserved in the isolated chromatin, it will be possible to pursue further the molecular basis of the nature of genetic repression.

REFERENCES

1.   Chamberlin, M., and Berg, P., Proc. Natl. Acad. Sci. U. S. A., 48, 81, 1962.

2.   Huang, R. C., and Bonner, J., Proc. Natl. Acad. Sci. U. S. A., 48, 1216, 1962.

3.   Bonner, J., Huang, R. C., and Maheshwari, N., Proc. Natl. Acad. Sci. U. S. A., 47, 1548, 1961.

4.   Nirenberg, M., and Matthei, J. H., Proc. Natl. Acad. Sci. U. S. A., 47, 1588, 1961.

Vincent G. Allfrey
and Alfred E. Mirsky

ROLE OF HISTONE
IN NUCLEAR FUNCTION

The work to be described deals with the structure and synthetic activities of chromosomes and isolated cell nuclei, with particular emphasis on some negative correlations between the presence of the histones and the synthesis of RNA's.

Before presenting our recent findings on histone effects and some surmises on the role of histones, it will be advisable to present a brief account of the nature and properties of the test systems we have used.

SYNTHETIC ACTIVITIES IN ISOLATED NUCLEI

One of the most useful and informative experimental systems is the isolated cell nucleus, and most of the work to be described was done on suspensions of nuclei isolated from calf thymus tissue. The isolation method is gentle and rapid; it involves a brief homogenization in isotonic sucrose or in slightly hypotonic sucrose [1, 2], followed by differential centrifugation to give a nuclear sediment.

Nuclear fractions obtained in this way are better than 90% pure, but they still contain a few whole cells (2-8%) and some cytoplasmic debris (Fig. 1A). When necessary, the cells and cytoplasmic contamination can be removed by layering or density-gradient techniques, centrifuging the nuclei through dense solutions of dextran, Ficoll, or sucrose [1]. The cells are lighter than nuclei and are trapped at the interface between the light and heavy suspension media (Fig. 1B). The nuclei, because of their high density, sediment to the bottom of the tube (Fig. 1C).

Thymus nuclei purified by these procedures can still carry out a surprising range of biosynthetic activities, including the synthesis of ATP [3, 4], of RNA [5-8], and of protein [2, 9, 10].

Unequivocal evidence for protein synthesis <u>within</u> the isolated nucleus has recently been obtained [1]. High resolution autoradiography with the electron microscope has shown that H^3-leucine uptake occurs inside the nucleus and is not due to cytoplasmic contamination (Fig. 2).

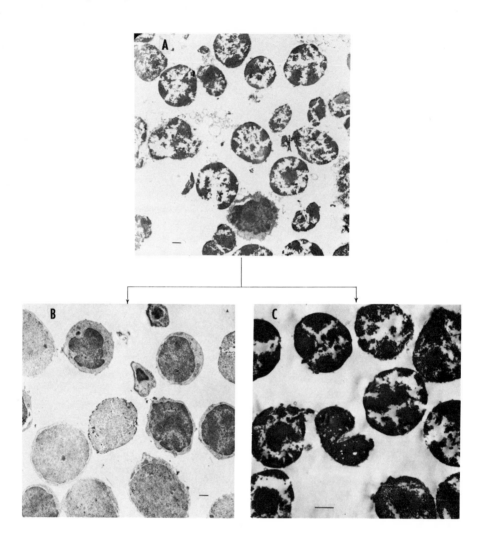

Fig. 1.—Electron micrographs showing stages in the purification of calf thymus nuclear suspensions. (A) Nuclear sediment obtained after homogenizing thymus tissue in 0.21 M sucrose and differential centrifugation in 0.25 M sucrose. Note the presence of an intact cell and some cytoplasmic debris in this section. (B) Cell-rich fraction trapped at the interface when the crude nuclear suspension (A) is centrifuged by layering over Ficoll (a cross-linked bacterial dextran) dissolved in isotonic sucrose. (C) Purified nuclear sediment after centrifugation through the Ficoll-sucrose density barrier.

One of the great advantages of the isolated nucleus is its susceptibility to attack by enzymes, such as DNAase or trypsin, to which whole cells

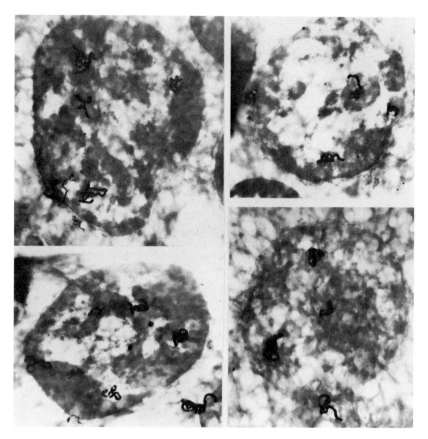

Fig. 2.—Electron microscope autoradiographs showing grain distributions over isolated cell nuclei following incubation in vitro with H³-leucine and extensive purification in a Ficoll density gradient. Note that most of the grains are centrally located over these very thin (600 Å) sections through the isolated nuclei.

are resistant. Thus, the use of DNAase has made it possible to remove all or most of the DNA from the isolated nuclei and to test for the effects of DNA removal on nuclear function [2, 11]. In practice, one finds that most of the DNA is readily removed from isolated nuclei, even at low enzyme concentrations (Fig. 3), but the removal of the last 15-20% of the DNA is more difficult, and requires more DNAase or more prolonged incubation. The experiments to be described below indicate that the easily removable DNA is inactive or repressed, while the remaining DNA is actively engaged in RNA synthesis.

NUCLEAR MESSENGER RNA'S

RNA synthesis in the nuclei is easily followed by tracer techniques,

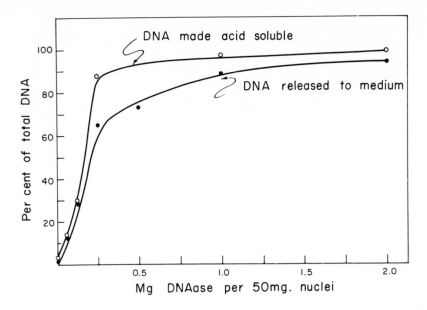

Fig. 3.—Curves showing the extent of DNA breakdown and release when isolated calf thymus nuclei are incubated in the presence of increasing concentrations of pancreatic DNAase (for 30 minutes at 37 C). The upper curve shows the DNA extractable in a 2% perchloric acid extract of the nuclei; intact DNA is not removed under these conditions. The lower curve shows the amount of DNA lost from the nuclei and found in the supernatant medium after centrifugation.

with purines, nucleosides, orotic acid, or P^{32}-orthophosphate as RNA precursors [2, 5-8]. It has been calculated that 10^9 nuclei (about 40 mg dry weight) can synthesize about 14 μg of RNA per hour in vitro. The extent of the synthesis can be better appreciated from the calculation that, in this interval, the average nucleus is making over 6,000 molecules of RNA (of one million average molecular weight).

The RNA made, as judged by pulse-labeling experiments with P^{32}, is largely of the messenger type; i.e., its base composition compares fairly closely to that of the thymus DNA [8]. This is illustrated by the data in Table 1, which presents the P^{32} distribution in the four major nucleotides derived from RNA by alkaline hydrolysis, and, for comparison, the base composition of thymus DNA.

The clear predominance of P^{32} in the adenylic and uridylic acids indicates that the RNA being made is of the high A + U type and is not ribosomal RNA (in which guanylic and cytidylic acids predominate). The data agrees with earlier findings that these nuclei are not very active in the synthesis of ribosomal RNA's [5, 7]. The probable explanation is that thymus lymphocytes are not dividing rapidly and are not required to make more ribosomal RNA for daughter cells.

TABLE 1

Evidence for the synthesis of messenger RNA in isolated nuclei*

Nucleotide	Radioactivity in isolated nucleotide	Activity relative to P^{32} content of adenylic acid	Distribution of P^{32}	Calculated nucleotide composition of RNA synthesized	Nucleotide composition of nuclear RNA's† messenger ribosomal		Base composition of thymus DNA	
	total cpm		% of total				Base	moles per 100 atoms P
Adenylic	3,677	10.0	25.9	25.9	26.3	20.4	adenine	27.1
Uridylic	3,991	10.85	28.1	28.1	28.7	18.6	thymine	28.3
Guanylic	3,319	9.02	23.4	23.4	22.5	32.7	guanine	22.6
Cytidylic	3,206	8.73	22.6	22.6	19.9	28.2	cytosine	19.9

*Based on P^{32}-orthophosphate uptake into RNA nucleotides. From Allfrey and Mirsky [8].
†From Sibatani et al. [7].

The presence of RNA's resembling DNA in their over-all base composition has been verified directly by isolation of a messenger RNA fraction from isolated thymus nuclei [7]. The method used involved a nuclear fractionation in salt solutions [5], followed by a phenol extraction of the residue insoluble in 1 M NaCl. The RNA with the highest rate of synthesis occurred at the interface layer between the aqueous phase and the phenol phase, and it could be isolated in quantity. Unfortunately, the RNA isolated was of relatively small size (3-4 S), probably due to nuclease activity during the salt extractions. A current method uses successive extractions with phenol at progressively higher temperatures [12]. Both procedures yield DNA-like RNA fractions with high rates of synthesis, but the latter procedure gives RNA fractions in the 20-22 S range.

The question arises whether such RNA's do indeed have a messenger function in protein synthesis. Two lines of evidence indicate that they do. First, it was observed in 1957 that if nuclear RNA synthesis is blocked, then protein synthesis shows a progressive inhibition beginning about 30 minutes later [2]. These early experiments used a benzimidazole derivative (DRB) [13] to stop nuclear RNA synthesis.

More recently, this type of experiment was repeated, with actinomycin D [14] as an inhibitor of DNA-dependent RNA synthesis. The results are shown in Figure 4, which compares the time courses of RNA and protein synthesis in the presence and absence of the antibiotic.

It is clear that RNA synthesis is immediately affected by the addition of actinomycin D and, after about 90 minutes, uptake into RNA has virtually ceased. However, protein synthesis, as judged by amino acid uptake, is not immediately inhibited, but shows the effects of a shortage of messenger RNA's about 30-60 minutes later.

In other tests for messenger RNA function, the DNA-like RNA isolated from calf thymus nuclei was added to thymus nuclear ribosomes. About a 70% stimulation of leucine uptake was observed [15]. (An RNA fraction prepared from yeast by a similar procedure has also been found to stimulate amino acid uptake by yeast ribosomes [16].)

COMPLETE DNA DEPENDENCE OF NUCLEAR
RNA SYNTHESIS

It was mentioned above that much of the DNA is readily removed from the nucleus, but that 15-20% is resistant to DNAase treatment. When DNA is removed in this way, it is found that up to 70-80% removal has no obvious effect on nuclear RNA synthesis—provided precautions are taken to protect the nuclei from adverse effects due to the release of histones previously bound to DNA. Protection is easily obtained by the addition of polyanions of high molecular weight, such as polyethylene sulfonate (PES) or polyacrylic acid [11].

When DNAase is added to a nuclear suspension in the presence of

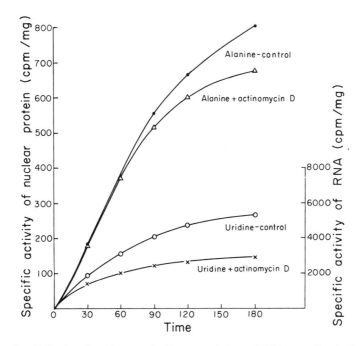

Fig. 4.—Effects of actinomycin D on protein and RNA synthesis in isolated thymus nuclei. The amount of isotope incorporated into protein (or RNA) is plotted against the time of incubation at 37 C. The precursors used were alanine-1-C^{14} and uridine-2-C^{14}. Note the rapid inhibition of RNA synthesis, beginning at the outset of the experiment. Amino acid uptake into nuclear proteins is not immediately inhibited, but decreases after 30-60 minutes.

PES, 70-80% of the DNA is removed after incubation at 37 C for 15 minutes. This has no effect on the subsequent capacity of the nuclei to incorporate adenosine-8-C^{14} or orotic acid-6-C^{14} into RNA. It follows that the DNA removed must have been inactive in RNA synthesis (i.e., unable to act as a primer for RNA polymerase).

However, if the remaining DNA is removed, then RNA synthesis comes to a halt. This is shown by the experiments summarized in Figure 5, which plots the uptake of orotic acid-6-C^{14} into RNA as a function of the residual DNA content of the nucleus [8]. The points lie on a straight line, which extrapolates back through the origin, and it can be concluded that removal of all of the DNA from the nucleus results in complete cessation of RNA synthesis.

The question that arises now concerns the mechanism of DNA activation and DNA repression. The thymus nucleus contains the full DNA complement characteristic of the diploid somatic cells of the organism [17], yet much of this genetic information will not be expressed in the lymphocyte. For example, the gene loci concerned with the synthesis of

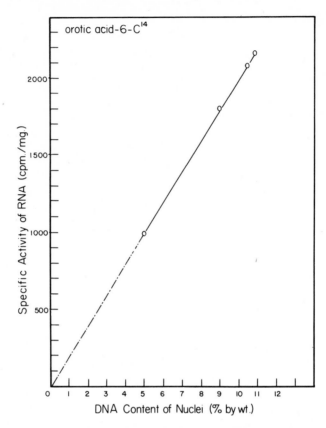

Fig. 5.—The relationship between the residual DNA content of nuclei treated with DNAase, and their ability to incorporate orotic-6-C[14] acid into RNA. Nuclei were preincubated with the enzyme, some losing more DNA than others, but all losing more than 70% of the original DNA content. They were then incubated with C[14]-orotic acid and fractionated according to their DNA contents in a density gradient. The specific activity of the RNA in the separate fractions is plotted against the DNA content of the fraction. Extrapolation of the line between experimental points leads through the origin. Similar data exist for adenosine-8-C[14] and guanosine-8-C[14] uptakes.

hemoglobin, serum albumin, the enzymes of digestion, myosin, and the structural proteins must all be inactive. What has prevented the bulk of the thymus DNA from serving as a primer for messenger RNA synthesis? The experiments to be described now implicate the histones as part of the mechanism for the suppression of DNA activity.

THE EFFECTS OF HISTONES ON SYNTHETIC
REACTIONS IN ISOLATED NUCLEI

In 1961 it was observed that the addition of basic proteins (histones and protamines) to isolated thymus nuclei caused an inhibition of RNA synthesis [8, 18, 19].

Unfortunately, this is not a specific target effect; added histones inhibit many other synthetic reactions in nuclei, as well as in mitochondria and isolated enzyme systems.

One such effect is illustrated in Figure 6, which shows the effects of added histones on ATP synthesis and respiration in thymus nuclei and thymus mitochondria [4]. The latter are very sensitive to added histone—a predictable finding, since Person and Fine [20] had reported earlier that histones inhibit the action of cytochrome oxidase.

Added histones also inhibit amino acid transport into thymus nuclei [21] and block amino acid uptake into nuclear proteins. The latter effect was first observed in intact nuclei [11, 22], but it has also been shown in suspensions of isolated nuclear ribosomes [23]. A comparison of different histones has shown differences in the extent to which they inhibit amino acid uptake, but this will not be reported here.

In considering histone effects on nuclear RNA synthesis, we have

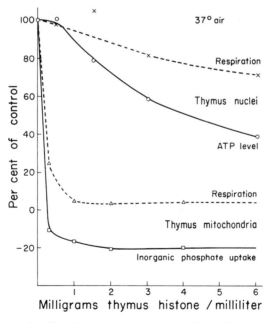

Fig. 6.—Effects of adding increasing amounts of total thymus histones on ATP synthesis and respiration in suspensions of isolated thymus nuclei and thymus mitochondria (from McEwen et al. [4]).

tested different histones by adding them to nuclei and then measuring the ability of the nuclei to incorporate radioactive precursors into RNA. An experiment of this sort is presented in Figure 7, which compares adenosine and guanosine uptakes into RNA in the presence of increasing amounts of (a) total thymus histones, (b) lysine-rich histones (i.e., the F1 fraction prepared by perchloric acid extraction of isolated thymus nuclei, following the method of Johns and Butler [24]), and (c) arginine-rich histones (i.e., the F3 fraction prepared by ethanolic-HCl extraction as described by Johns et al. [25]).

In these tests, the F3, or arginine-rich, histone fraction was clearly more inhibitory to nuclear RNA synthesis than were the F1 fractions [26]. Correspondingly low inhibitions were observed when the lysine-rich histone fractions prepared by the method of Daly and Mirsky [27] were added to the nuclei.

Apart from the different effectivenesses of different histone fractions, a matter to be discussed below, it is evident that histones can inhibit nuclear RNA synthesis. This fact is in accord with the results of the elegant

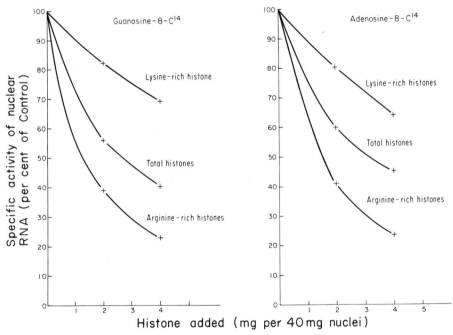

Fig. 7.—Comparative effects of adding increasing amounts of different thymus histones on the uptakes of adenosine-8-C[14] and guanosine-8-C[14] into RNA. Nuclei were incubated at 37 C for 30 minutes. The amount of histone added is plotted against the relative specific activity of the total nuclear RNA. The lysine-rich histones were prepared by the PCA extraction method of Johns and Butler [24]; the arginine-rich histones, according to Johns et al. [25].

experiments of Huang and Bonner [28], showing that histone-DNA complexes are unable to act as primers for RNA synthesis in the presence of an RNA polymerase from pea seedling nuclei.

Yet, considering the wide spectrum of inhibitory effects produced by histones, affecting as they do ATP and protein metabolism in the nucleus as well as RNA synthesis, we felt that a new experimental approach was needed. For this reason we tested the effects of removing histones on the capacity of thymus nuclei to synthesize RNA.

HISTONE REMOVAL BY TRYPSIN

Such tests are possible because of the susceptibility of isolated nuclei to attack by enzymes added to the medium. The enzyme selected was beef pancreatic trypsin, which, because of its preferential hydrolysis of peptide bonds involving arginine and lysine, would be expected to hydrolyze the histones preferentially. When trypsin was added to nuclear suspensions (at levels of 0.5 mg/ml, or 1 mg of enzyme per 40 mg of nuclei), much of the histone was hydrolyzed and released; e.g., about 70% of the total histones was degraded and released in 30 minutes, while the losses of nonhistone proteins were comparatively small [26]. It has been found that the nuclear RNA polymerase is not inactivated by trypsin under similar conditions [29].

ENHANCEMENT OF RNA SYNTHESIS

Removal of the histones by trypsin results in a marked stimulation of nuclear RNA synthesis [8]. Table 2 summarizes some of the results obtained with orotic acid, adenine, guanosine, and P^{32}-orthophosphate as RNA precursors. Stimulations in uptake range from 200-400% [26].

Because extensive tryptic digestion disrupts nuclear structure and releases free chromatin strands (about 50 Å in diameter), methods were devised for preserving nuclear morphology by moderating the action of the enzyme. Soybean trypsin inhibitor [30] was used for this purpose, and it effectively retarded and controlled the action of the enzyme on the nuclei.

The effects of trypsin treatment on nuclear RNA synthesis are shown in Figure 8, which plots the specific activity of nuclear RNA against the time of incubation. The lower curves show the time courses of incorporation of guanosine-8-C^{14} and adenine-8-C^{14} by "control" nuclei. The upper curves indicate the much higher incorporations induced by histone removal. Nuclei treated with the combination of trypsin and soy inhibitor retained their spherical shape and also showed stimulation; about a 70%

TABLE 2

Increased incorporation of RNA precursors by thymus nuclei following histone removal

Conditions of experiment	Precursor added	Specific activity of RNA nucleotides		
		Total nucleotides cpm/mg	Adenylic acid cpm/μmole	Cytidylic acid cpm/μmole
Nuclei alone	orotic-6-C^{14} acid	74.1		
Nuclei + 0.5 mg trypsin	" "	157		
Nuclei + 1.0 mg trypsin	" "	330		
Nuclei alone	adenine-8-C^{14}	330	97	
Nuclei + 1.0 mg trypsin	" " "	887	256	
Nuclei alone	guanosine-8-C^{14}	663		
Nuclei + 1.0 mg trypsin	" " "	1,390		
Nuclei alone	P^{32}-orthophosphate	1,388	9,380	6,400
Nuclei + 1.0 mg trypsin	" " "	3,330	26,070	18,860

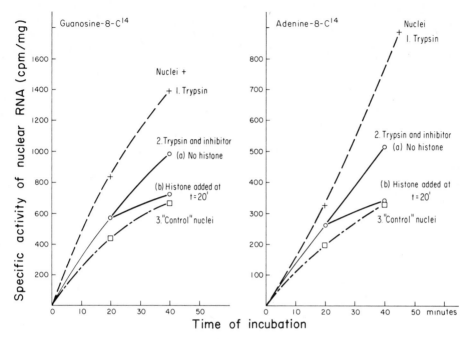

Fig. 8.—Effects of histone removal (with trypsin) on the uptake of guanosine-8-C[14] and adenine-8-C[14] into nuclear RNA. The lower curve (3) shows the time course of RNA synthesis in control nuclei (no histone added). The upper curve (1) shows the uptake in nuclei incubated with trypsin to remove about 70% of their total histones. Curve 2a is for nuclei treated with a mixture of trypsin plus soy inhibitor to moderate enzyme action and preserve nuclear structure. Curve 2b shows that addition of more histone to histone-depleted nuclei again represses nuclear RNA synthesis.

increase in the uptake of RNA precursors was observed (curve 2a). Furthermore, when histones were added back to trypsin-treated nuclei, the synthesis of RNA was again inhibited (curve 2b).

INCREASED SYNTHESIS OF MESSENGER RNA'S IN
HISTONE-DEPLETED NUCLEI

It was mentioned earlier that thymus nuclei contain and actively synthesize an RNA fraction of base composition similar to that of thymus DNA. We have isolated this messenger RNA fraction from P[32]-labeled nuclei and tested the effects of histone removal on its synthesis. In control nuclei the specific activity of the messenger RNA fraction after incubation for 30 minutes was 29,960 cpm per mg RNA-P; in trypsin-treated nuclei, the corresponding figure was 90,150 cpm per mg RNA-P, an increase of over 300%.

Three experiments have measured the distribution of P^{32} in the different nucleotides released by alkaline digestion of the total nuclear RNA after labeling trypsin-treated nuclei. The counts in the separate nucleotides (after elution from columns of Dowex-1) were different from those usually observed in control thymus nuclei; for example, higher P^{32} counts were found in guanylic and uridylic acids. These results, though preliminary, suggest that the removal of the histones has activated previously repressed DNA primers of different average base composition, perhaps opening up gene loci concerned with the synthesis of ribosomal RNA's as well as new messenger RNA's. If true, the thymus nucleus should be capable of new synthetic functions after histone removal. This attractive possibility remains to be investigated.

EFFECTS OF DIFFERENT HISTONES ON A THYMUS RNA POLYMERASE

A number of tests have been made, comparing the effects of different thymus histones on the activity of an RNA polymerase fraction prepared by saline extractions of calf thymus nuclei [29].

The enzyme system incorporates C^{14}-ATP and C^{14}-UTP very readily to form an acid-precipitable, and RNAase-digestible product. Incorporation occurs only if all four nucleoside triphosphates are present in the incubation medium. Uptake is inhibited by actinomycin D or by treatment with DNAase, and is clearly DNA-dependent by these tests.

Table 3 presents some results obtained by adding different histones to the thymus RNA polymerase. It is usually observed that histones inhibit the RNA polymerase reaction, but that inhibition becomes less marked as the salt concentration is raised (presumably because high salt concentrations dissociate the ionic bonds linking the histones to the DNA primer). It should be mentioned that the thymus polymerase preparations already contain thymus histones and DNA, so that the tests consist in adding more histone to a system that is already largely repressed.

When different histone fractions were compared, it was repeatedly observed that the F1 histone fraction (prepared by extraction of the nuclei in 5% perchloric acid or by chromatography on columns of carboxymethyl-cellulose [24, 25]) is a less effective inhibitor than the F3 histone fraction. These results were first interpreted in terms of the relative lysine and arginine contents of the different histone preparations, since F1 is lysine rich, and F3 is arginine rich. On this basis, our results seemed to be in direct conflict with the data of Huang and Bonner [28], who observed that a lysine-rich fraction prepared by chromatography on Amberlite IRC-50 [31] was a very potent inhibitor of RNA polymerase activity in prepara-

TABLE 3

Effects of different thymus histones on activity of thymus RNA polymerase*

Histone fraction added	Specific activity of RNA ppt. after uptake of			
	C^{14}– UTP		C^{14}– ATP	
	cpm/mg	% of control	cpm/mg	% of control
A. Control, no histone added	102.3	100	65.7	100
From IRC–50 column				
Ia (lysine–rich)	41.7	40.8		
Ib (lysine–rich)	42.0	41.1	26.3	40.0
IIb	54.4	53.2	57.7	87.8
III	73.8	72.1	69.0	105
IV (arginine–rich)	77.3	75.6	73.2	111
F1 extracted in 5% PCA, undialyzed	91.7	89.6	60.4	91.9
F1 extracted in 5% PCA, dialyzed			59.5	90.6
F1 (lys:arg. 13:1) after guanidination substituting 31% lysine epsilon amino groups†	47.1	46.0	23.5	35.8
F3 (extracted in ethanol–HCl)	22.8	22.3	50.7	77.2
B. From carboxymethylcellulose column				
Control, no histone added	55.0	100	29.0	100
F3 peak	19	34.5	9	31.0
C. Control, no histone added	102	100	106	100
F1 peak (lysine:arg. = 14.2)	92	90.2	73	68.9

* From Faulkner et al.[29].
† We are indebted to Dr. R.B. Merrifield of the Rockefeller Institute for the preparation of this substituted histone.

tions from pea seedlings (and Escherichia coli). The conflict has now been resolved after we tested the very same histone preparations on the thymus RNA polymerase. (These histone fractions were generously given to us by Dr. Kenneth Murray of Stanford University.) The results are included in Table 3. As far as the activity of these lysine-rich histones is concerned, they agree completely with the findings of Huang and Bonner for the RNA polymerase of the pea seedling. Peaks Ia and Ib, both lysine rich, are powerful inhibitors of RNA synthesis in the thymus.

It follows that the inhibitory capabilities of different thymus histones, when added to RNA-synthesizing systems, cannot be simply attributed to their lysine or arginine contents. Other factors (mode of isolation, surface charge distribution, secondary structural modifications induced by acids or by drying, aggregation between different histones in solution, differences in coiling due to differences in proline content) may all play a role in determining the net inhibitory effects when histones combine with DNA in the RNA polymerase assay.

EFFECTS OF HISTONES ON CHROMOSOME STRUCTURE

Another test system of considerable interest is the lampbrush chromosome (of amphibian oocytes) which, because of its enormous size and intense activity in RNA synthesis, affords unique opportunities to relate structure and function in a highly developed chromosome.

Lampbrush chromosomes from newt oocytes are illustrated in Figure 9. Their structure is now understood, largely as a result of the brilliant work of Callan and Lloyd [32] and of Gall [33]. The chromosome consists of two long, DNA-containing strands, tightly coiled in some regions (centromeres) and loosely extended at hundreds of sites along the chromosome to form loops which project outward at right angles to the chromosomal axis. The work of Gall and Callan [34] and Izawa, Allfrey, and Mirsky [35], shows that the loops are active sites of RNA synthesis.

Izawa, Allfrey, and Mirsky reported that RNA synthesis in the loops is completely suppressed by the addition of actinomycin D to suspensions of isolated Triturus viridescens oocytes. When this occurs, the changes in loop morphology are striking. Figure 10A shows that the loops have largely disappeared (retracted) after exposure to the antibiotic. A much less effective inhibitor of RNA synthesis, N-β-aminoethyl-actinomycin C3, was also tested. The presence of this modified actinomycin did not cause a corresponding retraction of the loops (Fig. 10B).

In other experiments, puromycin was added to oocytes to inhibit chromosomal protein synthesis, but this did not appreciably modify the appearance of the loops.

It seems clear that by combining with DNA, actinomycin D not only blocked the synthesis of RNA but also caused a condensation of the characteristic extended loop structure.

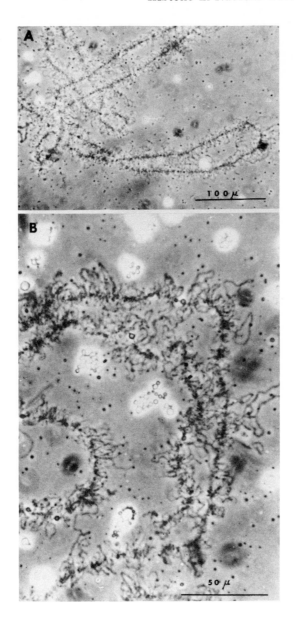

Fig. 9.—Lampbrush chromosomes from oocytes of Triturus viridescens. (A) Low-power view showing pair of homologues joined at chiasmata. (B) Higher magnification showing the loops projecting from the main chromosomal axis. Autoradiographs of these structures after labeling with C^{14}-uridine shows heavy grain deposits over the loops (Gall and Callan [34], Izawa et al. [35]).

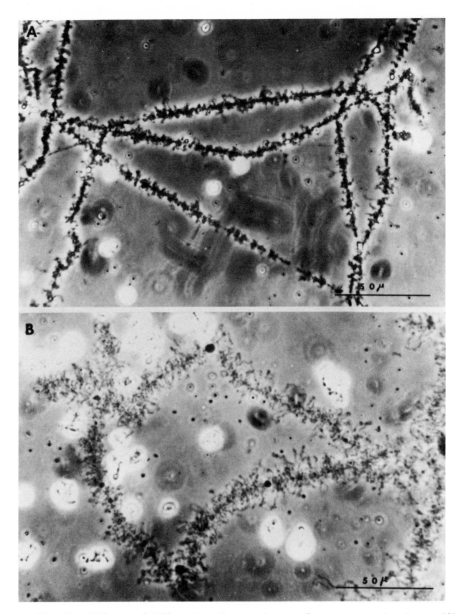

Fig. 10.—Effects of different actinomycins on chromosome structure. (A) View of lampbrush chromosomes after exposure to 2 µg/ml actinomycin D for 20 minutes at 16 C. Note disappearance of the loops. Autoradiographs (not presented) show that actinomycin D completely stops RNA synthesis in the loops. (B) View of chromosomes after 90 minutes of exposure to 2 µg/ml N-β-aminoethyl actinomycin C3. This compound does not block RNA synthesis. Note retention of the loops.

By analogy, this could be one mode of action of the histones. By combining with DNA to yield a condensed nucleohistone coil, they would serve to inhibit the activity of the DNA as a primer for RNA synthesis. To test this hypothesis, different histones were added directly to isolated lampbrush chromosomes. The F3 (arginine-rich) fraction caused retraction of the loops within 3 minutes (Fig. 11A). In contrast, the F1 histone preparation we tested did not induce a corresponding loss of structure; even after 15 minutes, more than half of the loops remained (Fig. 11B).

These results support the view that histones, by complexing with the DNA at active sites on the chromosome, cause it to contract or condense into a tight coil which is not active in RNA synthesis. It should be pointed out, however, that similar effects on lampbrush chromosome structure can be obtained with other polycations. For example, both D- and L-polylysine, cause loop retraction (Fig. 11C).

Recent tracer studies of lampbrush chromosomes have shown that the isolated chromosomes retain a capacity to synthesize RNA from the nucleoside triphosphates and from C^{14}-labeled nucleosides [36]. The RNA produced along the loops appears to be released in a structurally organized cluster of small nucleoli, arranged along a DNAase-sensitive fiber.

Summary and Conclusions

Experiments are described in which the addition of histones to suspensions of isolated calf thymus nuclei inhibited a number of their biosynthetic reactions, including the synthesis of RNA.

The selective removal of the histones with trypsin led to a marked stimulation of nuclear RNA synthesis. Much of the newly synthesized RNA appeared in the nuclear messenger RNA fraction.

The addition of different kinds of histones to nuclei or to an RNA polymerase preparation from calf thymus indicates that different histones differ greatly in their ability to inhibit the uptake of radioactive RNA precursors. At present, there is no simple, evident correlation between the degree of inhibition observed and the lysine or arginine contents of the particular histone fractions tested.

RNA synthesis in lampbrush chromosomes occurs on DNA-containing loops, which extend at right angles from the main axis of the chromosome. When actinomycin D combines with DNA in these chromosomes, RNA synthesis stops and the loops retract. The addition of histones to the isolated chromosomes also causes retraction of the loops.

The experimental findings in thymus nuclei and in isolated lampbrush chromosomes are consistent with the view that histones, by combining with DNA, cause it to assume a condensed state, no longer active as a primer in the synthesis of ribonucleic acids.

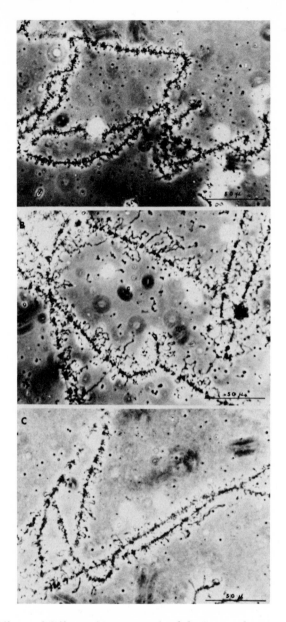

Fig. 11.—Effects of different histones and polylysine on chromosome structure. (A) View of isolated chromosomes exposed to 0.15 μg/ml F3 histone fractions (arginine-rich) from calf thymus nuclei. Note retraction of loops. (B) Chromosomes after 15 minutes of exposure to equal concentration of F1 fraction (lysine-rich). Note that the loops are still present. (C) View of chromosomes exposed to poly-L-lysine (0.15 μg/ml) for 2 minutes at 16 C. Note that many of the loops have retracted.

REFERENCES

1. Allfrey, V. G., Littau, V. C., and Mirsky, A. E., J. Cell Biol., In press, 1963.

2. Allfrey, V. G., Mirsky, A. E., and Osawa, S., J. Gen. Physiol., 40, 451, 1957.

3. Osawa, S., Allfrey, V. G., and Mirsky, A. E., J. Gen. Physiol., 40, 491, 1957.

4. McEwen, B. S., Allfrey, V. G., and Mirsky, A. E., J. Biol. Chem., 238, 758, 1963.

5. Allfrey, V. G., and Mirsky, A. E., Proc. Natl. Acad. Sci. U. S. A., 43, 821, 1957.

6. Breitman, T., and Webster, G. C., Nature, 184, 637, 1959.

7. Sibatani, A., de Kloet, S. R., Allfrey, V. G., and Mirsky, A. E., Proc. Natl. Acad. Sci. U. S. A., 48, 471, 1962.

8. Allfrey, V. G., and Mirsky, A. E., Proc. Natl. Acad. Sci. U. S. A., 48, 1590, 1962.

9. Allfrey, V. G., Proc. Natl. Acad. Sci. U. S. A., 40, 881, 1954.

10. Wang, T.-Y., Biochim. Biophys. Acta, 49, 108, 239, 1961.

11. Allfrey, V. G., and Mirsky, A. E., Proc. Natl. Acad. Sci. U. S. A., 44, 981, 1958.

12. Campagne, R. N., Allfrey, V. G., and Mirsky, A. E., Unpublished observations, 1963.

13. Tamm, I., Folkers, K., and Shunk, C. H., J. Bact., 72, 54, 1956.

14. Reich, E., Franklin, R. M., Shatkin, A. J., and Tatum, E. L., Science, 134, 556, 1961.

15. de Kloet, S. R., Allfrey, V. G., and Mirsky, A. E., Unpublished observations, 1962.

16. Barnett, L. B., Frens, G., and Koningsberger, V. V., Biochem. J., 84, 89P, 1962.

17. Mirsky, A. E., and Ris, H., Nature, 163, 666, 1949.

18. Allfrey, V. G., In O. Lindberg (ed.), Functional Biochemistry of Cell Structures (Oxford: Pergamon Press, 1961).

19. Allfrey, V. G., In The Molecular Basis of Neoplasia (Austin: Univ. of Texas Press, 1962), p. 58.

20. Person, P., and Fine, A., Science, 132, 43, 1960.

21. Allfrey, V. G., Meudt, R., Hopkins, J. W., and Mirsky, A. E., Proc. Natl. Acad. Sci. U. S. A., 47, 907, 1961.

22. Allfrey, V. G., and Mirsky, A. E., Trans. N. Y. Acad. Sci., Ser. 2, 21, 3, 1958.

23. Frenster, J. H., Allfrey, V. G., and Mirsky, A. E., Biochim. Biophys. Acta, 47, 130, 1961.

24. Johns, E. W., and Butler, J. A. V., Biochem. J., 82, 15, 1962.

25. Johns, E. W., Phillips, D. M. P., Simson, P., and Butler, J. A. V., Biochem. J., 77, 631, 1960.

26. Allfrey, V. G., Littau, V. C., and Mirsky, A. E., Proc. Natl. Acad. Sci. U. S. A., 49, 414, 1963.

27. Daly, M. M., and Mirsky, A. E., J. Gen. Physiol., 38, 405, 1955.

28. Huang, R.-c.C., and Bonner, J. Proc. Natl. Acad. Sci. U.S.A., 48, 1216, 1962.

29. Faulkner, R. M., Allfrey, V. G., and Mirsky, A. E., Manuscript in preparation, 1963.

30. Kunitz, M., J. Gen. Physiol., 30, 291, 1947.

31. Rasmussen, P. S., Murray, K., and Luck, J. M., Biochemistry, 1, 79, 1962.

32. Callan, H. G., and Lloyd, L., Phil. Trans. Roy. Soc. London, Ser. B, 243, 135, 1960.

33. Gall, J. G., In W. D. McElroy and B. Glass (eds.)The Chemical Basis of Development (Baltimore: Johns Hopkins Press, 1958), p. 103.

34. Gall, J. G., and Callan, H. G., Proc. Natl. Acad. Sci. U. S. A., 48, 562, 1962.

35. Izawa, M., Allfrey, V. G., and Mirsky, A. E., Proc. Natl. Acad. Sci. U. S. A., 49, 544, 1963.

36. Izawa, M., and Mirsky, A. E., Proc. Natl. Acad. Sci. U. S. A., in press, 1963.

Daniel Billen
and Lubomir S. Hnilica

INHIBITION OF DNA SYNTHESIS BY HISTONES

Stedman and Stedman [1] suggested that the histones may act as regulators of gene activity. More recently, Huang and Bonner [2] reported that histones influence the ability of DNA to function as primer for RNA synthesis in vitro. Allfrey et al. [3] came to a similar conclusion from experiments in which histones in intact calf thymus nuclei were digested with trypsin; RNA synthesis substantially increased. The histone suppressed RNA was in the messenger RNA fraction. This study of the effect of histones on DNA synthesis in vitro was motivated by an interest in their possible role as regulators of the DNA and RNA synthesis.

Partially purified DNA polymerase preparation used in these studies was prepared from Escherichia coli strain $15T^- A^- U^-$, as described elsewhere [4]. The standard reaction mixture for assay of DNA-synthesizing activity consisted of: deCTP, deATP, and deGTP, 5 mμmoles each; MgC1$_2$, 1 μmole; 2-mercaptoethanol, 0.15 μmole; 5 μg calf thymus DNA; 0.02 ml M glycine buffer (pH 9.2); and DNA polymerase (17.5 μg protein). Synthesis of DNA was followed by incorporation of label from (^{3}H)-thymidine triphosphate (TTP) into the cold acid-insoluble fraction. To each reaction mixture was added 2.5 mμmoles of (^{3}H)-TTP (S.A. = 7,000 counts per minute per mμmole). The final volume was 0.2 ml. The complete reaction mixture was incubated at 37 C for 10 minutes. Radioactivity of the cold acid-insoluble precipitate was determined by a paper-disc method of scintillation counting [4]. Calf thymus histone and the histone fractions F1, F2a, F2b, and F3 were obtained as described by Johns and Butler [5] and by Hnilica and Busch [6]. The purity of the histone fractions was controlled by amino acid analysis, N-terminal amino acid analysis, and by electrophoresis in starch gels. Histones, DNA, and DNA polymerase solutions were in 0.02 M phosphate buffer, pH 7.4. (The substitution of 0.01 M sodium acetate buffer, pH 7.2, did not change the qualitative effects but did influence the quantitation.)

The influence of whole calf thymus histones on DNA replication in vitro is illustrated in Table 1. The data show that, at sufficiently high concentrations, DNA synthesis was completely suppressed. Greater

TABLE 1

The effects of histone fractions on the in vitro synthesis of DNA

Rate of DNA synthesis in mμmoles of nucleotide incorporated in 10 min.

System*	Histone fraction added					
	None	WhH†	F1	F2a	F2b	F3
Complete	0.900	--	--	--	--	--
Complete plus 1 μg histone	--	0.685	0.785	0.830	0.826	0.819
Complete plus 10 μg histone	--	0.391	0.074	0.592	0.414	0.000
Complete plus 40 μg histone	--	0.010	0.043	0.007	0.027	0.032
Some characteristics of histone fractions						
Lys:arg	--	1.7	12.0	0.9	2.1	0.8
Basic: acidic amino acids	--	1.9	5.5	1.8	2.0	1.7

*17.5 μg (protein) of DNA polymerase preparation was used with 5 μg of calf thymus DNA as primer.
†WhH, whole histone, is the abbreviation used for the unfractionated sample of calf thymus histone.

than 50% inhibition was observed when the ratio of the weight of histone to DNA was 2:1.

The four fractions derived from the whole histone were capable of preventing DNA replication when they were present in concentrations of 20 μg or more (ratio > 4:1 of histone to DNA). However, a differential effectiveness was found at concentrations below 20 μg. Table 1 shows that 10 μg of fractions F1 and F3 completely inhibited DNA synthesis. This is to be compared with the partial inhibition produced at this concentration by the whole histone and fractions F2a and F2b. At 5 μg per reaction vessel, only fractions F1 and F3 inhibited this system (a ratio of histone to DNA of 1:1). To determine whether the basic amino acid composition of the two fractions could be the basis for correlation of the limited specificity observed, their amino acid compositions were

TABLE 2

Amino acid composition of calf thymus histone fractions

Amino acid	F1	F2a	F2b	F3
Lysine	30.0	10.6	16.4	10.2
Histidine	–	2.5	2.7	2.2
Arginine	2.5	11.6	7.9	13.1
Asp. Acid	2.2	5.7	5.2	6.3
Threonine	6.0	5.3	6.7	6.3
Serine	7.5	3.2	9.3	5.0
Glut. Acid	3.7	7.8	8.3	8.4
Proline	8.6	2.7	2.3	4.9
Glycine	6.1	13.0	7.6	6.6
Alanine	21.9	10.0	11.2	13.4
Valine	5.3	7.1	7.0	6.1
Methionine	–	0.9	1.3	0.6
Isoleucine	1.3	4.5	5.1	5.0
Leucine	4.0	10.2	5.9	8.2
Tyrosine	0.4	2.9	2.0	1.6
Phenylalanine	0.6	1.5	0.9	2.9
ϵ-N–Methyl–Lysine	–	0.5	–	–

compared. No simple correlation is evident between inhibition of DNA synthesis and the ratios of lysine to arginine or of basic to acid amino acids (Tables 1 and 2).

Increasing the concentration of DNA brought about an almost complete reversal of the inhibition of DNA synthesis by histone. Figure 1 compares the effects of increasing DNA concentration on F3 and F2a inhibition. The more selective inhibition by F3 is reflected by the requirement for a greater quantity of DNA for reversal of inhibition. In all experiments the in vitro inhibition was accompanied by formation of a fibrous nucleo-histone precipitate and loss of ultraviolet-absorbing material, which paralleled the decline in DNA synthesis (Fig. 2). Similar inhibitory effects

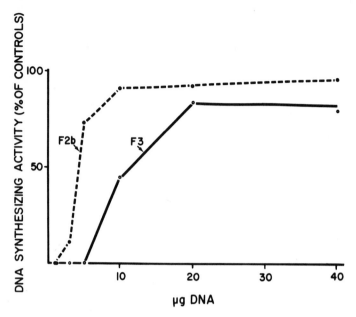

Fig. 1.—Inhibition of DNA synthesis by histone, and its reversal by DNA; 10 μg of the histone fractions was present in each assay except the controls. Controls were run at each DNA level, but without added histone.

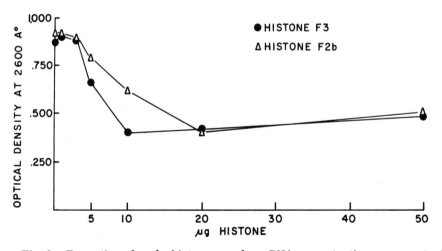

Fig. 2.—Formation of nucleohistone complex. DNA concentration was constant (5 μg/0.2 ml). Conditions were the same as described for the DNA polymerase assay.

of histone fractions were observed when denatured calf thymus (100 C for 10 minutes, followed by rapid cooling) or homologous Escherichia coli DNA was substituted as primer.

At 40 μg per reaction vessel, the following nonhistone proteins were tested and found to be without effect on the in vitro system: bovine albumin (Nutritional Biochemical Corp.); bovine gamma globulin (Fr. II, Pentex Labs.); human gamma globulin (kindly supplied by Dr. B. Jirgensons); B_1-metal-combining globulin (Cutter Labs.); egg albumin (5 x recrystallized, Pentex Labs.); bovine betalactoglobulin (Pentex Labs.); and calf globin prepared in the laboratory. Lysozyme showed some inhibition at higher concentrations and polylysine was found almost four times as active as any of the histone fractions. Lysine and arginine (10 μmoles) were without effect. This data indicate that not only positive charge but also some minimal size and probably the primary and secondary structures of the interacting protein molecules are important for the formation of nucleohistone complex. Indeed, as shown in Figure 3, the tryptic digestion at 0 C of the F1 and F2b histone fractions resulted in a loss of their inhibitory effect; amounts equivalent to 10 μg of undigested proteins are completely inactive after one hour of exposure to trypsin. When the amount of digest per reaction vessel was increased to 20 μg, some inhibitory activity, still detectable after one hour of digestion, was completely abolished in 120 minutes of trypsinisation (Fig. 3). The ability

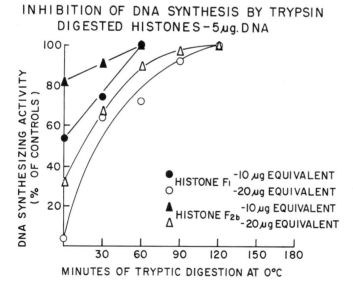

Fig. 3.—Inhibition of DNA synthesis in vitro by trypsin-digested histones; 5 μg of DNA was used for each assay. The tryptic digest was equivalent to 10 or 20 μg of undigested histone in each assay.

of histone fractions to form fibrous precipitate with DNA (nucleohistone) was completely lost after the first 30 minutes of digestion.

To investigate the minimal size of histone molecules required for interaction with DNA resulting in the inhibition of the DNA polymerase reaction, samples of the F2b, the least composite and best defined fraction of mammalian histones (molecular weight, 22,000), were incubated with trypsin in 0.1 M ammonium bicarbonate at 0 C. Parts of the reaction mixture were taken at 10, 20, 30, 45, and 60 minutes; the tryptic activity was arrested by adding trypsin inhibitor (soybean, California Biochemical). After lyophilization, the samples were analyzed by electrophoresis in starch gel, by paper electrophoresis, and by ultracentrifugation.

Trypsin at low temperature induces rapid breaks in the histone molecule. That the fragments are large is suggested by their position on starch gel and by their stainability with Amido black 10B. The starch-gel electrophoretic pattern for the undigested histone fraction F2b, as well as for the digested samples, is shown in Figure 4. The original single

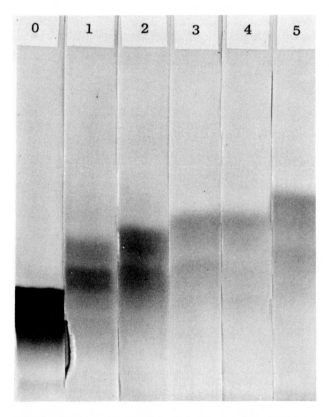

Fig. 4.—Electrophoresis in starch gel of trypsin-digested histone F2b; Amido black 10B stain; starch gels were made in 0.01 N HCl and run horizontally. 0 = undigested sample; 1 = 10 minutes, 2 = 20 minutes, 3 = 30 minutes, 4 = 45 minutes and 5 = 60 minutes of digestion by trypsin at 0 C.

band of the F2b fraction is split by the action of trypsin into four bands, electrophoretically faster than the original F2b fraction. An essentially identical picture was obtained by electrophoresis on paper. After 10 minutes of digestion, five or six ninhydrin-positive spots were detected. The intensity of fast-moving spots increased with time of digestion, indicating that trypsin first produced several large fragments, which were further split into shorter peptides. Large fragments are obviously still active in inhibiting the DNA synthesis in vitro, because the decrease in their concentration was almost parallel to the increase of newly synthesized DNA.

Data obtained by sedimentation in the ultracentrifuge further support this conclusion. As Figure 5 shows, fragments produced by short tryptic digestion are quite large and sediment is at 50, 740 rpm. The heterogeneity of the sedimenting material increases, and the concentration of large fragments decreases, with time of tryptic digestion. Some low-molecular material, seen at the meniscus, makes numerical evaluation of the sedimentation constant very inaccurate. The S value of calf thymus F2b histone exposed to trypsin increases immediately from 1.12 to 2.80,

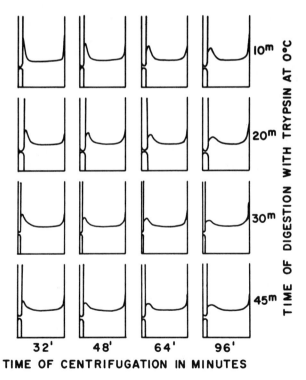

Fig. 5.—Sedimentation of the trypsin-digested samples of histone F2b; time of digestion 10, 20, 30, and 45 minutes. 1% solutions in 0.2 M potassium acetate buffer pH 4.2. Speed 50, 740 rpm.

a value that persists for the whole time of digestion. A formation of trypsin-histone complex is possible.

The DNA-histone interaction, which is based on electrostatic forces between phosphate groups of the nucleic acid and between the free amino groups of histones, is apparently structure dependent. The minimal size of a polycationic molecule still sufficient for establishing a firm electrostatic bond with DNA is not known, but as can be concluded from the presented data, the F2b fraction is close to this minimal required size, inasmuch as even a short exposure to trypsin at low temperature decreases the binding capacity of F2b histone rapidly. This decrease is paralleled by the loss of the inhibitory effect on the DNA synthesis in vitro.

Summary

DNA synthesis in vitro is strongly inhibited by histones, apparently because of the aggregation and precipitation of DNA in the form of DNP. Different histone fractions show some specificity. The very lysine-rich F1 and the arginine-rich F3 fractions were more effective than the slightly lysine-rich fractions F2a and F2b. The lysine and arginine content of F3 fraction is very similar to the lysine and arginine content of the F2a fraction. However, these two fractions are quite different in their inhibition of DNA synthesis in vitro. Some specific arrangement of the basic residues seem to be essential, because the tryptic digestion destroyed the inhibitory activity rapidly.

Results obtained with polylysine, with nonhistone proteins, and with timed tryptic digestion of F2b histone suggest that the basic amino acid residues must be placed and available at distinct distances or points along the DNA molecule to form the nucleohistone complex.

Acknowledgment

The authors wish to acknowledge the skillful technical assistance of Mrs. G. M. Willard, Mr. G. N. Jorgensen, and Mr. C. W. Taylor. This project was supported in part by grant AT-(40-1)-2695 from the Atomic Energy Commission and by grants from the United States Public Health Service.

REFERENCES

1. Stedman, E., and Stedman, E., Nature, 166, 780, 1950.

2. Huang, R.-c. C., and Bonner, J., Proc. Natl. Acad. Sci. U. S. A., 48, 1216, 1962.

3. Allfrey, V. G., Littau, V. C., and Mirsky, A. E., Proc. Natl. Acad. Sci. U. S. A., 49, 414, 1963.

4. Billen, D., Biochim. Biophys. Acta, 68, 342, 1963.

5. Johns, E. W., and Butler, J. A. V., Biochem. J., 82, 15, 1962.

6. Hnilica, L. S., and Busch, H., J. Biol. Chem., 238, 918, 1963.

Samuel B. Weiss
and C. Fred Fox

THE EFFECT OF POLYAMINES ON THE
DNA-DEPENDENT SYNTHESIS OF RNA

Enzymes that catalyze the DNA-primed synthesis of RNA are widely distributed in nature. The presence of RNA polymerase in mammalian [1, 2], plant [3], and bacterial extracts [4-7] has been well documented. The reaction catalyzed by this enzyme is summarized below.

$$nATP + nUTP + nCTP + nGTP \xrightarrow[Mn^{++}]{DNA} (ApUpCpGp)n + 4nPPi$$

All the experiments described in this report were conducted with an enzyme preparation from Micrococcus lysodeikticus, which was purified approximately 500-fold and had a $280/260$ mμ absorbance ratio of approximately 1.74.

This enzyme catalyzes the assembly of ribonucleotides into ribopolynucleotides under various conditions and with different primers. These different reactions may be listed in an arbitrary fashion as shown in Table 1. In the presence of enzyme and the appropriate cofactors, RNA synthesis occurs under the direction of a DNA or RNA primer, and also with no primer [8]. Native or denatured DNA serve as active primers in the RNA polymerase system. Two different kinds of RNA may be formed with DNA primers: (1) In the presence of all four ribonucleotides, ribopolymers are assembled that are complementary in base composition and in base sequence to the DNA primer [9]. (2) In the presence of a single ribonucleotide, the reaction leads to the formation of an RNA homopolymer that contains only a single base [10]. Both reactions are catalyzed by the same enzyme, and although the conditions for synthesis are similar in some respects, they differ in a number of ways. One difference is that a polyamine of low molecular weight is required for maximal synthesis when native DNA primes the formation of complementary RNA. In none of the other reactions listed in Table 1 has a polyamine requirement been observed.

TABLE 1

Reactions catalyzed by M. lysodeikticus RNA polymerase

Primer	No. of nucleotides present during reaction	Nature of RNA product	
		Base composition	Dissociated or complexed with primer
Native DNA	4	complementary	dissociated
Native DNA	1	homopolymer	dissociated
Denatured DNA	4	complementary	partially complexed
Denatured DNA	1	homopolymer	dissociated
RNA (natural and synthetic)	4	complementary	complexed
None	1	homopolymer	

The synthesis of complementary RNA requires all four ribonucleoside triphosphates, a divalent metal ion, DNA, and enzyme. In the absence of one of these components, no appreciable polymerization occurs (Table 2). Table 2 also indicates that the addition of spermidine significantly enhances the amount of CMP^{32} incorporated into RNA. RNA polymerase also catalyzes the exchange of inorganic PP with the two terminal phosphates of ribonucleoside triphosphates [11, 12]. This exchange reaction requires nucleic acid, a divalent metal ion, and at least one ribonucleotide. Although polyamines enhance RNA synthesis, organic cations have not been observed to affect the PP exchange reaction.

In the presence of a DNA primer, manganese ion, only one ribonucleoside triphosphate, polymerase catalyzes the assembly of an RNA homopolymer (Table 3). This reaction was first demonstrated by Chamberlin and Berg [10]. The addition of more than one ribonucleotide inhibits polymerization, but when a full complement of nucleotides is present, normal synthesis occurs once more. Table 3 also indicates that the polymerization of a single ribonucleotide is inhibited, and not enhanced, by the addition of spermidine. This inhibition is found for either poly A synthesis when calf thymus DNA is used as primer, or poly C synthesis with Pseudomonas DNA primer. In the latter case, synthesis may be repressed by the addition of pancreatic RNAase. Polyamines have been reported to partially protect RNA degradation from the action of RNAase [13]. Since the addition of spermidine inhibits poly C formation, it ap-

TABLE 2

Requirements for the four-nucleotide, DNA-primed
reaction

Additions	CMP^{32} incorporated
	mµmoles
Complete	10.3
Omit ATP	<0.2
Omit UTP	<0.2
Omit GTP	0.5
Omit Mn^{++}	<0.1
Omit DNA	<0.1
Omit spermidine	7.6
RNAase	0.4
DNAase	0.2

TABLE 3

Requirements for the single-nucleotide, DNA-primed reaction

Primer: calf thymus DNA substrate: ATP^{32} experiment 1		Primer: P. fluorescens DNA substrate: CTP^{32} experiment 2	
Additions	AMP^{32} incorporated	Additions	CMP^{32} incorporated
	mµmoles		mµmoles
Complete	63.7	Complete	5.2
GTP	32.3	ATP	1.3
GTP, CTP	1.6	ATP, GTP	0.6
GTP, CTP, UTP	24.5	ATP, GTP, UTP	27.6
Spermidine	44.8	Spermidine	3.9
Omit Mn^{++}	1.3	Omit Mn^{++}	<0.1
Omit DNA	0	Omit DNA	0
RNAase	74.8	RNAase	<0.1
DNAase	20.7	DNAase	0.7

pears unlikely that the polyamine stimulation of complementary RNA synthesis is due to the inhibition of trace quantities of RNAase that may be present in the reaction system.

RNA polymerase will also utilize RNA primers to direct the synthesis of de novo RNA [14, 15]. Initially, we demonstrated that RNA homopolymers could prime the synthesis of complementary RNA molecules. Thus polycytidylate primed the assembly of polyguanylate, and polyadenylate primed the synthesis of polyuridylate. More recently, we have shown that natural RNA's will also serve as primers in this system. Table 4 gives the base composition of various infectious RNA's. Analysis of the products formed in the presence of these primers and a full complement of ribonucleotides, catalyzed by RNA polymerase, indicates that the RNA's synthesized are also complementary in base composition (Table 4). The RNA-directed synthesis of RNA does not require polyamines. In this reaction, organic cations may inhibit synthesis slightly or have no effect.

Our evidence to date suggests that only one enzyme is responsible for the various types of RNA synthesis discussed above. Nevertheless, only under certain conditions do we find an enhancement of RNA formation with polyamines, that is, when native DNA serves as primer and all four ribonucleotides are simultaneously present. The rate and extent of RNA synthesis is significantly reduced in the absence of added spermine when the reaction is primed by native DNA (Fig. 1). If spermine is added after

TABLE 4

Base composition of viral RNA-primed product
(limited reaction: 5 minutes)

Base	Base proportions: mole %							
	TYMV RNA			TMV RNA			MSØ2 RNA	
	$(A)^*$	$(B)^\dagger$	Primed product	$(A)^*$	$(B)^\dagger$	Primed product	$(B)^\dagger$	Primed product
G	17	19	39	25	27	18	27	27
A	23	20	19	30	26	30	22	27
C	38	39	23	19	18	25	25	24
U	22	22	19	26	29	27	26	22

* Reported values.
† Determined values.

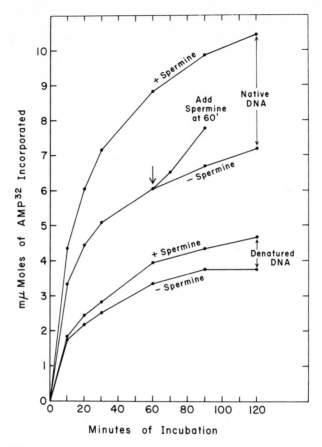

Fig. 1.—Time course of DNA-dependent RNA synthesis in the absence and presence of spermine.

synthesis has started to level off (in the reaction where polyamine is omitted), an increased rate of nucleotide polymerization is found once again. The exact interpretation of this phenomenon is still unclear. Figure 1 also demonstrates that heat-denatured DNA is less efficient for RNA synthesis than native DNA. The addition of polyamines to the reaction mixture when denatured DNA serves as primer only slightly alters the extent of RNA formation.

A number of different organic cations of low molecular weight stimulate the native DNA-primed reaction (Table 5). Spermine, spermidine, putrescine, and cadaverine are active in this system, optimal effects with each of these compounds being obtained at different molar concentrations. At very high concentrations, a number of these polyamines inhibit synthesis since they induce precipitation of the DNA primer. Table 5 also indicates that polyamines of high molecular weight, such as calf thymus histone, protamine, and polylysine, have no effect at the relatively low

TABLE 5

The effect of various polyamines on RNA synthesis

Additions	GMP^{32} incorporated
	mμmoles
None	7.80
Spermidine (0.4 μmoles)	10.35
Spermidine (1.0 μmoles)	11.30
Spermine (0.1 μmoles)	9.78
Spermine (0.2 μmoles)	14.30
Putrescine (2.0 μmoles)	8.96
Putrescine (10.0 μmoles)	13.50
Cadaverine (2.0 μmoles)	8.75
Cadaverine (10.0 μmoles)	9.56
Calf thymus histone (20 μg)	7.98
Protamine (20 μg)	7.84
Polylysine (10 μg)	7.34

concentrations used. At higher concentrations, DNA precipitation results in reduced synthesis.

The polyamine stimulation reported here occurs with a variety of native DNA primers (Table 6). The DNA's tested were derived from different species and varied widely in their base composition. In each case, the inclusion of spermidine in the reaction mixture enhanced the amount of ribopolynucleotide formed by about 35-50%. The polyamine stimulation cannot, therefore, be attributed to DNA's rich in a particular base, but seems to be a general property of the reaction system itself.

TABLE 6

The effect of spermidine with various DNA primers
(4 NTP reaction)

Primer DNA	Spermidine	Polynucleotide synthesized
		mμmoles
Calf thymus	+	31.5
	–	21.5
Rat liver	+	33.3
	–	24.2
Bacteriophage T2	+	35.4
	–	22.3
Bacteriophage T4	+	16.0
	–	10.9
Salmon sperm	+	42.9
	–	32.8
Sea urchin sperm	+	28.1
	–	21.7
E. coli	+	34.6
	–	25.0
S. marcescens	+	33.0
	–	24.2
P. fluorescens	+	42.9
	–	30.2
A. aerogenes	+	37.2
	–	27.4
M. lysodeikticus	+	31.1
	–	22.1

Discussion

Of the various reactions catalyzed by RNA polymerase that result in RNA synthesis, only one is stimulated to any significant extent primarily by polyamines—the four-ribonucleotide reaction carried out in the presence of native DNA. When RNA polymerase catalyzes the formation of an RNA homopolymer or when RNA primes more of itself, no enhancement of the polymerization process has resulted from the addition of organic cations. When stimulation is observed, organic cations of low molecular weight are active, whereas macromolecular polyamines are without effect.

Various polyamines have been shown to bind readily with polynucleotides. In general, nucleic acid-polyamine complexes appear more resistant to nuclease degradation and demonstrate a somewhat higher degree of secondary structure as measured by helix-coil temperature transition studies [16]. The latter phenomenon occurs primarily with DNA's rich in adenine and thymine [17]. These properties of nucleic acid-polyamine complexes could account, in part, for the enhanced synthesis of RNA reported here. However, it is possible that organic cations serve another function in the RNA polymerase reaction, especially since our preparations of enzyme and primer appear to be relatively free in nucleases, and also because the polyamine stimulation occurs with DNA primers rich in guanine and cytosine as well as those high in adenine and thymine. One possible function of polyamines in this system might be to enhance the release of newly formed RNA from its double-stranded DNA template. In the absence of added polyamine, the depressed rate of RNA synthesis could be due to DNA-RNA complexes that dissociate less readily than when organic cations are present. Although speculations of this kind are attractive, we have not been able to detect the formation of DNA-RNA hybrids during synthesis, either in the absence or presence of polyamines.

Acknowledgments

This investigation was supported in part by funds from the Joseph and Helen Regenstein Foundation.

REFERENCES

1.   Weiss, S. B., and Gladstone, L., J. Am. Chem. Soc., 81, 4118, 1959.

2.   Weiss, S. B., Proc. Natl. Acad. Sci. U. S. A., 46, 1020, 1960.

3.   Huang, R.-c. C., Maheshwari, N., and Bonner, J., Biochem. Biophys. Res. Commun.,3, 689, 1960.

4.   Stevens, A., Biochem. Biophys. Res. Commun., 3, 15, 1960.

5.   Hurwitz, J., Breslar, A., and Diringer, R., Biochem. Biophys. Res. Commun., 3, 15, 1960.

6.   Weiss, S. B., J. Biol. Chem., 236, PC18, 1961.

7.   Ochoa, S., Burma, O. P., Kruger, H., and Weill, J. D., Proc. Natl. Acad. Sci. U. S. A., 47, 670, 1961.

8.   Fox, C. F., Robinson, W. S., and Weiss, S. B., Fed. Proc.,22, 463, 1963.

9.   Geiduschek, E. P., Nakamoto, T., and Weiss, S. B., Proc. Natl. Acad. Sci. U. S. A., 47, 1405, 1961.

10.   Chamberlin, M., and Berg, P., Proc. Natl. Acad. Sci. U. S. A., 48, 81, 1962.

11.   Furth, J. J., Hurwitz, J., and Anders, M., J. Biol. Chem., 237, 2611,1962.

12.   Fox, C. F., and Weiss, S. B., J. Biol. Chem., in press, 1963.

13.   Tabor,H., Tabor, C. W., and Rosenthal, S. M., Ann. Rev. Biochem.,30, 579, 1961.

14.   Nakamoto, T., and Weiss, S. B., Proc. Natl. Acad. Sci. U. S. A., 48, 880, 1962.

15.   Krakow, J. S., and Ochoa, S., Proc. Natl. Acad. Sci. U. S. A., 49, 88, 1963.

16.   Mahler, H. R., Mehrotra, B. D., and Sharp, C. W., Biochem. Biophys. Res. Commun., 4, 79, 1961.

17.   Mandel, M., J. Mol. Biol., 5, 435, 1962.

R. Vendrely

THE ENZYMATIC DEGRADATION
OF NUCLEOHISTONES

In 1958, we reported [1] the effect of aseptic autolysis on the nucleo-histone of calf kidney. During the course of this autolysis, the nuclei become pycnotic (Fig. 1). From calf kidney that had undergone autolysis for 24 hours at 37 C, we isolated a material that behaved as, and had the expected chemical composition of, a nucleohistone. (N-P ratio 3.88, arginine 12%, lysine 15.6%, histidine 2.2%.) The essential differences between the nucleohistone isolated from this material and that from non-autolyzed tissue were physical; it had a lower viscosity and apparently a lower degree of polymerization.

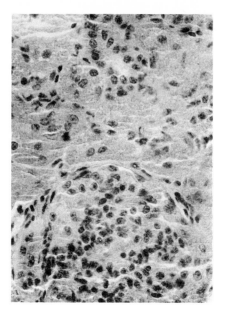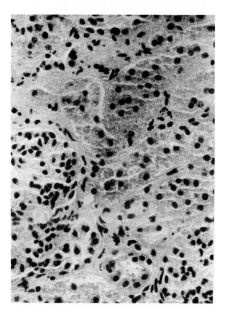

Fig. 1.—Sections of calf kidney, Feulgen counterstained with fast green. Left, control; right, pycnotic.

307

We believed that autolysis might make it possible to study the whole histone complex by facilitating isolation of components with different amino acid compositions from that of the total histone, therefore permitting demonstration of the heterogeneity of histones which has been shown only on the basis of the isolated products. Only a few attempts have been made [2-4] to fractionate the whole nucleohistone complex.

We first attempted to study the kinetics of this autolytic process with time and to compare the effects with those due to the action of purified enzymes known to act on DNA and histones. This would permit us to see if the effects of autolysis could be accounted for by the action of DNAase and proteases of the cell or whether it might represent the presence of a depolymerase for nucleohistone.

In these studies we used crude chromatin and nucleohistone isolated at low ionic strength from calf thymus instead of the whole tissue. In some experiments, chicken erythrocyte nuclei were used.

MATERIAL AND METHODS

Preparation of the chromatin. The nuclear material was obtained from ground calf thymus by resuspension and isolation in isotonic saline with citrate, followed by a number of washings in noncitrated saline.

Preparation of nucleohistone. Nucleohistone was prepared as follows. 100 g of calf thymus was homogenized in 500 ml of cold 0.14 M NaCl, pH 7, with sodium citrate. The mixture was centrifuged for 5 minutes at 4000 x g, the pellet washed three times with centrifugation successively at 3,000, 2,000, and 1,000 x g. After the last washing with distilled water the pellet was suspended in 1,000 ml of distilled water and dialyzed overnight in the cold.

The viscous dialysate was diluted to 4,000 ml by adding distilled water, and it was shaken for 6 hours in the cold. The insoluble fraction was removed by centrifugation for 2 hours at 45,000 x g (Spinco). The nucleohistone was precipitated by adding NaCl to make the solution 0.14 M. It was then resuspended in 800 ml of distilled water and redissolved by dialysis overnight against distilled water (2-4 C). The nucleohistone was diluted to 2,000 ml by adding distilled water and shaking in the cold. Clarification was achieved by centrifugation for 1 hour at 45,000 x g to eliminate any traces of insoluble material. The final dry product was obtained by lyophilization.

Aseptic autolysis of calf thymus chromatin. A crude chromatin was suspended in isotonic saline saturated with chloroform (100 ml per 25g of initial fresh thymus) and submitted to autolysis at 37 C in sterile flasks. The kinetics of the autolysis were followed over time by removing aliquots at various times and dialyzing them overnight in the cold against distilled water, which was changed frequently. An equal volume of the cold water

was then added and after shaking for 2 hours, the suspension was centrifuged at 6,000 x g and NaCl added to make the solution isotonic. The
precipitate so obtained was collected and washed with alcohol-acetone,
dried in vacuum, and held for analysis.

The fractions were analyzed for their phosphorous and DNA content,
and the major fractions for their amino acid composition by the Stein and
Moore method performed directly on a hydrolysate of the whole nucleohistone. The nucleotide composition of the DNA was also determined.

Action of purified enzymes on nucleohistone.   1. Action of DNAase.
The solution of nucleohistone described above was divided into 100 ml
fractions. To each fraction was added 1.2 mg of DNAase, (crystallized
GBI), and 0.15 mM $MgCl_2$. Aliquots were taken at various times and
saline added to precipitate any remaining intact nucleohistone. The
amount of nucleohistone was determined.

2. Action of chymotrypsin. To nucleohistone solutions as above,
50 μg per ml of chymotrypsin crystalline (Armour) and 0.05 mM calcium
chloride was added. At suitable intervals aliquots were removed, made
isotonic with NaCl and the amount of intact nucleohistone determined.
The phosphorous content of the samples were also determined.

Autolysis of isolated nuclei of chicken erythrocytes. Chicken erythrocytes free of cytoplasm were obtained by a procedure described earlier
[5]. They were submitted to aseptic autolysis in the same manner as the
crude chromatin.

Results

1. Autolysis experiments on crude chromatin of calf thymus. The
amount of material remaining after autolysis is plotted against time in
Figure 2. The results indicate a slow process and a resistance of the
nucleohistone complex to autolysis; 96% of the material was still precipitable after 4 hours, 38% after 18 hours, and 28% after 24 hours. To
determine whether a possible inhibitor of DNAase exists in this preparation, we also allowed DNAase to act on a homogenate of thymus. After
2 hours, the material exposed to DNAase was so extensively digested
that no nucleohistone could be isolated, even in a partly depolymerized
condition. Therefore it appears that this preparation contains no inhibitor of DNAase (pancreatic).

Precipitates obtained at different times of autolysis exhibited the
characteristics of a nucleohistone and were similar in composition. The
degree of polymerization, however, was lower. The final precipitates
appear in the form of short fibers and finally as a powder. The viscosity
of the solutions was progressively lower. For analyses see Table 3.

2. Action of DNAase. The action of the DNAase was very rapid at
37 C, as indicated by the curve in Figure 2. After 4 hours, the amount
of residue does not change. Analysis indicates that this residue consists

essentially of histones to which some resistant nucleotide fractions remain attached (Table 1).

3. <u>Action of chymotrypsin</u>. After 3-4 hours, no nucleohistone pre-

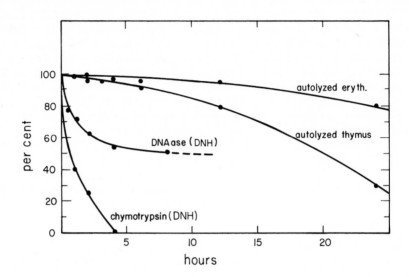

Fig. 2.—Effects of autolysis on crude chromatin of calf thymus and of erythrocytes and of enzymes on deoxyribonucleohistone. Amount remaining precipitable
as a function of time.

TABLE 1

Action of DNAase on calf thymus nucleohistone isolated at low ionic strength*

Hours of digestion	0	1/2	1	2	4	8
Dry weight, %	100	80	75.2	65.8	57.5	54.8
N : P	3.88	4.71	5.54	5.62	7.11	9.14
Digested DNA, %	0	36.2	46.6	56.0	67.2	73.0
Collected protein, %	100	94.7	94.3	85.3	80.3	79.3
$\dfrac{(A + T)}{(G + C)}$	1.30		1.31			1.10

*Analysis of the fractions precipitated in 0.14 M NaCl.

cipitate appeared in isotonic saline. After only 1 hour, 25% of the initial product could still be collected (Fig. 2). The phosphorous content of the samples at 1 or 2 hours showed a progressive increase (Table 2).

During the same time period, DNA progressively increased and was precipitable in 1 volume of alcohol. This DNA had small amounts of histone, which became less with time. The N-P ratio of this mixture reached a value of 2.10 after 20 hours.

4. <u>Autolysis of chicken erythrocyte nuclei</u>. The curve of autolysis obtained with chicken erythrocyte nuclei (Fig. 2) indicates a more resistant nucleohistone than the thymus nucleohistone. After 24 hours, 80% of the nucleohistone was still precipitable in isotonic saline.

5. <u>Examination of the products of 24-hour autolysis</u>. We studied a fraction that is not precipitated in isotonic saline and contains nucleo-histone of low molecular weight. To the supernatant from the above fraction the addition of dilute acetic acid to pH 4.7 caused the formation of a finely divided precipitate. This was purified by redissolution in bi-carbonate buffer and reprecipitation at pH 4.7. The product, representing 16% of the original nucleohistone, possessed an N-P ratio characteristic of nucleohistone, 3.75 (3.72 for the original nucleohistone), as well as a similar amino acid composition (Table 4).

Discussion

The results obtained by autolysis of chromatin or nucleohistone as compared to the effects of the purified enzymes, chymotrypsin, and DNA-ase indicate that two different processes are occurring. These enzymes

TABLE 2

Action of chymotrypsin on calf thymus nucleohistone isolated
at low ionic strength*

Hours of digestion	0	1	2	4
Dry weight, %	100	25.2	16	0
N : P	3.75	3.28	3.18	
Digested protein, %	0	52.9	71.7	100
Collected DNA, %	100	59.1	40.4	0

*Fractions precipitated in 0.14 M NaCl.

TABLE 3

Autolysis of calf thymus chromatinic material*

Duration of autolysis in hours	0	1	2	4	6	12	18	24
Dry weight, %	100	99.1	95.2	96.1	90.5	79	58.3	28.3
N : P	3.88	3.88		3.89	3.75	3.79		3.93
mg amino acids % of proteins								
lys	15.00	15.00		15.40		13.77		13.44
arg		12.50		12.60		12.19		12.68
hist		2.47		2.25		1.74		1.53
(A + T) / (G + C)	1.30							1.20

*Analysis of the fractions precipitated in 0.14 M NaCl.

act upon their specific substrate only and do not appear in the whole nucleohistone molecule. On the other hand, during autolysis, the nucleo-histone appears to be undergoing depolymerization without any other action. The point of attack on the nucleohistone is not evident from the studies undertaken so far.

The results of the experiment with whole homogenate and added DNAase indicate that DNAase was not partially inhibited. Van Lancker and Holtzer [6] reported data that suggested an inhibitor of DNAase in liver nuclei.

The nucleohistone of chicken erythrocytes appears to be more re-sistant than that of the thymus nucleohistone. This may be interpreted in two ways: (1) The enzymes concerned with autolysis are of cytoplasmic origin and are more abundant in the material extracted from calf thymus. (2) The enzymes are nuclear but are more abundant in thymus nuclei than in erytirocyte nuclei. It would be interesting to study the chromatin material from metabolically more active cells, such as liver or pancreas.

All the experiments seem to indicate that in the autolysis of nuclear material, the process is not a simple digestion by nuclease or proteolytic enzyme, but apparently a depolymerization of the nucleohistone. Further work is in process to study the electrophoretic properties of some of the nucleohistones isolated after autolysis. Fractionations with the ultra-centrifuge and ion-exchange columns are also in process. It is hoped

TABLE 4

Amino acid compositions of nucleohistone before and after 24 hours of autolysis

Amino acid	Moles per 100 atoms nucleic P		Grams residue per 100 g protein	
	Initial DNH	Final DNH	Initial DNH	Final DNH
Aspartic acid	17.3	15.7	5.14	5.50
Glutamic acid	27.4	33.2	9.02	11.90
Threonine	20.3	19.5	5.38	5.61
Serine	17.8	16.3	4.16	4.15
Proline	22.7	18.3	5.81	5.11
Alanine	40.5	41.0	8.11	8.83
Valine	22.4	21.0	5.83	5.97
Methionine	1.1	1.4	0.35	0.51
Isoleucine	14.2	15.7	4.13	4.97
Leucine	25.4	27.3	7.41	8.72
Tyrosine	9.0	8.0	3.63	3.44
Phenylalanine	6.9	6.6	2.56	2.61
Lysine	43.5	41.5	14.13	14.65
Arginine	31.5	28.0	11.12	12.50
Histidine	5.7	6.1	2.00	2.30

that further studies will permit use of the data from these studies to examine the mode of association of protein and DNA in the nucleohistone complex.

Summary

The effect of autolysis on nucleohistones of calf thymus and chick erythrocyte nuclei was studied. It compared with the effect of purified enzymes (DNAase and chymotrypsin). The autolytic process differs from the digestion with purified enzymes. It appears to involve a depolymerization of the complex without dissociation of the DNA and histone. The depolymerized products appear to be similar to the initial nucleohistones in composition and do not reveal any heterogeneity of the histones themselves.

Comment

Ermoleva has reported (Biokhim. 26, 897, 1961) that an enzyme contained in the rabbit appendix possesses the ability to release DNA from calf thymus chromatin. Separation of chromatin from the released DNA was accomplished by centrifugation at 10,000 x g; the chromatin sedimenting at this speed and ultraviolet-absorbing material remain in the supernatant. Bonner and Huang (unpublished) have repeated Ermoleva's experiment, using enzyme prepared from rabbit appendix. Not readily sedimented ultraviolet-absorbing material was released by the enzyme preparation, as described by Ermoleva. Melting profile studies have shown that the released material is, however, nucleohistone identical with the nucleohistone component of whole chromatin. The enzyme appears to degrade the chromosomal structure, preferentially releasing nucleohistone.

REFERENCES

1.   Vendrely, R., Alfert, M., Matsudaira, H., and Knobloch, A., Exptl. Cell Res., 14, 295, 1958.

2.   Chargaff, E., Crampton, C. F., and Lipshitz, R., Nature, 172, 289, 1953.

3.   Lucy, J. A., and Butler, J. A. V., Nature, 174, 32, 1954.

4.   Bakay, B., Kirschner, L. B., and Toennies, G., Biochem. Biophys. Res. Commun., 2, 459, 1960.

5.   Vendrely, R., and Vendrely, C., Experientia, 4, 434, 1948.

6.   Van Lancker, J. L., and Holtzer, R. L., Lab. Invest., 12, 102, 1963.

VI. ROLE OF HISTONES
IN DEVELOPMENT

 Ulrich Clever

PUFFING IN GIANT
CHROMOSOMES OF *DIPTERA* AND
THE MECHANISM OF ITS CONTROL

All cellular functions in adult organisms, as well as the processes concerned with embryonic or postembryonic development, depend on genic activity. Among the cells of each individual there is considerable diversity of function, structure, and chemical composition. They all, however, possess identical sets of genes. It follows that identical genomes do not necessarily lead to identical phenotypes or, in other words, that there must exist some mechanism which controls the phenotypic expression of the genes in the developmental processes. This might be explained by the assumption either of uniform genic activity in all cells and a cell-specific selection of the genic messages at the cytoplasmic level, or differential gene activity patterns. Tissue-specific differences in the activity patterns of genes have been clearly demonstrated in Dipteran giant chromosomes, and the possibility of influencing the activity of individual genes independently of the rest of the genome has been shown in many cases, particularly in microbial systems. There is no doubt, therefore, that differential gene activation is the chief cause of the different phenotypic expression of identical genomes under various conditions. Many of the problems of development, therefore, will ultimately be analyzed in terms of nucleocytoplasmic interactions and of mechanisms controlling gene activity.

In the past few years, studies on microorganisms have yielded important results concerning the mechanism of regulation of gene activity. The mechanisms discovered reversibly and permanently regulate the actual rate of synthetic gene activity. On the other hand, differentiation in higher organisms is, at least in many cases, more or less irreversible. It may be questioned whether it is feasible to assume the same mechanism for the control of gene activity in higher organisms as has been proposed for microorganisms. To attack this problem, it is necessary to have some knowledge of the mode of behavior of gene activity in the course of animal development and of the relationships between alterations of gene activities and the correlated developmental processes. Giant chromosomes of Diptera offer a very suitable object for studies along these lines, because it is possible to distinguish morphologically active chromosomal loci from inactive ones. The results of recent studies on giant chromosomes will be reviewed in this article and will be discussed in the light of recent theories concerning the regulation of gene activity.

The structure of giant chromosomes and the alterations during puffing have recently been reviewed by Beermann [1]. We will briefly describe some data important for our discussion on the mechanism of puffing. According to the views of Koltzoff [2], Bauer [3], and Bridges [4], which are now generally accepted, giant chromosomes are to be considered as polytene bundles of chromosome fibers, each of which is equivalent to a normal chromosome (chromatid). The single strands are held together in a cable-like fashion (Fig. 1d). Most of the DNA in giant chromosomes is located in the bands; small amounts are, however, found in the interbands. According to a hypothesis first proposed by Ris and Crouse [5], which is now widely accepted, bands (chromomeres) and interbands differ in the degree of coiling of the constituent nucleohistone fibers of the chromatids. The chromomeres may be considered as tightly folded portions of these fibers. The pattern of bands and interbands is characteristic for each chromosome. Homologous chromosomes from all tissues show identical banding patterns [6-8]. The banding pattern of giant chromosomes is, therefore, generally regarded as reflecting the genetic organization of the constituent chromosome strand.

The structure of physiologically active loci becomes modified (Fig. 1); this phenomenon is called "puffing." Puffs are the chromosomal sites of RNA synthesis [9, 10]. The RNA's synthesized by different puffs differ from each other in base composition [11]. Genetically, puffs are equivalent to single-informational gene loci [12]. Thus, puffs may be considered as being the sites of messenger RNA production. In this sense, they are the loci of active genes, as was deduced by Beermann [13] from his morphological comparison of puffing patterns in different tissues and stages of development.

According to Beermann, the structural modification of puffed loci consists of an unfolding of the tightly coiled chromosome fibers of the related chromomeres into long, looplike threads (Fig. 1d). This was established by electron microscopic investigations of the structure of the Balbiani rings by Beermann and Bahr [14]. Thus, in terms of a single chromatid, the structure of the Balbiani ring is comparable to that of the loops of lampbrush chromosomes (cf. Gall, [15]). Puffs, and even Balbiani rings, regress as soon as the modified locus becomes inactive [16]. Furthermore, puffing is not an all-or-none effect; the structural modification of an individual locus may range from a very slight, diffuse, swelling of a single band, which is then hardly to be distinguished from a normal one, to the blown-up structure of a Balbiani ring (Fig. 1, a-c). The size of the puffs formed at homologous loci in different animals is correlated with the actual degree of synthetic activity.

Within the loops of Balbiani rings and the puffed regions of chromosomes, a protein is accumulated. This protein is not stainable with fast green after the method of Alfert and Geschwind [17] at pH 8; it is stainable, however, with fast green at pH 2 [18] and with light green at pH 5 [19]. It cannot, therefore, be a histone. The pattern of histone

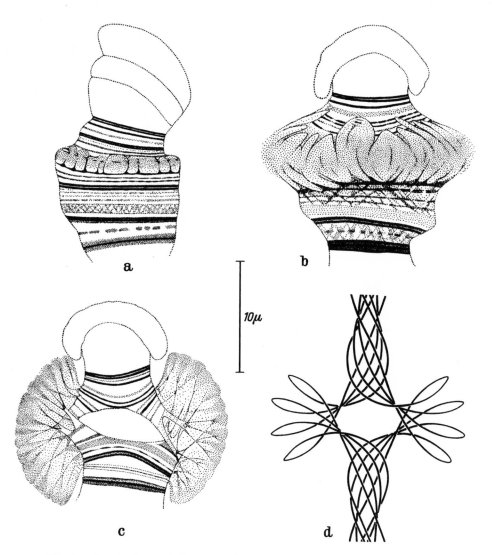

Fig. 1.—(a–c) Several degrees of puffing of the Balbiani ring locus BR_1 in salivary gland chromosome IV of <u>Chironomus tentans</u>. (d) Beermann's interpretation of the course of the chromosomal fibers in the regions of the Balbiani rings (after Beermann [7]).

distribution in giant chromosomes corresponds to the pattern of DNA distribution [20]. The content of DNA and histone apparently remains unchanged during puff formation [18, 21]. The puff protein may be homogeneously distributed throughout the puffed region, or it may form droplets (compare the puff [narrow] and the Balbiani ring in Fig. 2). Pelling ([9] and unpublished) found no labeling of the puffs with radioactive amino

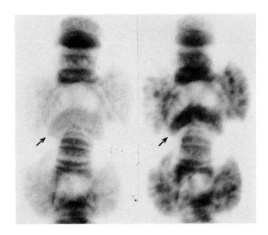

Fig. 2.—Salivary gland chromosome IV of <u>C. tentans</u>, stained with orcein–light green at pH 5, photographed in green (a) and red (b) light to demonstrate the green–stained protein in puffs (narrow) and Balbiani rings.

acids after short incubation. In new experiments, we injected ecdysone and tritiated leucine simultaneously. Ecdysone induces some new puffs within less than two hours. Two hours after the injection, the newly formed puffs were still found to be absolutely unlabeled, although rather large amounts of the protein had accumulated. The protein, therefore, seems not to be synthesized in the puffs and its function is still unknown. One might speculate that it is RNA polymerase. It also seems possible, however, that it is involved in the transport of the newly synthesized RNA, or that it has some function in the mechanism of puffing.

Within an individual larva, the puffing patterns are identical in all cells having the same function, but vary specifically from tissue to tissue [7, 13, 16]. In salivary gland cells of <u>Chironomus tentans</u>, puffing is restricted to about 200-300 loci (Clever, [22], Pelling, unpublished). Whereas puffs in some of these loci always occur in every larva, others are found infrequently (Fig. 3). Therefore, the patterns of those loci which are actually puffed in the salivary gland cells of different animals vary from larva to larva. The puffing frequency of each locus may be altered experimentally. We have concluded that in loci with low puffing frequencies, periods of activity alternate with periods of inactivity in each larva [22]. It follows from these results that it is necessary to distinguish between (1) a pattern of potentially active loci, which is identical in all larvae, and (2) a pattern of loci which are actually puffed. The latter differs in different larvae. Besides the puff size, puff frequencies may be used as a second measure of activity of the loci concerned. We have used both measurements to study the relationships between the behavior

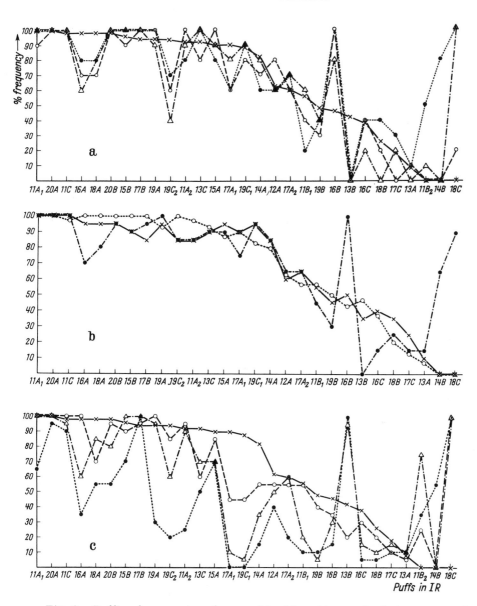

Fig. 3.—Puffing frequencies of several loci in salivary gland chromosome I of <u>C. tentans</u> during the third and the last larval instar. (a) Third instar and larval molt; o young third instar larvae, Δ larvae at the beginning of the molt, ● larvae at the end of the molt. (b) Last instar before beginning of pupal molt; larval age: ● 0-1 day, × 7-8 days, o 12-13 days. (c) Pupal molt; o young prepupae, Δ prepupae of middle age, ● old prepupae. ×, in (a) and (c), average frequencies of (b) for comparison.

of gene activities and the developmental processes during the third and the last (fourth) larval instar of Chironomus tentans [22, 23].

Provided the conditions of the external milieu remain constant, the puffing frequencies of most loci remain unchanged during larval life from the young third instar—and probably from the beginning of larval life—until the beginning of metamorphosis at the end of the last larval instar (Fig. 3). The decrease of puff frequencies in older prepupae (Fig. 3c) is probably due to the beginning of the breakdown of the gland cells. It must be concluded, therefore, that the activity of these loci is not related to any developmental process, but to the basal or functional metabolism of the gland cells. In most of these loci, the puffing frequency is below 100%. Furthermore, the size of the homologous puffs differs from larva to larva. It follows that, even in those loci involved in the everyday functions of the cells, phases of puffing alternate with phases of nonpuffing. Because of the constancy of all, even the low, puffing frequencies, the puffing phases must be distributed evenly throughout larval life. Fig. 4 (A and B) shows some characteristic time patterns of puffing of loci belonging to this group.

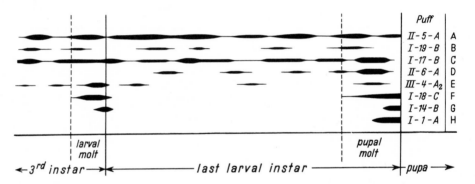

Fig. 4.—Typical time patterns of puffing in the salivary gland chromosomes of C. tentans during the third and the last larval instar.

There is a further group of loci at which puffs are present only during molting periods (e.g., I-18-C and I-14-B in Fig. 3; puffs F- I in Fig. 4). In other loci, puffs are always extremely large during the pupal molt, whereas they reach this size only occasionally during intermolts (e.g., I-17-B). The activities of the genes represented by the former group of puffs are related to cellular processes that are specific for molting periods. Genes of the latter group are involved in processes that are not specific for, but are regularly enhanced during, this period. After the beginning of molting, the different loci react successively in a regular sequence. Some of them react immediately after the induction of molting (I-18-C); others only some days later (I-14-B). Molting in insects is induced by ecdysone, a hormone secreted by the prothoracic glands. Target organs of this hormone are the individual cells of the various tissues.

The work of several authors indicates that all the puffing events characteristic for molting are, in some way, under the control of the hormone [19,
24-27]. From the facts mentioned above, it follows that this control
usually must be indirect. In a few loci, however, puffing seems to be
regulated by ecdysone more directly.

Ecdysone, isolated in 1954 by Butenandt and Karlson [28], is a steroid
closely related to cholesterin (cf. Karlson [29]). Molting in insects can be
induced experimentally by injecting the hormone. Soon after injection of
ecdysone into young, last instar larvae of Chironomus tentans, puffs are
formed in loci I-18-C and IV-2-B of the salivary gland chromosomes [19,
24]. The appearance of puff I-18-C (Fig. 5a) is recognizable after 15-30
minutes, that of puff IV-2-B (Fig. 5b) after 30-60 minutes. Enlargement
of the puffs is complete after about two hours (Fig. 6). The induction of
these gene activities specific for molting is the first known effect of ecdysone. The relationship between gene activation and hormonal control
of molting in insects has been reviewed recently by Clever [30].

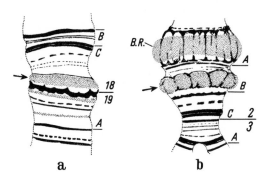

Fig. 5.—Sections of salivary gland chromosomes I and IV of C. tentans, with
puffs I-18-C (a) and IV-2-B (b).

In normal development, puffs I-18-C and IV-2-B are, at least when
large, specific for periods when ecdysone is present in the hemolymph,
i.e., for the molting periods [22, 23, 25]. The fact that puffing of these
loci depends on the presence of ecdysone is clearly demonstrated experimentally. The duration of the induced puffing phases of both loci depends
on the dose of hormone injected. The result of a typical experiment is
given in Figure 6 [19]. After injections of lower doses, the puffs regress
still earlier—e.g., after injection of 2×10^{-5} μg of ecdysone, the regression
of both puffs is complete after eight hours [31]. Both puffs reappear when
ecdysone is injected again immediately after their disappearance. The
puffs disappeared, therefore, because of an elimination of the ecdysone
injected. The size of the puffs decreases gradually. The hormone is also
eliminated gradually; the time required for its elimination is longer the
greater the amount of hormone injected. From these results we have
concluded that activity of loci I-18-C and IV-2-B as indicated by puffing
is controlled by the ecdysone concentration.

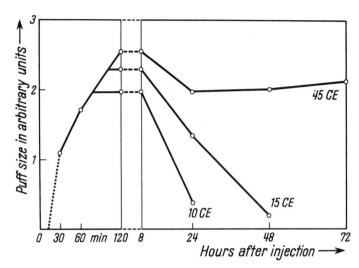

Fig. 6.—Changes in puffing of locus I-18-C during 72 hours after injections of various doses of ecdysone. C. E. = Calliphora units.

One may interpret our results to mean that puffing of both loci is controlled by ecdysone in essentially the same way. In normal develop- ment, however, and to some extent even in the experiment, there are periods of characteristic differences in the behavior of the two loci [19, 22, 23, 25]. (1) In normal development, the appearance of puff I-18-C in a larva at the end of a larval instar is the first sign of the beginning of molting. In contrast to the experiment, however, puff IV-2-B appears only one to two days later than puff I-18-C, although even here, locus IV-2-B reacts earlier than any other loci. Furthermore, in normal de- velopment, both puffs increase in size gradually, whereas in the experi- ment, they reach their maximal size about two hours after the injection (periods I and III in Fig. 7). (2) At the end of the larval molt, puff IV-2-B regresses much earlier than puff I-18-C, and in young, last instar larvae, puff IV-2-B is absent while puff I-18-C is still present (period II). (3) During the pupal molt, puff I-18-C does not disappear and reaches its maximal size only in older prepupae. Puff IV-2-B, however, attains maximal size in the middle of the prepupal period, then becomes smaller and finally disappears (period IV). These results indicate that regulation of activity of loci I-18-C and IV-2-B differs to some extent.

    Assuming the interpretation of our former experimental results to be correct—puffing of loci I-18-C and IV-2-B depends on the concentration of ecdysone—the behavior of the puffs in period III (and I) leads to the following conclusions: (1) The concentration of ecdysone must rise gradu- ally during the course of the molt; (2) Loci I-18-C and IV-2-B must differ in their reaction thresholds. To test the hypothesis, we have compared the sizes of the puffs induced with various amounts of ecdysone after three

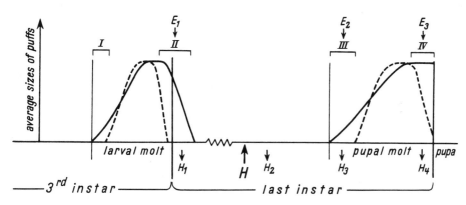

Fig. 7.—Puffing of loci I-18-C (————) and IV-2-B (- - - -) during the course of the third and the last larval instar of <u>C. tentans</u>. I-IV indicate periods of different behavior of the two puffs. E_1-E_3, injections of ecdysone. H, injection of hemolymph from donors H_1-H_4.

hours of incubation [31]. The reaction threshold for locus I-18-C was at a concentration of about 10^{-7} μg, that for locus IV-2-B at a concentration of about 10^{-6} μg of ecdysone per mg of larval weight. The concentration within the cells corresponds, then, to about 10-100 molecules of ecdysone per haploid set of chromatids. Both puffs increase gradually with increasing hormone doses. The maximal sizes are reached at concentrations of 10^{-2} μg (I-18-C) and 10^{-4} μg (IV-2-B) of ecdysone per mg of larval weight. Thus, puff IV-2-B reacts within a smaller range to the concentration of ecdysone than puff I-18-C, and this range lies within that of puff I-18-C. When the average sizes of the induced puffs are plotted against the hormone doses, the resulting curves are very much like those in which the puff sizes are plotted against time in normal development (Fig. 8). We conclude that puffing of loci I-18-C and IV-2-B at the beginning of molts is regulated by the changing hormone titer, and that the differences in their behavior are due to the different reactivities of the two loci.

Next we tried to answer the question whether the behavior of puff I-18-C and/or that of puff IV-2-B at the end of molts (periods II and IV in Fig. 7) might also be due to the actual hormone concentrations. If the size of puff I-18-C corresponds to the hormone concentration, ecdysone is present in the hemolymph during both periods, and its concentration should be higher in period IV than in period II. Puff IV-2-B, then, should not be inducible by injections of ecdysone during these periods. In a first series of experiments, therefore, we injected ecdysone into larvae that were expected to have puff I-18-C, but not puff IV-2-B (E_1-E_3 in Fig. 7). It was possible to induce puff IV-2-B by injections E_1 and E_2, but not by injection E_3. This led to the working hypothesis that the concentration of ecdysone is very high in larvae during period IV, but very low during period II. To test this hypothesis, a second series of experiments was

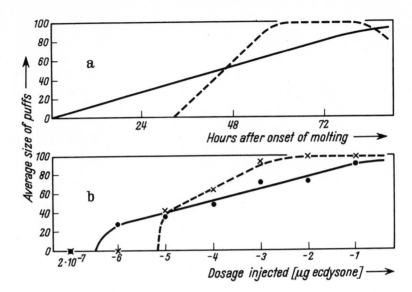

Fig. 8.—(a) Puffing of loci I-18-C (—————) and IV-2-B (- - - -) in the salivary gland chromosomes of <u>C. tentans</u> during the course of the pupal molt. (b) Dependence of the size of the induced puffs on the dose of ecdysone.

undertaken, in which we injected hemolymph into larvae of stage H (Fig. 7), using larvae at different stages of development as donors (H_1-H_4). Because of the sensitivity of puffs I-18-C and IV-2-B, they should be induced by these injections if any appreciable amounts of ecdysone were present. The following results are of interest in this connection. (1) Hemolymph from old prepupae (H_4) induces large puffs at both sites, even if puff IV-2-B is not present in the donors. (2) Hemolymph from very young, last instar larvae (H_1) never induces puff IV-2-B and very seldom induces a small puff I-18-C. The results of injection H_3 correspond to that of H_1, and injection H_2 never induces either puff (Clever, unpublished).

It follows from these results that in period II the titer of ecdysone is very low. The absence of puff IV-2-B in contrast to puff I-18-C during this period, therefore, is interpreted as being due to the different reaction thresholds of the two loci. The early regression of puff IV-2-B may, however, be initiated by the same factor that is effective in the pupal molt. At the end of the pupal molt (period IV), puff IV-2-B loses its activity, although high amounts of ecdysone are still present. It follows that in prepupae of this stage some other process is at work that, with regard to this gene locus, is antagonistic to that of ecdysone. The changes undergone by puff I-18-C are, by contrast to those of puff IV-2-B, due only to corresponding changes in the hormone concentration.

   Puffing of both loci, therefore, is regulated permanently by specific
cytoplasmic factors during the whole period of larval development we
have studied. Generalizing from these results, the view seems to be
justified that, normally, puffing of all chromosomal loci is permanently
controlled by cytoplasmic factors, each of which is responsible for regulating the activity of one or a few chromosomal loci. In some cases,
effects on puffing of unspecific factors—such as heat treatment, changes
in ionic concentrations or explanation—have been reported [7, 13, 22,
32-34].
   While these results generally support the idea that puffing is controlled by cytoplasmic factors, the mode of their interference with the
normal regulatory mechanisms in the cell is not yet understood. In any
case, puffing in giant chromosomes seems to be entirely dependent on the
cytoplasmic environment at any one time. This result demonstrates that
at least a part of the gene activity in higher organisms is regulated in a
way similar to that regulating gene activity in bacteria (cf. Monod and
Jacob, [35]). The mechanism of this regulation, therefore, may be expected to be similar in both. The fast reaction of the loci just described
to specific changes in the cytoplasmic environment should be ineffective
if a stable messenger RNA were produced and accumulated in the cytoplasm. One may interpret our results, therefore, as supporting the view
that even in higher organisms, some messenger RNA is short-lived like
most or all messenger RNA in bacteria (cf. Levinthal et al. [36]).
   To obtain further information about the mechanism of the action of
ecdysone, we tested the effects of some antibiotics known to interfere with
cell metabolism at different levels. In various temporal combinations
with ecdysone, we injected puromycin, chloramphenicol, actinomycin C,
and mitomycin C. Actinomycin and mitomycin partially or totally inhibited
the induction of puffs I-18-C and IV-2-B by ecdysone, whereas puromycin
and chloramphenicol had no effect (Tables 1 and 2). Actinomycin was
more effective than mitomycin. If these antibiotics are injected after
the ecdysone, their effects differ markedly: actinomycin always causes
a decrease in size of all puffs, Balbiani rings, and nucleoli. Mitomycin
does not affect puffs present at the time of its injection, and if injected
after the ecdysone, therefore has no effect on puffs I-18-C and IV-2-B.
   Actinomycin is known as a specific inhibitor of DNA-dependent RNA
synthesis; probably it is tightly bound to the DNA and suppresses the
activity of RNA polymerase [37-39]. Mitomycin causes a degradation of
DNA in bacteria and tumor cells [40, 41] and inhibits the induction of
β-galactosidase in <u>Escherichia</u> <u>coli</u> [42]. Puromycin and chloramphenicol
interfere with protein synthesis at the level of amino acid from soluble
RNA to the protein [43-45]. Our results indicate that those antibiotics
which interfere with nucleic acid metabolism inhibit puff induction by
ecdysone. The results with mitomycin are in agreement with the hypothesis
of Cheer and Tchen that only "dormant" loci are affected by this antibiotic.
Antibiotics that interfere with protein synthesis seem to have no influence
on the induction. It seems, therefore, that the induction of activity in loci

TABLE 1

Effects of some antibiotics on the induction of puff I-18-C by ecdysone*

		No. animals in size class†			
		0	1	2	3
Control (untreated)		15	5	–	–
Ecdysone		–	–	5	14
Puromycin ⟶ Ecdysone		–	–	4	9
Mitomycin ⟶ Ecdysone		6	7	2	1
Actinomycin ⟶ Ecdysone		11	3	1	–
Ecdysone ⟶ Mitomycin		–	1	4	7
Ecdysone ⟶ Actinomycin		8	3	–	–

* Size classes of the puff after Clever [19]. Concentrations of the antibiotics: puromycin, 10 µg/ml; actinomycin, 3 µg/ml; mitomycin, 10 µg/ml.
† Size classes are classified from 0 (no puff) to 3 (maximal puff).

TABLE 2

Effects of some antibiotics on the induction of puff IV-2-B by ecdysone*

		No. animals in size class†		
		0/1	2	3
Control (untreated)		19	–	–
Ecdysone		–	1	18
Puromycin ⟶ Ecdysone		–	1	11
Mitomycin ⟶ Ecdysone		9	4	2
Actinomycin ⟶ Ecdysone		14	1	–
Ecdysone ⟶ Mitomycin		1	2	7
Ecdysone ⟶ Actinomycin		9	2	–

* Size classes of the puff after Clever [19]. Concentrations of the antibiotics same as in Table 1.
† Size classes are classified 0 (no puff) to 3 (maximal puff).

I-18-C and IV-2-B by ecdysone does not involve the synthesis of new proteins. Our results are consistent with the hypothesis that the hormone acts directly at the genic level.

According to the model of Jacob and Monod [46], which was deduced from biochemical and genetic studies of enzyme induction in bacteria, the regulation of genic activity acts primarily on the DNA of the genes itself. Cytoplasmic "effectors," which, as "inducers" or "co-repressors," influence the activity of structural genes in directing the synthesis of messenger RNA, do so by interfering with the repressor of the regulator-operator system. There is some evidence that regulatory systems of gene activity that involve genes with informational, and genes with regulatory, function are effective even in higher organisms [47-51]. In principle, the model of Jacob and Monod also seems suited to explain the action of regulatory factors such as ecdysone in our system. The action of ecdysone then, would be like that of an effector. It seems worth mentioning in this connection that the minimal concentration of ecdysone effective in inducing the puffs is of the same order of magnitude as that of the repressor in the β-galactosidase system of Escherichia coli (Ullman et al. cited by Jacob and Monod [52]).

Some of our results seem to indicate that loci I-18-C and IV-2-B are independent of each other in their reaction to ecdysone. If ecdysone acts directly on both loci, this might be regarded as a case of non-coordinate induction, comparable to the case of non-coordinate repression discussed for the arginine system in Escherichia coli [53-55]. Furthermore, if ecdysone is an effector of the IV-2-B locus, it would follow that activity of this locus is controlled by two antagonistic substances, comparable to inducer and co-repressor in bacteria. This type of regulation of gene activity by antagonistic effectors has been discussed in bacteria [56, 57]. In higher organisms, control mechanisms of this kind would, a priori, seem to be more adapted to the requirements of coordination of intracellular events than those acting only in one direction.

Enzyme induction in bacteria seems to be an all-or-none effect [58]. Puffing of loci I-18-C and IV-2-B, on the other hand, is regulated quantitatively by the concentration of ecdysone. Effects of effector concentration on the rate of enzyme synthesis have also been described, but they seem to be due to heterogeneous response of the cell population. More complicated mechanisms have, however, also been discussed [59]. For ecdysone—and other effectors regulating puffing—it may be speculated that with low concentrations only a few of the several thousand loci of which each band is composed are activated. It may also be that each individual locus is activated more frequently in a unit of time by high than by low concentrations. The size of the puff, then, may depend on the concentration only so far as it depends on the actual rate at which RNA can be produced.

So far, we have neglected the role histone may play in the regulation of puffing. In 1950, Stedman and Stedman [60] suggested that histone might act as a suppressor of gene activity. This view was recently supported strongly by experiments of Huang and Bonner [61] and Bonner and Huang [62]. According to these authors, about 80% of the DNA in the chromosomes of pea seedlings is bound to histone, and only the remaining 20% of free DNA is active in the sense that it acts as a primer to RNA synthesis in cell-free systems. It seems to be of interest that this percentage is of the same order of magnitude as that of the puff-forming loci in giant chromosomes.

If the regulator-operator model holds for the regulation of activity in puffs, one might speculate that histone is the repressor that blocks the operator locus. Indeed, Jacob et al. [63] and Garen and Garen [64] recently provided some evidence that the repressor is a protein. Paigen [65], on the other hand, has discussed a model with RNA as the repressor, and Sporn and Dingman [66] have found an RNA species in the nuclei of rat liver for which they discuss this function. In the course of animal development, adult histones are successively replaced by several other types of histones or by protamines [67, 68]. The assumption that histone acts as the repressor, therefore, leads to the inference that repressors are of different types during different stages of development. Moreover, Swift [18] found the amount of histone unchanged during puffing in giant chromosomes. It seems to us more probable, therefore, that histone plays some role other than taking part in the mechanism of the regulator-operator system.

As mentioned above, gene activation in giant chromosomes is always accompanied by an unfolding of the tightly coiled chromosome fibers in the related chromomeres. Similar modifications of chromosome structure in relation to genic activity are also known from other types of chromosomes (e.g., lampbrush chromosomes [15, 69]; Y-chromosomes in the spermatogenesis of Drosophila species [70, 71], whereas lack of modification of chromosome structure after a locus has become active has never been demonstrated. Therefore, the uncoiling of the nucleo-histone fiber seems to be an inevitable condition for gene activity in chromosomes. This view is also supported by results of Hsu [72] on differential rates of RNA synthesis in eu- and heterochromatin.

According to a model of chromosome structure recently proposed by Cole [73], the successive series of coilings of the chromosome fiber result from associations of DNA with histone protein. Uncoiling is caused by a dissociation of DNA with histone. Whether the details of Cole's model are correct or not, it seems tempting to speculate that the primary role of histone is to establish the coiled chromosome structure, and that through this function, it may act as a suppressor of gene activity. Dissociation of the DNA-histone complex within the region of a genetic locus would then be a prerequisite for messenger RNA synthesis and puffing. According to Cole, local changes in the ionic concentration may lead to the dissociation of RNA with histone. These could be produced by the reaction of a repressor with its specific operator locus. The view that the uncoiling is a secondary effect in the process of induction is in agreement with our observation that inhibition of RNA synthesis by actinomycin apparently causes reversion of even the large loops of Balbiani rings. It would be of interest, in this connection, to know whether the histone Swift [18] found in puffs is still bound to DNA.

As stated above, puffing in giant chromosomes seems to be permanently controlled by cytoplasmic factors. The view that an inactivation of certain parts of the genetic material, which is stable under the conditions of normal development, takes place in the course of cellular differentiation is, however, not disproved by these results. Briggs and King [74 and earlier articles] found that the potency of nuclei, as indicated in transplantation experiments, becomes more and more restricted in the course of amphibian development. In their experiments, the final potency of the nuclei seemed to be closely related to the type of donor tissue. Serial transplantations indicated that the restriction is irreversible [75]. In recent experiments, Gurdon [76] showed that a large fraction of differentiated intestinal epithelium cells of Xenopus contains totipotent nuclei. Furthermore, Hennen [77] found that karyotypic abnormalities account for the irreversible restriction of potency of nuclei transplanted into egg cytoplasm of other species. These results may suggest that the changes in nuclear potency observed by Briggs and King may be a consequence of the experimental procedure rather than of normal differentiation. However, the original interpretation—that their results indicate a stable type of nuclear differentiation—is as yet not disproved. Recently, Markert and Ursprung [78, 79] produced comparable irreversible changes in the potency of nuclei by injecting protein fractions from liver nuclei into eggs. Karyotypic abnormalities were not observed. It is conceivable, then, that histone in those loci which do not belong to the pattern of potential activity in the specialized donor cells is altered in its character. This assumption would also explain the results of several authors (e.g., Stedman and Stedman [60] and Cruft et al. [80])that the composition of histone varies in different tissues. By way of altering histone, the DNA-histone dissociation may become impossible under the conditions of induction, and a restriction in the genetic potency of the nuclei would therefore result.

Irreversible restriction of genetic potency has been discussed also on the basis of the regulator-operator system alone [35]. Bacteria, however, in which this kind of regulation may be the only one, have no equivalent of cellular differentiation. It seems tempting to speculate that development of a more complex chromosome structure with additional possibilities of regulation of gene activities was an inevitable condition for the evolution of organisms with cells having a high degree of differentiation and specialization.

REFERENCES

1.   Beermann, W., Protoplasmatologia IVD, (Wien: Springer-Verlag, 1962).

2.   Koltzoff, N. K., Science, 80, 312, 1934.

3.   Bauer, H. Z., Zellforsch., 23, 280, 1935.

4.   Bridges, C. B., Am. Naturalist, 69, 59, 1935.

5.   Ris, H., and Crouse, H., Proc. Natl. Acad. Sci. U. S. A., 31, 321, 1945.

6.   Beermann, W., Naturwissenschaften, 37, 543, 1950.

7.   Beermann, W., Chromosoma, 5, 139, 1952.

8.   Pavan, C., and Breuer, M., J. Heredity, 43, 152, 1952.

9.   Pelling, C., Nature, 184, 655, 1959.

10.   Sirlin, J. L., Exptl. Cell Res., 19, 177, 1960.

11.   Edström, J.-E., and Beermann, W., J. Cell Biol., 14, 371, 1962.

12.   Beermann, W., Chromosoma, 12, 1, 1961.

13.   Beermann, W., Z. Naturforsch., 7b, 237, 1952.

14.   Beermann, W., and Bahr, G. F., Exptl. Cell Res., 6, 195, 1954.

15.   Gall, J. G., In W. D. McElroy and B. Glass (eds.), The Chemical Basis of Development, (Baltimore: Johns Hopkins Press, 1958).

16.   Mechelke, F., Chromosoma, 5, 511, 1953.

17.   Alfert, M., and Geschwind, I. J., Proc. Natl. Acad. Sci. U. S. A., 39, 991, 1953.

18.   Swift, H., In J. M. Allan (ed.), The Molecular Control of Cellular Activity, (London/New York: McGraw-Hill, 1962), pp. 73-125.

19.   Clever, U., Chromosoma, 12, 607, 1961.

20.   Horn, E. C., and Ward, C. L., Proc. Natl. Acad. Sci. U. S. A., 43, 776, 1957.

21.   Rudkin, G. T., Genetics, 40, 593, 1955.

22.   Clever, U., Chromosoma, 13, 385, 1962.

23.   Clever, U., Chromosoma, 14, 651, 1963.

24.   Clever, U., and Karlson, P., Exptl. Cell Res., 20, 623, 1960.

25.   Clever, U., J. Insect Physiol., 8, 357, 1962.

26.   Panitz, R., Naturwissenschaften, 47, 383, 1960.

27.   Becker, H. J., Chromosoma, 13, 341, 1962.

28.   Butenandt, A., and Karlson, P. Z. Naturforsch., 9b, 389, 1954.

29.   Karlson, P., Angew. Chem., 75, 257, 1963.

30.   Clever, U., Proc. 16th Intern. Congr. Zool., 1963, In press.

31.   Clever, U., Develop. Biol., 6, 73, 1963.

32.   Becker, H. J., Chromosoma, 10, 654, 1959.

33.   Kroeger, H., Chromosoma, 11, 129, 1960.

34.   Ritossa, F., Experientia, 18, 571, 1962.

35.   Monod, J., and Jacob, F., Cold Spring Harbor Symp. Quant. Biol., 26, 389, 1961.

36.   Levinthal, C., Keynan, A., and Higa, A., Proc. Natl. Acad. Sci. U. S. A., 48, 1631, 1962.

37.   Rauen, H. M., Kersten, H., and Kersten, W., Hoppe-Seylers Z. Physiol. Chem., 321, 139, 1960.

38.   Hurwitz, J., Furth, J. J., Malamy, M., and Alexander, M., Proc. Natl. Acad. Sci. U. S. A., 48, 1222, 1962.

39.   Reich, E., Franklin, R. M., Shatkin, A. J., and Tatum, E. L., Proc. Natl. Acad. Sci. U. S. A., 48, 1238, 1962.

40.   Reich, E., Shatkin, A. J., and Tatum, E. L., Biochim. Biophys. Acta, 53, 132, 1961.

41.   Kersten, H., Biochim. Biophys. Acta, 55, 558, 1962.

42.   Cheer, S., and Tchen, T. T., Biochem. Biophys. Res. Comun., 9, 271, 1962.

43.   Yarmolinsky, M. B., and de la Haba, G. L., Proc. Natl. Acad. Sci. U. S. A., 45, 1721, 1959.

44.   Brock, Th. D., Bacteriol. Rev., 25, 32, 1961.

45.   Rendi, R., and Ochoa, S., J. Biol. Chem., 237, 3711, 1962.

46.   Jacob, F., and Monod, J., J. Mol. Biol., 3, 318, 1961.

47.   Horowitz, N. H., Fling, M., McLeod, H. C., and Sueoka, N., J. Mol. Biol., 2, 96, 1960.

48.   McClintock, B., Am. Naturalist, 95, 265, 1961.

49.   Paigen, K., Proc. Natl. Acad. Sci. U. S. A., 47, 1641, 1961.

50.   Motulsky, A. G., Nature, 194, 607, 1962.

51.   Manwell, C., Baker, C. M. A., Roslansky, J. D., and Foght, M., Proc. Natl. Acad. Sci. U. S. A., 49, 496, 1963.

52.   Jacob, F., and Monod, J., UNESCO Symp. Biol. Organization, 1962, In press, 1963.

53.   Gorini, L., Gundersen, W., and Burger, M., Cold Spring Harbor Symp. Quant. Biol., 26, 173, 1961.

54.   Maas, W. K., Cold Spring Harbor Symp. Quant. Biol., 26, 183, 1961.

55.   Vogel, H. J., Cold Spring Harbor Quant. Biol., 26, 163, 1961.

56.   Magasanik, B., Cold Spring Harbor Symp. Quant. Biol., 26, 249, 1961.

57.   McFall, E., and Mandelstamm, J., Nature, 197, 880, 1963.

58.   Novick, A., and Weiner, M., Proc. Natl. Acad. Sci. U. S. A., 43, 553, 1957.

59.   Marr, A. G., and Marcus, L., Biochim. Biophys. Acta, 64, 65, 1962.

60.   Stedman, E., and Stedman, E., Nature, 166, 780, 1950.

61.   Huang, R. C., and Bonner, J., Proc. Natl. Acad. Sci. U. S. A., 48, 1216, 1962.

62.   Bonner, J., and Huang, R. C., J. Mol. Biol., 6, 169, 1963.

63.   Jacob, F., Sussmann, R., and Monod, J., C. R. Acad. Sci., 254, 4214, 1962.

64.   Garen, A., and Garen, S., J. Mol. Biol., 6, 433, 1963.

65.   Paigen, K., J. Theoret. Biol., 3, 268, 1962.

66.   Sporn, M. B., and Dingman, W., Biochim. Biophys. Acta, 68, 387, 1963.

67.   Bloch, D. P., and Hew, H. Y. C., J. Biophys. Biochem. Cytol., 8, 69, 1960.

68.   Alfert, M., J. Biophys. Biochem. Cytol., 2, 109, 1956.

69.   Callan, H. G., and Lloyd, L., In P. H. B. Walker (ed.), New Approaches in Cell Biology (New York: Academic Press, 1960).

70.   Meyer, G. F., Chromosoma, 14, 207, 1963.

71.   Meyer, G. F., Hess, O., and Beermann, W., Chromosoma, 12, 676, 1961.

72.   Hsu, T. C., Exptl. Cell Res., 27, 332, 1962.

73.   Cole, A., Nature, 196, 211, 1962.

74.   Briggs, R., and King, Th. J., J. Morphol., 100, 269, 1957.

75.   King, Th. J., and Briggs, R., Cold Spring Harbor Symp. Quant. Biol., 21, 271, 1956.

76.   Gurdon, J. B., J. Embryol. Exptl. Morphol., 10, 622, 1962.

77.   Hennen, S., Develop. Biol., 6, 133 - 183, 1963.

78.   Markert, C. L., and Ursprung, H., Am. Zoologist, 2, 428, 1962.

79.   Markert, C. L., and Ursprung, H., Develop. Biol., 7, 560, 1963.

80.   Cruft, H. J., Mauritzen, C. M., and Stedman, E., Nature, 174, 580, 1955.

 David P. Bloch

GENETIC IMPLICATIONS
OF HISTONE DIFFERENTIATION

THE MEANING OF CHROMOSOME DIFFERENTIATION

One of the interesting questions that confronts the student of differentiation concerns the extent to which "differentiation of the genome" plays
a role in cellular differentiation. Weismann, in an early attempt to explain
cell differentiation, theorized a controlled but unequal partitioning of the
chromosome complement during division [1]. Although the later studies
of Boveri [2] on chromosome diminution in Ascaris established such
genome differentiation as a real phenomenon [3, p. 325], with time, chromosome constancy came to be regarded as the rule, and it seems that
although chromosome diminution, elimination [4], differential DNA synthesis [5], and other alterations of the complement may play a role, it is
a minor one and has little bearing on the process of development in most
organisms. The important generalizations of chromosome constancy
[2a and 3, p. 817], then DNA constancy [6], led to the view that variable
gene expression is a reflection of a materially constant genome responding
differently to changing cytoplasmic environments. The state of affairs ten
years ago was nicely summed up by Ephrussi [7]. "Unless development
involves a rather unlikely process of orderly and directed gene mutation,
the differential must have its seat in the cytoplasm." According to this
view, one would predict that were it possible to extract the genome from
a liver cell and transfer it to a muscle cell,* it would act in concert with
its new environment much as a chromosome taken from an Escherichia
coli in a given state of induction reacts appropriately when "injected" by
mating into a cell in another state [8].

---

*A distinction must be made between nucleus and genome. It is true that the nuclear
transfer experiments of Briggs and King showed a heritable differentiation of the
nucleus [30]. However, Prescott and Bender's [31] and Goldstein's [32] demonstrations of a nuclear material that fills the cytoplasm during mitosis, but is
recovered by the reconstituting nucleus after division, indicate that not all nuclear
heredity need be attributed to the chromosomes.

335

Although such transfer among metazoan cells cannot be done at present, recent findings suggest that the prediction would not be realized—that the chromosomes of metazoan somatic cells do undergo changes during development resulting in homologous loci that are able to respond differently, even when confronted with identical environments. Supporting evidence comes from: (1) studies on phase variation in Salmonella, which suggest that some genes may have the capacity for assuming alternative states [9]; (2) studies of paramutation in maize, indicating that alternation between states occurs in higher organisms and is subject to biological control [10]; and (3) existence of the heteropycnotic condition of homologous blocks of chromatin, such as the X chromosomes in the females of some mammals, in which genetically homologous regions exhibit differences in morphology [11], metabolism [12], and the expression of the genes contained therein [13]. Here, as in paramutation, alternative states are seen to coexist within the same cell—thereby precluding as its basis a simple repressor-operator type of mechanism such as operates in bacteria, where activity of a locus reflects only its environment. These phenomena must reflect differences intrinsic to the locus itself. Interestingly, these alterations are mitotically transmissible.

In brief, it would appear that:

$$\text{gene (state 1)} \rightleftharpoons \text{gene (state 2)}$$

both states exhibiting a degree of stability, having the capacity for replication, and resulting in characteristic phenotypic expression.

As stated, this idea may appear to flaunt the established view of a constant gene. One must bear in mind, however, that the gene of the geneticist is exposed to scrutiny only during stages of development in which its activity is normally realized. Barring mutation or gene interaction, this realization is the same, generation after generation, hence the geneticist's gene is constant only so far as it consistently repeats a pattern of behavior in successive generations of organisms. The classical genetic approach says little about the behavior of a gene within a generation, and it is here that controlled alteration of the genome may play its role.

If the gene itself (i.e., DNA) has an inherent capacity to exist in physiologically meaningful alternative states, which consist, for example, of alternative secondary or tertiary configurations that are inducible and capable of replication, one might speak simply of alternative gene states. If, on the other hand, the chromosomal unit in somatic division involves something more than the gene that bridges generations of organisms, this simple concept will not suffice. An "epigene" would need to be invoked [14]. Whatever the basis, the existence of alternative chromosomal states whose maintenance depends on intrinsic factors could legitimately be termed chromosome differentiation.

CHROMOSOME DIFFERENTIATION AND "HISTONE DIFFERENTIATION"

In 1950, Edgar and Ellen Stedman [15] proposed that histones, the basic proteins associated with DNA, exhibit a cell specificity. They found slight differences in the composition and prevalence of homologous histone fractions among different tissue types at a time when similar studies on DNA were leading to the concept of DNA constancy, and they suggested that the basic proteins of the chromosome may play a role in the regulation of gene activity.

These chemical investigations had a biological parallel. During the past two decades, geneticists have been accumulating observations of some rather bizarre aspects of chromosome behavior that implicate the genome in the control of its own activity and have led to a view of chromatin as a dual structure. Among these phenomena are activation [16], in which the expression of a gene of usual rank is modified by controlling genes; position effect [17], describing the influence of the position of a gene in the chromosome complement on its activity; and, most compelling, a historical effect, in which the expression of a gene is conditioned by its past as well as its present circumstances [10]. The last effect may be remarkably persistent, bridging many generations of cells, and even of organisms, having its ultimate expression in the phenomenon of paramutation, an inducible gene change that is carried through the germ line, yet which, unlike classical mutation, is under precise biological control [10]. It is clear in this instance, that the maintenance of a change of activity once induced can be an intrinsic function of the locus involved. Equally important in supporting this conclusion is the ability of homologous loci within the same cell to act in different ways. Observations such as these led Brink to advance the hypothesis that the chromatin consists of two components, a constant orthochromatin, or the genes proper, and a variable parachromatin, which imparts a quality of responsiveness of the orthochromatin to its environment. Brink proposed the following properties for this system to account for its effects. The parachromatin and orthochromatin are coextensive throughout the genome. The role of the parachromatin is epigenetic, controlling expression during development. The association is variable, and reaches a ground state during gamete formation. The parachromatin has its origin in a part of the orthochromatin (specific genes), and being thus limited in variety, is ambivalent, i.e., relatively homogeneous as compared with the orthochromatin with which it associates. The association is self-replicating in the sense that a particular pattern is reproduced during chromosome replication, and is mitotically transmissible. What appear as alternative gene states may be manifestations of alternative associations between the orthochromatin and parachromatin.

The behavior of the orthochromatin-parachromatin system as formulated by Brink and that of the DNA-histone association as inferred from limited observation of histone behavior show striking parallels.

THE ORIGIN OF HISTONES

Spermatogenesis in the grasshopper provides an excellent system for the study of histone synthesis. As in many species, there occurs in the spermatid a new histone, whose synthesis is independent of the process of chromosome replication. This protein can be readily distinguished from other histones because of its distinctive properties and reactions. An additional feature in the grasshopper is its synthesis very late in development of the sperm, when most of the other processes that contribute to sperm maturation are completed. There is little left in the cell to confuse the issue. The events leading to, and accompanying, histone synthesis are the following (Bloch and Brack, unpublished):

Shortly after meiosis, the production of RNA is stopped. All detectable RNA is lost from the nucleus, and most of the cellular RNA is lost during sloughing of the cytoplasm. The resulting intermediate spermatid is characterized by a spherical nucleus, devoid of RNA, surrounded by a thin layer of cytoplasm, and trailed by a long axial filament to which a few bubbles of cytoplasm still adhere. The RNA of this cell, representing only a small fraction of that present in earlier stages, is contained in the thin cortical cytoplasm surrounding the nucleus. The nucleus then begins an elongation that culminates in a hairlike structure, whose dimensions are similar to those of the tail. As elongation proceeds, the nucleus undergoes a progressive change in its staining properties, indicating an increase in protein-bound arginine, and accumulation of the characteristic sperm histone. The staining change is accompanied by incorporation of labeled arginine. Short-term experiments show that labeling first occurs within the cytoplasm in association with ribosomes that had themselves been synthesized at least a week earlier, and the protein then migrates into the nucleus, where it combines with the DNA.

The synthesis of grasshopper sperm histone is accomplished in a rather conventional manner, much like that of beta-galactosidase, hemoglobin, and other proteins whose syntheses have been extensively studied. It is mediated by an RNA which presumably owes its origin to the nucleus. A unique feature of this protein, however, is its entry into the nucleus and subsequent combination with the entire DNA complement. The gene (or genes) responsible for the production of sperm histone enjoys a special relationship to the remainder of the complement in that this gene becomes associated with the product of its activity.

HISTONE VARIATION AMONG CELLS

Unequivocal examples of histone variation are unfortunately rare. However, when variation is seen, it is usually very apparent. The classical example is the sperm cell, as noted above. The transition in grasshopper is a simple one. In many species it is more involved. In the squid, Loligo, a sequence of changes occurs, the intermediate spermatid containing a histone very rich in arginine, later spermatids containing a protamine, and mature sperms, still another protamine [18]. There may be some overlapping during these replacements. An intermediate cell may contain a minor fraction which was or will become the major fraction of another stage. However, the replacements ultimately involve the entire genome.

The significance of the uniqueness of sperm in unknown. A rather trivial function, packaging, has often been casually ascribed to the histone change. Alternative interpretations have been espoused. Brink proposed that parachromatin reaches a ground state during gamete formation. Perhaps this distinctive protein provides for obliteration of the developmental history that led to the formation of the mature sperm. It seems significant that the sperm is at once a highly specialized cell containing a completely totipotent (undifferentiated) nucleus.

The changes in sperm maturation appear to be but a part of a broader program of changes that extends into the early developing embryo. In the snail Helix aspersa, the protamine of the sperm is lost on fertilization, and replaced by a faintly basic protein that is demonstrably different from both the sperm proteins and the histones of the mature animal [19]. This histone persists until a later stage in development, near gastrulation, when the histones of the entire embryo are replaced by others as yet indistinguishable from those of the adult organism.

Thus histone variation, while limited in its manifestations, is apparent during a short but important span of the life cycle of many organisms. These variations are the result of replacements that cover most of the genome, if not the entire genome. The meaning of the changes is not known. One important consequence of their observation is the realization that most of the DNA of an organism is capable of combining with alternative histones.

AMBIVALENCE—VARIATION WITHIN CELLS

There are other aspects of the problem of histone variation. It has been well established that the histones constitute a heterogeneous class of proteins, even when obtained from a single cell type, and that the heterogeneity is extensive [20]. One may ask whether each DNA* within a cell associates with its own characteristic histone. The concept of coding provides an unequivocal answer [21]. The DNA-histone complex contains roughly equal weights of DNA and histone, approximately 3-4 amino acids per nucleotide. Since at least three nucleotides are needed for the specification of a single amino acid, there is insufficient information in a stretch of DNA to code the synthesis of its associated histone. The histone associated with a given segment must then, usually, have its origin in another segment. By similar reasoning, there is insufficient information in the entire complement of DNA to code a unique histone for each DNA. As a consequence, many different DNA's must associate with common histones, and these must have their origin in a limited fraction of the genome.

---

*A DNA is considered here to be a stretch of a helix that combines with a single histone molecule. Such stretches would average three or four turns long.

Histone variation, then, is two dimensional, occurring to a limited extent among the different DNA's within a given cell type, and also among homologous DNA's during development.

Since different DNA's can combine with the same histone, and a given DNA combines with alternative histones, the nature of the association between DNA and histone can hardly be attributed to inherent affinities between different types of molecules. It seems more probable that any DNA can combine with any histone. Although we have no clue to the nature of the determination of the spectrum of associations within a cell, it seems improbable that these associations should be random. This is one of the crucial questions. Although a regulatory role for histone has been sharply defined in the Stedman's inhibition hypothesis, the factors determining the association itself have yet to be surmised. One would assume, according to this hypothesis, that changes in the association would be a very specific response to a given set of conditions, the change to be maintained until key conditions bring about a further change.

REPLICATION OF THE ASSOCIATION

In 1955, Bloch and Godman[22] found parallel increases in the staining of both DNA and histone during the interphase period leading to division, and concluded that the DNA and histone are synthesized together. Similar results have since been obtained by others and similar interpretations given them [23, 24]. At the time, there seemed no reason to doubt that the two syntheses were intimately connected. Now, however, with our deeper understanding of protein synthesis, there seems no reason to expect them to occur together, and indeed every reason to expect the syntheses to be independent. In the past year, several reports have indicated that histones may be synthesized before or independently of DNA [25-27]. In any event, the observations of parallel increases in staining are reinterpreted as indicating complexing of the histone with DNA immediately on replication of the latter, the association perhaps rendering the previously synthesized histone stainable. Parallel syntheses, if they do indeed occur, probably reflect nothing more than an approximate temporal relationship.

When a given stretch of DNA is replicated in a medium containing a variety of histones, will the DNA associate with the same type of histone after replication as before replication? If it does, then the DNA-histone association, rather than the DNA, may be considered to be the hereditary unit of the somatic cell. That the same association will be recovered is conjecture, and has as its basis the unsupported yet untried postulate that the association is not random but meaningful for the cell. Such replication would be equivalent to the replication of the orthochromatin-parachromatin system in Brink's formulation.

HISTONE FUNCTION

Brink's hypothetical parachromatin plays an epigenetic role, mediating between the environment and the genome. The recent findings by Huang and Bonner [28] and Allfrey, et al. [29] that histones inhibit DNA-primed RNA synthesis provide the first direct evidence in support of the Stedmans' 13-year-old inhibition hypothesis. Granted the correctness of the inhibition hypothesis, and its sine qua non, a controlled variation in the DNA-histone association, histone's role would also be epigenetic. The objection has been voiced that the hypothesis does not really explain anything, but by adding another factor makes the problem that much more complicated. It may be true that an important explanation is still wanting. What controls the association? However, the objection is invalid because it presumes that the real problem is less complicated than it probably is. Histone may, and parachromatin does, impart an additional degree of freedom to the genetic system, which appears to be in force during differentiation. This is a relative degree of autonomy of the chromosome complement, permitting it to maintain alternative states that are physiologically meaningful and can be reproduced in the absence of continued extrinsic control. The usefulness of such a phenomenon can easily be imagined, but no excursions into its possible role in differentiation would be as eloquent an argument for its operation as the very fact of its existence.

Acknowledgments

This work was supported by grants from the National Science Foundation and the National Institutes of Health. It was also presented at the Second International Conference on Congenital Malformations, New York, 1963, with the title "Histone-Differentiation - An Expression of Gene Differentiation?"

REFERENCES

1.   Weismann, A., In Pouton, Schonland, and Shipley (eds.), Weismann on Heredity (Oxford: Oxford Univ. Press, 1891), pp. 163-255.

2.   Boveri, T., Anat. Anz., 2, 688, 1887.

2a   Boveri, T., Verhandl. Phys.-Med. Ges. Wurz., 35, 1902.

3.   Wilson, E. B., The Cell in Development and Heredity. (New York: MacMillan Co., 1925), pp. 325 and 917.

4.   Metz, C. W., Am. Naturalist, 72, 485, 1938.

5.   Stich, H. F., and Naylor, J. K., Exptl. Cell Res., 14, 442, 1957.

6.   Chargaff, E., and Lipshitz, R., J. Am. Chem. Soc., 75, 3658, 1953.

7. Ephrussi, B., Nucleo-cytoplasmic Interactions in Microorganisms (London/ New York: Oxford Univ. Press, 1953), p. 4.

8. Jacob, F., and Monod, J., J. Mol. Biol., 3, 318, 1961.

9. Lederberg, J., and Iino, T., Genetics 41, 743, 1956.

10. Brink, R. A., Quart. Rev. Biol. 35, 120, 1960.

11. Ohno, S., Kaplan, W. D., and Kinosita, R., Exptl..Cell Res.,18, 415, 1959.

12. Taylor, J. H., J. Biophys. Biochem. Cytol., 7, 455, 1960.

13. Lyon, M. F., Nature, 190, 732, 1961.

14. Ephrussi, B., J. Cellular Comp. Physiol., 52, 35, 1958.

15. Stedman, E., and Stedman, E., Nature, 166, 780, 1950.

16. McClintock, B., Brookhaven Symp. Biol., 8, 58, 1955.

17. Schultz, J., Proc. Natl. Acad. Sci. U. S. A., 22, 27, 1936.

18. Bloch, D. P., J. Histochem. Cytochem., 10, 137, 1962.

19. Bloch, D. P., and Hew, H. Y. C., J. Biophys. Biochem. Cytol., 8, 69, 1960.

20. Hnilica, L., Johns, E. W., and Butler, J. A. V., Biochem. J., 82, 123, 1962.

21. Bloch, D. P., Proc. Natl. Acad. Sci. U. S. A., 48, 324, 1962.

22. Bloch, D. P., and Godman, G. C., J. Biophys. Biochem. Cytol., 1, 17, 1955.

23. Alfert, M., In Symposium on Fine Structure of Cells, Leiden, 1954. (Gro- ningen: P. Noordhoff, Ltd., 1955), pp. 157-163.

24. Gall, J., J. Biophys. Biochem. Cytol., 5, 295, 1959.

25. Lindner, A., and Kutkam, T., Abstracts, 2d Ann. Meeting Am. Soc. Cell Biol., p. 105, 1962.

26. Dounce, A. L., This book.

27. Zeevaart, J. A. D., This book.

28. Huang, R. C., and Bonner, J., Proc. Natl. Acad. Sci. U. S. A., 48, 1216, 1962.

29. Allfrey, V. G., Littau, V. C., and Mirsky, A. E., Proc. Natl. Acad. Sci. U. S. A., 49, 414, 1963.

30. King, T. J., and Briggs, R., Cold Spring Harbor Symp. Quant. Biol. 21, 271, 1956.

31. Prescott, D. M., and Bender, M. A., J. Comp. Physiol., 62 Suppl., 175, 1963.

32. Goldstein, L., Exptl. Cell Res., 15, 635, 1958.

 Jan A. D. Zeevaart

CHEMICAL BASIS OF INDUCTION

INTRODUCTION

Since the discovery of photoperiodism by Garner and Allard in 1920, it has been known that flowering in many plants is not an autonomous act, but is controlled by one environmental factor—the lengths of day and night. In this paper, only short-day plants will be discussed. These plants flower only if exposed, in a 24-hour cycle, to a dark period of a certain minimum length. For example, most short-day plants flower when exposed to 8 hours of light and 16 hours of darkness per day.

Short-day plants convenient to experiment with are <u>Xanthium penn-sylvanicum</u>, the cocklebur, and <u>Pharbitis nil</u>, the Japanese morning glory. Both these plants respond to exposure to one 16-hour dark period by initiation of floral primordia. The Japanese morning glory is particularly suitable for experimentation, since four-day old seedlings are fully sensitive to the 16-hour inductive night. Six to seven flower buds per seedling, including a terminal flower, are produced in response to such treatment. Seedlings grown continuously under short nights produce no flower buds. Thus, the differentiation of flower buds in this plant can be induced at will by the simple act of providing one inductive night.

FLOWER HORMONE

The next question is, if plants respond to one long night by initiation of floral primordia, which organ of the plant perceives the length of the night? By darkening either the leaf or the apex, one finds that the leaves perceive the night length, even though the ultimate result, the formation of flower buds, becomes apparent in the apex. Therefore, since plants possess no nervous system, some chemical message must move from the leaf to the apex, there to induce the formation of flower buds. This chemical has been designated the flower hormone, florigen.

343

The results of an experiment that clearly demonstrates the production and translocation of the flower hormone in Pharbitis nil are presented in Figure 1. When plants are exposed to dark for 12 hours or less, no flower buds form. With more than 12 hours of darkness, flower buds form, and their number reaches a peak with 14-15 hours of darkness. The upper curve of Figure 1 may be thought of as that of cumulative production of flower hormone. The data of the lower curve were obtained by removing the cotyledons from the seedlings at the ends of dark periods of different lengths. As compared with the first curve, there is a lag of 4-5 hours before the number of flower buds reaches a peak. If the cotyledons are cut off before the hormone has been translocated in sufficient quantities to cause flowering, flowering does not occur. The lower curve thus represents the translocation of the hormone from the cotyledons. In sum, the flower hormone of short-day plants is produced and released in the leaves during the long night and thereafter transported to the apex.

The chemical nature of the flower hormone is not yet known. Among the various metabolic inhibitors that have been applied to leaves during photoperiodic induction, only one specifically inhibits hormone production [1]. This inhibitor, SK&F 7997 [tris-(2-dimethylaminoethyl)-phosphate trihydrochloride] inhibits the biosynthesis of cholesterol in animal tissues. Thus, it has been postulated [1] that the flower hormone may be a steroid- or isoprenoid-like compound with mevalonic acid as its precursor.

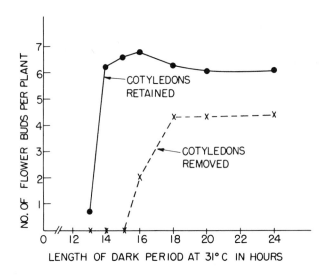

Fig. 1.—Translocation of flower hormone from cotyledons of Pharbitis nil. Four-day-old seedlings were exposed to one dark period, varying from 12 to 24 hours at 31 C. When transferred to light, the seedlings were either left intact (upper curve), or the cotyledons were cut off (lower curve).

DIFFERENTIATION

Flower hormone acts at the apex. Before photoperiodic induction, the apex produces only leaf primordia. On arrival of the hormone, the growing point enlarges and differentiates into a flower bud or an inflorescence. A new program is started in the apex as soon as the hormone appears. Present knowledge concerning the expression of genetic information leads us to the following hypothesis: All cells of a higher plant contain the same genetic information, but not all information is expressed at the same time. When a new structure, as a flower bud, is differentiated, genes previously repressed are activated in the apex by the flower hormone.

The first expression of more or new genetic information would be expected to be RNA synthesis followed by protein synthesis. This, indeed, has been observed by Gifford and Tepper [2], who have also reported a decrease in the histone-DNA ratio in the apex. This is followed by massive increases in RNA and protein synthesis. These findings were made by histochemistry and microautoradiography.

A further interesting fact concerning the action of the flower hormone is that DNA replication must continue while the hormone is at the apex. If the antimetabolites 5-fluorouracil or 5-fluorodeoxyuridine are applied to the apex before arrival of the hormone, flower formation is completely suppressed. This inhibition can be fully overcome by the timely application of thymidine, thymidylic acid, or deoxyuridine [3, 4]. In animal and bacterial systems, 5-fluorodeoxyuridine is a competitive inhibitor of the enzyme thymidylate synthetase, and the results obtained with Pharbitis indicate that the same holds for plants.

Since DNA multiplication is the primary process blocked by 5-fluorodeoxyuridine, these results have been interpreted to indicate that the flower hormone can only act and express itself in subsequent formation of flower buds when multiplying DNA is present in the apex. It follows that the genes for flowering can be activated only when they are in a state of replication.

In summary, reproductive development in short-day plants is controlled by one environmental factor, a long night. Exposure to such a dark period results in the production of the flower hormone in the leaves, which, after transport to the apex, triggers the formation of floral primordia, presumably activating genes previously repressed.

MECHANISM OF HORMONE ACTION

It has been suggested above that the flower hormone acts by turning on the floral genes in the cells of the apex. So far, no direct experimental evidence supporting this idea has been obtained.

In insects, metamorphosis is induced by the hormone ecdysone, a sterol [5]. Clever [6] has shown that shortly after injection of ecdysone into Chironomus larvae, a particular gene becomes activated, and that this can be observed as a new puff at a particular locus in the giant chromosomes of the salivary glands. This demonstrates directly that, during development, genes previously repressed become active under the influence of the hormone. Karlson [7] has suggested that hormones may generally act by activating genes. The results presented in several recent papers concerning the action of animal steroid hormones can be interpreted in favor of this hypothesis.

Butenandt, Günther and Turbe [8] found that injection of testosterone caused a fourfold increase in the incorporation of C^{14}-leucine into proteins of the seminal vesicles.

Shaw and Koen [9] studied an esterase present in mature male mice, but absent in females. Injection of testosterone caused production of the enzyme in females as well as in immature animals.

Liao and Williams-Ashman [10] tested the in vitro incorporation of transfer RNA-valine-C^{14} into protein by prostatic ribosomes. Incorporation was slight by ribosomes from castrated rats, but treatment of the castrated animals with testosterone caused the prostate gland to produce ribosomes that incorporated much greater amounts. Addition of polyUG (U:G = 6.7, containing the code word for valine) to the system markedly increased valine incorporation by preparations from castrated animals, but its addition to ribosomes from testosterone-treated animals had little effect. These results are interpreted to mean that removal of testosterone results in deficiency of messenger RNA in the prostate, a deficiency repaired by addition of testosterone.

Finally, Hamilton [11] has shown that injection of estrogens into immature rats increases the rate of RNA synthesis in the uterus, and that this is followed by an increase in protein synthesis.

All of the above observations concerning the action of hormones in higher organisms support the general working hypothesis that hormones act by activating genes, and that they direct the differentiation of higher organisms by activating particular genes at specific times and places.

Comment

The notion that steroid hormones function as regulators of gene action is generally attractive, but difficult to implement specifically. There are two particularly difficult points.

The first is, as has been pointed out earlier, that steroid hormones appear to interact most strongly with denatured DNA, and relatively little with native DNA. We must bear in mind, however, that studies of the binding of nonpolar compounds with DNA molecules by hydrophobic interaction have shown that such interaction in general tends to unwind, to melt out, DNA. Whether unwinding of DNA has a biological function is unknown.

The second difficulty is to imagine how a steroid hormone could recognize a specific locus on a chromosome. There are, however, many types of steriods, and it remains for the future to determine whether the mechanisms of binding these different materials by DNA are different. Certainly, at the moment, no molecular model can be proposed to account for recognition of a specific gene by a specific hormone. It is now, however, possible to determine experimentally whether this is actually the case or not. As has been pointed out by Karlson [7] and Karlson, Maurer, and Wenzel [5], it is feasible to determine the distribution of tritiated-ecdysone after injection into insect larvae, and thus to see if this hormone is bound specifically to the gene it activates. This should conclusively answer whether there is a direct interaction between the hormone and DNA, or an indirect action via the cytoplasm. Studies in vitro with isolated giant chromosomes may provide further clues [7].

Acknowledgments

The author's work was supported by grants from the Herman Frasch Foundation for Agricultural Chemistry and from the National Science Foundation (G-17483).

REFERENCES

1. Bonner, J., Heftmann, E., and Zeevaart, J. A. D., Plant Physiol., 38, 81, 1963.

2. Gifford, E. M., Jr., and Tepper, H. B., Am. J. Botany, 49, 706, 1962.

3. Zeevaart, J. A. D., Plant Physiol., 37, 296, 1962.

4. Zeevaart, J. A. D., Science, 137, 723, 1962.

5. Karlson, P., Maurer, R., and Wenzel, M., Z. Naturforsch., 18b, 219, 1963.

6. Clever, U., Chromosoma, 12, 607, 1961.

7. Karlson, P., Colloq. Ges. Physiol. Chem., 13, 101, 1962.

8. Butenandt, A., Günther, H., and Turbe, F., Hoppe Seylers Z. Physiol. Chem., 322, 28, 1960.

9. Shaw, C. R., and Koen, A. L., Science, 140, 70, 1963.

10. Liao, S., and Williams-Ashman, H. G., Proc. Natl. Acad. Sci. U. S. A., 48, 1956, 1962.

11. Hamilton, T. H., Proc. Natl. Acad. Sci. U. S. A., 49, 373, 1963.

Marko Zalokar

THE RELATIONSHIP OF GENE ACTION
TO EMBRYONIC INDUCTION
AND COMPETENCE

One of the basic manifestations of embryonic development is the formation of new proteins (or a change in their formation rate) at a particular time or in a particular place. Much work has been done on the appearance of new proteins or enzymes during development with the hope of finding the causes of development. As a result of this effort, we are now able to express developmental changes not as the appearance of buds, primordia, and so forth, but as the appearance of specific enzymes. The real causes remain as obscure as before, but the chemical knowledge gives us materials that are more open to experimental analysis.

We now know the chemical nature of genes, and we generally accept the theory DNA→RNA→protein. This means that whenever a new protein is being made in the cell, a gene is involved. We can, therefore, assume that during development, genes must be differentially active or inactive. The control of the final manifestation of gene activity can be exerted at several levels: (1) the gene itself, (2) the RNA-protein synthesis mechanism, (3) the protein (enzyme) function, and (4) the substrate interactions. All of these controls probably function in development, but the control at the gene level must be considered as most important and most specific.

To understand the control mechanisms involved in gene action, we should first study the physical and chemical state of an active or inactive gene, and second, how the change of this state is initiated, maintained, and terminated in an orderly fashion, as required by development.

If we assume that DNA is freely exposed to precursors and necessary enzymes, then it should continuously produce RNA, unless certain controls exist. One such control could exist if the product remained associated with the DNA molecule. The activity of DNA would then depend on a mechanism that removes the product (RNA). It has been suggested by several speakers that a DNA-RNA complex may be formed, and that the liberation of RNA would depend on breaking the bonds between the two types of molecules. If such a mechanism exists, then we should find DNA-RNA complexes in cells in which most of the genes are inactive, and the ratio of DNA to RNA should be close to 2:1 (assuming a double-strand DNA and one-strand RNA complex). In many nuclei, this ratio is much higher, so that this mechanism may have only a restricted significance in the control of gene function.

348

Another way to prevent the continuous activity of DNA could be a special mechanism required to initiate the synthesis of each new RNA molecule. If we consider a model in which the two strands of DNA separate to make RNA, then a strand-separating mechanism could function as an initiator of the synthesis. If the double-strand DNA acts as an entity, then there could be a mechanism needed to arrange nucleic acid precursors in proper spaces, or one to start RNA polymerase action. All these mechanisms would derive their specificity by interacting with a coded part of the DNA molecule as a condition for initiation.

In a more complex arrangement, DNA could be prevented from functioning by having its active sites masked, physically or chemically. A gene may be covered (associated) with other molecules, and the removal of these molecules would be needed for initiation of the synthesis. Or, the association with other molecules may induce a structural re-arrangement of the DNA molecule so that active sites are not exposed. In both cases, the activation will require unmasking—by a specific destruction of the masking material, by changing the nature of this material so that it loses affinity for DNA, or by a removal of this material to sites with greater affinity for it.

Whichever system of control is real, it must be specific for each gene. This requires at least two specific factors—a specific inducer, and a specific site to respond to the inducer. There is no real need to look for a more complicated system, as that of operon, where an operator gene is needed to initiate synthesis by a structural gene, and a regulator gene to produce a controlling molecule, which reacts specifically with the inducer and then acts on the operator.

The situation could be much simpler. If we assume that inactive genes are masked, being unmasked during activation, there is no need for a specific mask for each gene (a gene-specific histone). It is enough that one of the partners of the complex is specific, and that the demasker has a special affinity for the specific partner, the gene. The mask can be anything that can be pushed away by the remover (demasker).

The next step in our search for gene activation during development, will be to look for an inducer, or whatever we choose to call it. In development, genes should be activated at the proper time and proper place. It would be difficult to explain this by an internal rhythm of gene action, the way Goldschmidt implied in his studies of timing of manifestation of gene action. It is more probable that the gene is informed of the state of the cytoplasm and that this information is time- and space-dependent. Briefly, when the cytoplasm, or a more complex entity of cellular organization, reaches a certain stage, a signal is sent to the gene, asking for its contribution. The signal should be specific so that it acts only on the genes concerned.

This signal has been often compared to the bacterial inducers, in which a substrate or a product of enzyme action regulates the production rate of the enzyme. Such induction must play only a restricted role in development, in which the signal should evoke the formation of an entirely new set of enzymes, or of a structural protein without enzymatic action.

It would be better to compare the signal to a hormone. It is known that hormone action stimulates certain enzymatic activities, which may be due to new, or increased production of, enzymes. It could be assumed that either the hormones themselves, or some immediate products of their activity, activate genes. In this case, the gene products are not related to the inducing agent, as would be true in the previous case. The genes must have a special structure able to accept this signal. If one signal activates several unrelated genes, they will have this structure in common. If we assume that all of the DNA molecule contains a code for a protein, this special structure may then also be a code for a part of the protein, so that all proteins evoked by the same signal may contain a partially identical amino acid sequence.

After this short discussion of the genetic side of the problem, we will turn to the embryological side. The classical and central theme of experimental embryology is Spemann's organizer, which induces the neural crest in early embryos. A tremendous amount of work has been done to find its chemical nature, which remains unknown, although it is believed now to be either protein or RNA.

I would like to discuss another system of embryonic induction, which entails less complicated processes, but shows all the typical problems of induction, namely lens formation.

At a certain stage in embryonic development the optic cup comes into contact with overlying epiderm and induces in it formation of a lens. Studies showed that in most cases, the inducing stimulus of the cup is needed for lens production. The cup can be removed and placed under the epiderm elsewhere, or the epiderm can be transplanted over the cup: a lens will be induced, whenever the epiderm is competent. The exploration of competence shows that early ectoderm (gastrula) does not react, and that the reaction disappears gradually after tail bud stage. Although during the neurula stage, the epiderm of any region of the body reacts, at later stages the competence narrows down to the epiderm in the vicinity of the eye cup.

There is another system in which lens formation can be used to study developmental processes, the so-called Wolffian lens regeneration. After removal of a lens in some Urodeles (Triturus, Salamandra), a new lens is formed from the upper rim of the iris. This formation, as in the embryo, is induced by the eye cup, the retina in this case. The competence is restricted to a small area of the iris. It is remarkable that iris epithelium, derived from tissues that had no competence to form lens during embryonic organization, acquire this competence later. But more interesting still, iris is a differentiated tissue, which, under the influence of an inducer, first becomes dedifferentiated and then assumes a new function. Part of these changes can be easily expressed in chemical terms and should be open to experimental approach. Iris epithelium is heavily pigmented; one function of its genes is to direct the production of enzymes connected with the formation of melanin granules. During lens induction, this function is stopped, melanin is removed from the cell, and a new function starts—synthesis of specific lens proteins.

The process of induction must activate genes involved in new functions. Genes responsible for the formation of lens proteins are of special interest—lens proteins are structural proteins, not enzymes. There is no substrate or end-product of enzyme action that could serve as an inducer. The stimulus for induction comes from the eye cup (or retina) and not from the responding tissue. Clearly, this induction is of a different nature than enzyme induction.

Besides inducing new protein formation, the lens inducer must inactivate the genes responsible for melanin formation. The exact nature of this process is an open question. Were the iris-epithelium-genes normally under the influence of a "melanin" inducer reverting to an inactive state with the change in cell processes, or did the lens inducer inactivate them directly?

But most important is the question of competence. Not all cells can respond to the action of inducers. This may be entirely due to some obscure cytoplasmic effects, interacting with the inducer, but we prefer to think that there is a more direct relationship between competence and gene action. In this case, only cells with competence have genes in a state receptive to the inducer. We must then assume at least two independent mechanisms of control of gene action in development.

One mechanism determines a certain state of genes, so that they are potentially able to respond to inducing action. The other mechanism initiates gene action itself. We find a similar situation in the case of hormonal controls. Thyrotropic hormone, for example, activates the production of thyroxine and thyreoglobulin, but this only in competent cells, that is to say, cells of the thyroid gland.

What is competence, then; what is induction? Competence has to do with the masking of genes, induction, and initiation of RNA synthesis. In terms of our concern with histones, we can imagine that histones keep genes incompetent; the removal of histones does not make genes active, but only makes them susceptible to the action of inducers.

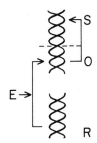

VII. THOUGHTS
FOR THE FUTURE

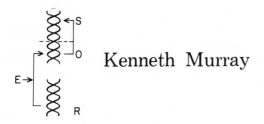

Kenneth Murray

THE STATE OF HISTONE CHEMISTRY

One of the most outstanding features of histones is the complex array of proteins contained in a given preparation from a single source. The application of a new method for protein fractionation has thus far served to show that previously isolated histone fractions are still heterogeneous. Thus, although we have been presented with a variety of procedures for both analytical and preparative fractionation of histone extracts (variations on chromatographic and zone electrophoretic techniques have proved the most popular), it is clear that none of the several fractions and subfractions so far prepared is homogeneous. In fact, some of the fractions are still complex mixtures about which we know very little.

The complexity of histones is a barrier to the resolution of discrete histone components, and, therefore, to detailed chemical studies of these proteins and to the quest for variations in histones prepared from different species and different cell types. Nevertheless, considerable effort has been devoted to investigations of histones from a wide variety of sources and although the various preparations have, at least in general, a great qualitative similarity, some outstanding differences have been observed. It has been shown that pea embryo, rice embryo, and wheat germ histones differ markedly from mammalian histone preparations and the histones from wheat germ contain little or no histone fractions with a high proportion of arginine residues. Furthermore, a histone fraction prepared from chicken erythrocyte nuclei has not yet been found in other histone preparations. Comparisons of histones of normal and tumor tissues have revealed far more similarities than differences between these two classes generally, although small differences have been indicated.

Obviously, extensions of studies on fractionation of histones are essential. Methods based on chemical fractionation or column chromatography possess the advantage of high capacity. However, zone electrophoresis in gels (either starch or polyacrylamide) offers a higher degree of resolution and is a good analytical method, but the low capacity of the gels limits their use in preparative experiments. It is possible that polyacrylamide gels will provide useful preparative procedures if a reasonable capacity can be attained, but at the present there seems little alternative to the use of combined procedures, and hence the separation of a given fraction of histone is tedious and yields are low.

In spite of the need for improved procedures for the fractionation of histones, further investigations into the heterogeneity of histone fractions and into differences between histones from various species and cell types must continue. The most promising approach to studies of this type probably lies in careful, detailed, quantitative work on the peptides furnished by various partial hydrolytic procedures. The need for care in the fractionation and recovery of peptides so derived and the importance of quantitative recovery of the peptides as well as their quantitative amino acid analysis cannot be overstressed. Work of this nature is necessarily tedious and time consuming, but may be greatly facilitated by the use of in vivo labeling experiments.

Studies of partial hydrolysates of histone fractions do, of course, provide information pertaining to the primary structure of the histone components, but the heterogeneity of histone fractions makes it impossible to progress far in the elucidation of complete amino acid sequence. However, the limited information available is of interest and use in considerations of some aspects of the association of the various histone fractions with DNA. An irregular arrangement of basic amino acids along the polypeptide chains has been demonstrated for several histone fractions.

The complexity of histones obtained from a given source is well established and it is improbable that this complex array of proteins is produced artificially during preparation. It is not known how many proteins are contained in a given histone preparation, but the number may be quite large. In my opinion, it is not yet possible to assign, with any confidence, even an order of magnitude to the probable number of different histones. Another problem raised by the complexity of histones is that of histone nomenclature, a matter discussed elsewhere in this volume.

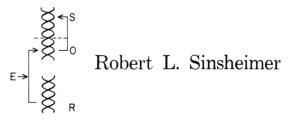

Robert L. Sinsheimer

THE STATE OF
NUCLEOHISTONE STRUCTURE

We have as yet only the most vague and general ideas of the structures of nucleohistones. At least three different structures have been proposed. One, implicit in much discussion, is the older idea that the histone is wrapped in the large groove of one, or perhaps two, parallel DNA molecules. A second proposal, put forward by Zubay, is essentially a sheet-like structure, in which DNA molecules run in one direction, and histone molecules run at an angle of 37° to them, thus matching up every other large groove. This is an interesting proposal, particularly if one thinks of it in terms of the coiling of chromosomes as they condense in preparation for mitosis. The kind of arrangement Zubay has proposed will, if the histones are disposed on only one side of the DNA, tend to cause the DNA to coil up. This is certainly reminiscent of the things one sees in condensing chromosomes. A third structure, that proposed by Richards, suggests that histone molecules are located between pairs of DNA molecules. Support for this structure is vague at present, however.

To understand the structure of nucleohistones, we should understand the secondary and tertiary structure of histones themselves. Although there has been much talk about native histones, it is not in fact clear, other than as a general concept, what a native histone is. Whether histones possess secondary or tertiary structure beyond that which can be obtained by putting them in ethylene chlorohydrin, or whether there is some secondary structure that is maintained during association of histone with DNA, is as yet unknown.

In this connection, it would appear that the methods used to prepare histones—extraction by acid or sequential passage through solutions of high and low ionic strength—must inevitably lead to preparations that, at one stage or another, lose any secondary structure they might have had. Whether such secondary structure can be reconstituted in the sense that polyglumatic acid can undergo the coil-helix transition reversibly has not yet been established. Whether the structures of histones in the reconstituted nucleohistones of Bonner and Huang bear any simple relationship to the structures of histones as they exist in native nucleohistone is unknown.

357

Perhaps the closest approach as yet attained to native nucleohistone is the material Bonner and Huang obtain by gentle shearing of chromatin in media of low ionic strength. It would be highly worthwhile to carry on more detailed studies with material of this sort.

Both Zubay and Richards have laid some emphasis upon the 37-Å spacing they find by X-ray diffraction analysis of nucleohistone preparations. This spacing has also been found in X-ray studies of erythrocyte nuclei. These facts support the notion that the 37-Å spacing may constitute a basic datum of nucleohistone biology.

A further point of interest concerns whether there are differences in the secondary and tertiary structures of the different kinds of histone that have been isolated. I suppose that Bonner has this in mind when he discusses the question of the different proline contents of different histones. Differences in proline content obviously influence the possible amount of α-helix that may be formed in any particular histone, and this in turn may influence the extent to which histone can combine with one or more DNA molecules. It is not immediately obvious that an α-helix can be positioned in the large groove of a single DNA molecule. In all probability, it would be much too stiff. The α-helix content of the histone of nucleohistone preparations is quite evidently something that needs to be studied. This may require new and special methods. The interesting results of Bradbury were based on deuterium exchange. Supporting data by other methods will be desirable, however.

Finally, and most importantly, we should understand in more detail the question whether a histone can select a particular DNA molecule, a particular informational sequence. No experimental results have yet been reported as to whether there is differential binding of different histones to different DNA's of different base composition or to synthetic polynucleotides of different composition. This will provide an important subject for further investigation of nucleohistone structure.

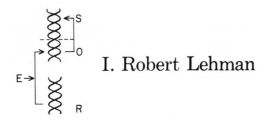

I. Robert Lehman

ENZYMOLOGY RELATED
TO THE NUCLEOHISTONES

I have had two recent encounters with histones. The first was the description Professor Arthur Kornberg gave me of an experiment in which he had observed a dramatic inhibition of the DNA polymerase from Escherichia coli by preparations of calf thymus histone. He finally traced this effect to a quantitative precipitation of the DNA primer by the histone. Since the enzyme exhibits an absolute requirement for DNA, its action is inhibited by DNA precipitation. I concluded from this experience that the ability of histones to precipitate DNA, while technically interesting and useful, was biologically uninteresting. My second recent experience with histones has been the discussions assembled in the present volume. My take-home lesson is "Histones are not to be dismissed so lightly."

It is apparent that histones do more in the cell than simply act as DNA precipitants. One encouragement for this point of view comes from the contribution of Bonner and Huang, who have shown that soluble complexes of DNA and histone can be prepared by a careful reconstitution process. Such reconstituted nucleohistones can be characterized by their melting temperatures, by their sedimentation constants, and by their contents of histone and DNA. With such soluble complexes in hand, it is certainly possible to do meaningful enzymology.

The experiments of Bonner and Huang provide some support, albeit not direct, for Stedman's hypothesis that histones are inhibitors of gene action. Bonner and Huang have demonstrated rather clearly that histones inhibit the action of RNA polymerase, both that purified from Escherichia coli and that from pea chromatin. If we accept current ideas concerning protein synthesis, RNA polymerase, of course, occupies a central role in the phenotypic expression of a gene.

Of interest, too, is the correlation found by Bonner and Huang between the degree of inhibition of RNA priming activity of a given histone fraction and its content of lysine, the lysine-rich fractions being the more effective, and the correlation of this relation to the stabilization of DNA against melting by the same histone. Histone fractions of high lysine and low arginine content raise the T_m of the reconstituted nucleohistone substantially, and completely abolish the ability of the DNA to support RNA synthesis. On the other hand, fractions rich in arginine and poor in lysine exert no effect on T_m of the DNA, and inhibit but little RNA synthesis.

Supporting the notion that the reconstituted complexes are not entirely artifacts, nucleohistones have also been isolated from several tissues and shown to be without activity in the priming of RNA synthesis, as would be predicted on the basis of the reconstitution experiments.

Other workers, too, have reported in this volume on the effects of histones in various states of purity on the ability of DNA to support RNA synthesis by RNA polymerase. The results are generally in agreement. One can, in general, find conditions under which histones inhibit RNA polymerase in vitro. There is general agreement, too, between the groups of Bonner and Huang, Butler, Hnilica (who worked with DNA polymerase) and Allfrey, that the lysine-rich histones are more effective inhibitors of the polymerases they have studied, and the arginine-rich histones less effective. In only one study, that reported by Weiss, who used highly purified micrococcal RNA polymerase, was no effect of the addition of histone on rate of RNA synthesis detected. In this instance the amount of histone added to the system was substantially below that required for equivalence of DNA and histone. The absence of inhibition may simply have been due to suboptimal levels of histone.

An important question concerning the enzymology of histone action in the RNA polymerase system is the degree of specificity of the inter-action of histone and DNA. This is obviously but one facet of a major question that concerns all workers in the field. How specific is the action of histone in the various systems and situations in which it has been studied—histologically, cytochemically, enzymatically, and so on? Is the histone simply acting as a nonspecific polycation, which binds polyanionic structures, such as nucleic acids, and effectively removes them from the scene? Or is there some more important and subtle specificity? As yet, there is no definitive answer to this question. One interesting point re-garding specificity has been raised in Hnilica's studies with DNA poly-merase of Escherichia coli, in which he found that lysine-rich histones are potent inhibitors of the enzyme. This inhibition closely correlated with the ability of a particular histone to precipitate DNA, so that in these experiments, inhibition and precipitation went hand in hand. But the in-teresting observation, regardless of its relevance to gene action, is that treatment of the histone with trypsin for increasing periods causes the histone to lose both its inhibitory activity and its ability to precipitate DNA. These changes in properties of the histone appear when their phys-ical changes, as measures by sedimentation, are relatively minor.

In the elegant experiments of Weiss, a stimulation of the rate of action of RNA polymerase (that of M. lysodeikticus) resulted from the addition of what may be the bacterial counterpart of histones, the poly-amines. The mechanism of this stimulation is not clear, but physical studies are now under way in a number of laboratories, whose purpose is to develop an understanding of the binding of polyamines to DNA. An important advantage of polyamines over the histones is that their struc-ture is known with some degree of certainty. One can look forward to at least some meaningful physical chemistry of the binding of polyamines to DNA, and to meaningful studies of the activity of such complexed DNA's in a wide variety of enzymatic systems.

Finally, an important contribution to the enzymology of nucleohistones and histones is contained in the paper in this volume by Flamm and Birnstiel, or more specifically, in the last table of their paper. This table summarizes the results of experiments that indicate a limited, but nonetheless significant, incorporation of labeled amino acids into histone-like material. These experiments were done with cell-free extracts—with isolated nucleoli. This is an encouraging beginning in the understanding of the cell-free biosynthesis of histones. If one may predict on the basis of enzymatic studies carried out in other areas, it would be my prediction that studies of cell-free synthesis of histones, in addition to providing information about their biosynthetic pathway, cannot help but shed some light on the role of histones in cellular metabolism.

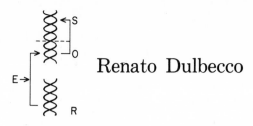

Renato Dulbecco

THE HISTONES AS CANDIDATES
FOR A ROLE IN GENETIC REPRESSION

It is obvious that today we do not have enough information to determine whether histones have any relevance to developmental processes. For this reason, I propose not so much to analyze what has previously been said and written on the subject, but rather to consider the whole problem as it appears today. In doing so, I do not believe that one can decide whether histones have a determining role in development, but one can perhaps decide whether it is possible that they are involved, and perhaps how they might be involved.

Zalokar (this volume) puts it well when he says that development consists of the synthesis of a specific protein at a specific time. I agree, too, with his comment that the memory of the system is important; that previous experience of the system determines its response at the moment of the experiment. The problem of development is, then, the problem of gene regulation in a complex organism. We can think of a differentiating cell as a black box into which we feed information that may be either in the form of a substance or substances or in the form of cell-to-cell contact. Out of our cell comes some kind of response. The cell possesses a new attitude as a result of the input.

The question is, then, what happens within the black box? The only logical way we can think about this problem today is to say that what happens in the black box is analogous to what we know happens in other black boxes. The analogy we use is that of the bacterial system, because this is the only system about which we know something. The basic information derived from bacterial studies is that there are two types of genes, regulator genes and structural genes. The structural gene makes a messenger RNA, which in turn codes the construction of a protein. The regulator gene controls the operation of the structural gene; determines whether or not it makes its characteristic messenger RNA. The regulator gene does this through a repressor that operates over some restricted area of the gene. It is known that there are substances that may enter the cell from the outside and influence the process by controlling the function of the repressor.

Is it possible that a mechanism of the type known for bacteria is operative also in development? We will assume that this is the case. We should recall that there are probably two principal types of regulatory systems in bacteria, one having to do with the regulation of the production of messenger RNA, as described above, and a second having to do with the regulation of DNA multiplication itself. The operation of these mechanisms in bacteria defines two types of functional units for the DNA of the cell. The first is the unit functional in the synthesis of RNA, the expression of gene function. This unit is called the operon. The second is the unit functional with respect to DNA replication, a unit of DNA we may designate as the replicon.

Now let us examine the facts with respect to the cells of higher organisms. Do we have any evidence that there are functional units in the chromosomes of the cells of higher creatures? I think that there is such evidence. It has, for example, been shown that chromosomes consist of chromomeres, that in some places the chromosome is condensed and in others, not. There is also the example of the loops of the lampbrush chromosome. These, too, appear to represent regions of some kind of unitary function, each including a large segment of the chromosome. There is, in addition, the heterochromatin, which is perhaps a DNA with a functional attitude different from that of other DNA. The units we here discuss—chromomeres, loops, heterochromatic pieces—are of course much larger than the functional units of bacteria. Each would involve perhaps ten times as much DNA as that of a bacterial operon. Differentiation into units such as chromomeres or loops cannot be produced by DNA alone; it requires something else. What is this something else? It is probable that it is a protein, and it is probable that it is histone, because histone is the protein always present in association with the DNA of chromosomes. The fact that there are many different chromomeres within the chromosome suggests that different types of molecules must cause their formation. If these are histones, then there must be many kinds of histones with different properties. These are, I would say, a priori requirements.

If we look again at the problem of regulation, bearing in mind that intracellular regulatory substances are involved, we can ask what are the a priori requirements for the substance which is to be a regulator? It would seem that such a regulator must possess at least two properties. It must be made by a gene, so as to have specificity with respect to its synthesis, and it must act on a gene, or a part of a gene, or a group of genes, and must therefore have specificity as to site of action. We may now look at the problem of the role of histones by asking whether histones have the degree of specificity required of such regulatory substances. This question has already been discussed from a structural point of view by other authors in this volume, and the question has been raised whether there are enough types of histones to provide, for example, a different repressor for each gene of the genome. If this were the case, we would expect to find in the cell perhaps a million different kinds of histone molecules.

Before we pursue this argument further, let us discuss in more detail the problem of histone specificity from a different standpoint. Is there any evidence that histones are synthesized, specified, by specific genes? One cannot help but be impressed by the fact that the histone chemists have shown that if one isolates the corresponding kinds of histones from very different kinds of cells—Walker carcinoma, calf thymus, pea seedlings, Chlorella—one obtains substances with very similar properties. Peptide analysis of the corresponding histone fractions of histones of different origins further establishes their similarity. Many of the peptides of corresponding histones of different origins are identical, and even those that are different are different by, say, one amino acid out of three or four. Since the peptides obtained by tryptic hydrolysis of histones are small, we might ask whether such similarity could be produced by chance from histones in which amino acids are randomly assorted. It can be calculated that the probability that such similarity as has been found among the peptides of histones of different origins is due to chance is extremely small. We must therefore conclude that the similarity of the peptide patterns of histones of different origins suggests strongly that the histones of different origins do actually correspond to one another, that, in other words, they are made by the same gene, similarly expressed in cells of many types. The differences that have been found recall the differences between, for example, the insulins of different species. It therefore appears likely that such differences among histones may have arisen by mutational differences. These considerations lend some conviction to the idea that histones are precisely gene-determined substances, and that they therefore must have some kind of precise and specific structures and effects.

Other points of view have been expressed. This is true, for example, of the investigators who have looked at the interaction between DNA and histone and have found that this interaction does not readily reveal any great degree of specificity. I think we should recognize, however, that in such studies one may be looking at only a very general characteristic of histone molecules, namely, the most obvious one of ionic interaction of the basic groups of histones with the acidic groups of nucleic acid. If there are other properties of the histone molecule that might lead to subtle interaction with DNA, these may very well have been missed. We cannot, therefore, give much weight to the fact that structural investigations have not as yet yielded any support to the idea of specificity of structure of these materials.

Considering now the effects of the histones, we would like to know whether here also there is any specificity. We should first note that the results of a number of kinds of experiments do not show specificity. This is true, for example, of the effect of histone on lampbrush chromosomes, described by Mirsky. These effects were, in fact, obtained in a highly heterologous system (Triturus chromosomes, calf thymus histone). The ability of histones to produce effects in heterologous systems does not exclude the possibility of their possessing specificity, because again, the effects thus far studied result from the least specific and most obvious type of interaction, that of histone as a polycation rather than as an information unit.

On the other hand, other findings suggest that there is specificity in the histone and in the histone-DNA interaction. One simple fact is that the DNA of sperm in some species does not possess histone, but is complexed with protamine, and that during the development of the fertilized egg, histones are formed and caused to replace the protamine. This is a hint that histones are something important, and not just cations for the polyanionic DNA. In this connection, the problem of the heterogeneity of the histones becomes an important one. This point has already been discussed, but I wish to bring out two further facts. First of all, a chromatographically or electrophoretically homogeneous histone fraction yields, on peptide analysis, a limited number of peptides. This seems to me to support the view that in each histone fraction there are not a great many different kinds of histones. It might be objected that this point is invalid because the peptide analysis reflects only the structure of the major histone components in the particular fraction, and that there may be a vast number of minor components, which we do not detect. This is, for the geneticist, not a convincing argument. If histones are specific and individual regulatory substances at the gene level, they should be made up of a mixture of many regulators, each one affecting a different gene. There is no reason to assume that there should be major and minor components, since the various regulator materials should each be present in the same amount. I therefore tend to agree with Bonner that the number of histones present in a cell is not tremendously large, but is limited to perhaps a hundred or a thousand, not to a million.

If this is so, can we still maintain that histones are regulatory substances? How might they operate? In this connection it is a welcome discovery that bacteria have been found to contain histones, or at least molecules comparable to histones. If these molecules are associated with the bacterial DNA, the finding is an important one, since it would suggest a universality in the role of histones, a fact which would be in agreement with their possible regulatory function.

A second important point in this connection is that the histones are of small molecular size. Since histone molecules are small, and since there is a sufficient supply of histone in the cell to cover essentially the full complement of DNA, we are faced with two alternatives. One is that histones are regulatory substances and that many histone molecules correspond to an individual gene. Regulation would be produced by a cooperative effect over many molecules of histone. This is a distasteful notion. The second possibility is that some histone molecules act at a specific point of the gene. According to this view, on each gene there would be one molecule of regulatory histone and many other molecules of histones that are not regulatory. This would, of course, complicate the situation a great deal. To avoid these difficulties, one tends to assume that there cannot be a great amount of specificity in the action of histones because, after all, histone-DNA interaction is based on the interaction of basic groups with the regulatory, spaced, phosphate groups of DNA. This does not, in fact, preclude the existence of other types of interaction. We can, for example, imagine that the histone molecule interacts ionically with the DNA molecule, but that, in addition, it can reach inside and interact with the specificity-conferring groups of the bases, particularly at such moments as the DNA chains open up in the performance of their functional activity. Since it is probable that a DNA chain operates cyclically, it would be possible for histone molecules to recognize specific sites on the DNA, recognition being made perhaps according to base sequence, and for the histone to become attached in stable configuration by interactions in addition to the nonspecific ionic one.

Now to more specific points of view concerning the role of histones in development. One of the more important points is the behavior of histones in the puffing of polytene chromosomes. It has been shown that histones persist during the puffing, and that the histone-DNA ratio is equal in puffing and nonpuffing regions. It would appear to me that this suggests that, if the histones have a regulatory function, they display it, not through their presence or absence, but because of their relationship to the DNA itself. These considerations raise a further question. What is the role in the over-all picture of exogenous substances obviously involved in the regulation of development—hormones, for example, specific growth factors, etc. ? Since it seems impossible for any of these substances to recognize directly the DNA of a particular gene, there must be some other intermediary substance that assists in specific recognition. It appears probable that the intermediary substances are not histones, because these do not appear, as we have seen, to possess sufficient specificity for such recognition. This suggests, then, that the action of histone on DNA may be mediated by a substance or substances that recognize DNA informational sequences, substances that act as specific keys. Such keys could be part of the histone molecule or could be separate molecular species. The key, in general, would recognize the exogenous substances, such as steroids, that contribute to regulation. This suggests also that the differing degrees of inhibition of RNA synthesis by different histones, as observed in the work of Bonner and Huang, perhaps have to do with variable contaminations of the various histone fractions by substances with the property of the key described above.

And now for a few final comments. These have to do with the possible role of histones in carcinogenesis. It has been shown by Stanfield Rogers that the virus-induced papilloma of rabbits contains a very active arginase and, in addition, a reduced amount of arginine-rich histone. Whether this reduction in the amount of histone has any relationship to the induction and persistence of the cancerous state is something that should most certainly be investigated.

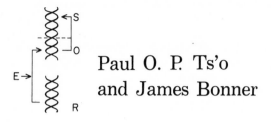

Paul O. P. Ts'o
and James Bonner

BIOLOGY AND CHEMISTRY
OF THE HISTONES: THE CHALLENGES

Recent advances in the biochemistry and biophysics of protein and nucleic acid synthesis encourage the formulation of concepts of reproduction, growth, and adaptation in bacteria at the molecular level. It now appears to be appropriate to try to formulate analogous concepts, or at least to raise similar questions, concerning the cells of higher organisms, plants, and animals. At the cellular level, the major difference between microorganisms and higher forms of life lies in the state of organization and complexity within the cell. Of the subcellular structures of higher organisms, the nucleus is of most interest and importance, since physically it is the principal seat of information storage and information transfer. A complete molecular description of the functions of the nucleus cannot, of course, be formulated until its structure, chemistry, and enzymology have been more thoroughly worked out. We can even now, however, start to pose pertinent questions about the nucleus. Among the many components of the nucleus, we focus our attention on the histones. We choose the histones not only because of the large quantities of this material in the nucleus, and not only because histones occur exclusively within the nucleus, but also because histones interact strongly with DNA. One may hope that studies of histones will yield information pertinent to the understanding of the mechanisms that regulate DNA replication, as well as of the mechanisms that regulate DNA-dependent RNA synthesis and thus control growth and differentiation. In addition to the many obvious questions concerning the chemistry of histones, such as their preparation and purification, fractionation and homogeneity, amino acid composition and sequences, molecular weights and secondary structures, and so forth, we wish to ponder certain structural and chemical problems, the answers to which are critical and fundamental to the understanding of the function of histones. Many of the questions we raise have not previously been emphasized, or even asked, and the answers to them are not yet in sight. Presentation and discussion of these questions may serve a useful purpose.

I. NATURAL STATE OF HISTONE AND DNA IN THE NUCLEUS

Some specific spatial and structural relationship between histone and DNA is necessary if histones are to regulate the functioning of DNA effectively. It is, therefore, of importance to know whether the DNA-histone complex does in fact exist in the living cell. We divide the argument on this matter into two parts:

A. DNA and histone are not complexed in the living cell, and the nucleo-histones that have been isolated are artifacts.

Reflection will reveal that this statement contains a serious challenge, and is not as ridiculous as it might at first appear. One can imagine at least three situations inside the nucleus, all capable of rapid alteration as a result of nuclear damage, that could prevent complex formation between the polyanion, DNA, and the polycation, histone. These are (1) Histone and DNA are each bound to other structural elements within the nucleus and are prevented from coming into close contact with one another; (2) Histones and DNA are bathed in a high concentration of electrolyte contained inside the nucleus; (3) Other naturally occurring organic polyanions, such as diamines and dicarboxylic acids, are specifically concentrated in the nucleus and inhibit DNA-histone complex formation. Careful investigations of intranuclear electrolyte concentrations, and of the presence or absence in the nucleus of other small, organic polyions, will make decisions possible on situations (2) and (3). A definitive decision on the first situation is more difficult, since the question itself is not well defined.

There are at least two a priori reasons for supposing that histones play an important role in the nucleus by providing a structural basis for the functioning of DNA. The first is that at one particular period in the mitotic cycle, all of the DNA in the nucleus specifically aggregates to form condensed chromosomes. Histones, by their proximity to DNA (and ubiquity in higher organisms), are therefore the agents most probably concerned with the orientation and anchoring of the DNA in these super-structures. The second reason is that the biology of the nucleus suggests that all of its DNA molecules possess a structural and spatial relationship to one another. All data indicate that DNA molecules do not simply float freely inside the nucleoplasm, but have a definite order and are arranged in definite sequences. If we imagine that the nuclear DNA cannot function properly without the appropriate structural arrangement, then histones are the candidates of choice for the position of providing such structure. Indeed, it would be very difficult to suggest any function for the histones if this function is not to complex with DNA. We are led, therefore, to examine the structure of the DNA-histone complex and to consider how this structure is related to the function of DNA.

B. The properties and structure of the isolated DNA-histone complex may be different from that which exists in the living cell.

This possibility remains as the greatest challenge to direct experimental investigation of the DNA-histone complex. There are suggestions (see Zubay in this volume) that perhaps the major function of histones is to connect DNA molecules together in proper order in the chromosomal superstructure, but not necessarily to cover up the DNA and thus prevent it from functioning, as histone appears to do in the isolated nucleohistones. This point will be discussed in more detail below. It may be hoped that X-ray examinations of intact nuclei may contribute information concerning the exact nature of the association between DNA and histone in vivo.

A simple but relevant experiment is here proposed, an experiment which can tell us whether nucleohistone as at present isolated is an artifact. An exogenous DNA, heavily labeled with isotope, such as P^{32}, is to be mixed with isolated but intact nuclei. The nuclei are then disrupted in medium of low ionic strength and the nucleohistone isolated. Nucleohistone sediments more rapidly than DNA, and can therefore be readily separated from the free DNA. If the nucleohistone is found to be grossly contaminated with the exogenous DNA, then there is strong indication that artifacts are present in the commonly isolated nucleohistones. To serve as control on the thoroughness of mixing and on the possibility of interaction, nuclei and labeled exogenous DNA should also be disrupted in medium of high ionic strength (2 M NaCl). The mixture is then to be diluted to low ionic strength (for example, 0.2 M NaCl). The nucleohistone isolated under these conditions should contain the labeled exogenous DNA.

II. FORMATION OF THE DNA-HISTONE COMPLEX

For a DNA-histone complex to be biologically meaningful, it must satisfy at least two principal requirements, i.e., those of irreversibility and specificity. Our present knowledge indicates that there are not tens of thousands of kinds of histones, a situation that would be necessary if one specific kind of histone were required for interaction with each individual, functional unit of DNA. It is more realistic to assume that the same species of histone molecule can and does react with a variety of segments or functional units of DNA.

Irreversibility

Proper control within the cell of the binding of histone along the DNA strand requires a certain degree of irreversibility of the complex formation. It is essential that the complex, once formed, be required to surmount an energy barrier before dissociation can occur. For instance, particular histones are to be removed from the area X of DNA during the mitotic or life cycle. It is vital that the complex elsewhere in the genome not be weakened, and that histones do not move from other areas back to area X. An appropriate energy barrier should make such selective histone removal possible. Such an energy barrier to dissociation will also reduce the sensitivity of the complex to the local concentrations of DNA and of histone. Furthermore, it is expected from the behavior of polyelectrolytes that it will be difficult to maintain complete covering of the DNA (to maintain equivalence) with histone at all times. Electrostatic interaction will be greatly reduced at advanced stages of neutralization. At some times and some places along the DNA chain, histone would tend to dissociate unspecifically in the absence of an energy barrier to such dissociation. At least four types of experimental evidence support the notion that formation of the complex between DNA and histone is to a certain degree irreversible: (1) The molecular weight of nucleohistone is not sensitive to dilution [1]; (2) Histones exhibit secondary structure in nucleohistone, but uncoil and denature if they are dissociated from DNA (see both Zubay and Bradbury, this volume); (3) Such denatured histones can reform secondary structure if dissolved in a solvent in which they are sparingly soluble, or if cast into a surface film (see Bradbury, this volume); (4) Partially dissociated native nucleohistone yields a two-step melting profile (absorbancy vs. temperature), rather than a gradual transition (Bonner and Huang, this volume).

Unfortunately, the critical experiments related to this point are yet to be done. For instance, do we find any redistribution of histones when free DNA is added to a solution of nucleohistone ? Does denatured histone regain its helical content when recombined with DNA ? The existence of an energy barrier to dissociation may be due to changes, resulting from association, in environment and conformation of either or both histone and DNA. Thus, a change of histone conformation induced by complex formation with DNA would clearly indicate the source of the dissociation energy barrier. So far as the DNA is concerned, it is generally considered that there is no gross change of its conformation or shape as a result of formation of the nucleohistone complex. The E_p $_{259\ m\mu}$ (molar extinction coefficient for phosphorus) of nucleohistone is interestingly greater than that of DNA, about 10%, a value much too high to be attributed to the contribution of the histones, proteins poor in aromatic amino acids [2]. Furthermore, the increment in E_p appears to be decreased in the presence of 1 M NaCl, a salt concentration that, of course, causes substantial dissociation of the complex. Comparison of the optical rotary dispersion of nucleohistones in media of low ionic strength with that in media of high ionic strength (at least 2 M NaCl) may also provide interesting information.

By measuring the amount of crosslinkage induced by ultraviolet irradiation between the two strands of DNA, Glisin and Doty [3] detected pulsation along the double helix. What changes in such pulsation will result when DNA is in complex with histone ? These are but a few of many kinds of experiments whose results are essential to a better understanding of the nature of the DNA-histone complex.

Specificity

There are three aspects to specificity in a functional DNA-histone complex: (1) kinds of DNA (composition, sequence, and conformation) contained in a given complex and their relationships to nearby kinds of DNA (for proper superstructure); (2) kinds of histones contained in the complex and their relationships to nearby kinds of histones; (3) requirements of the programmed activity of the cell, that is, the aspect of the elements of time and sequence of events. It is quite possible that at different times or points along the developmental pathway, a particular DNA segment, a particular portion of the genome, may be combined with different species of histone, and vice versa, as demanded by the program of genetic activity with which the nucleus is provided.

One would, naturally enough, like to know whether a histone can recognize the base sequence of a segment of DNA. The histone, if it can, must presumably perform its task either by itself or with the assistance of some adapter to which it is attached, such as an oligonucleotide or a steroid. We have little information about, and equally little insight into, the nature of specific interaction between proteins and nucleic acid. We still do not understand the basis of specificity in the well-known and clear-cut case of the interaction between a specific transfer RNA and its specific amino acid-activating enzyme. Much more work on this important matter is needed before any theoretical treatment can be made of specificity in the DNA-histone complex.

Two major conclusions on specificity can be drawn from existing data (see related papers in this volume): (1) There are many types of histones and many varying degrees of binding strength between DNA and histones; (2) There are cell, organ and species specificities with respect to types of histones. The complexity of the picture certainly indicates the possibility of high specificity. Such specificity has not yet, however, been proved to have any biological meaningfulness. An attempt is now being made in our laboratories to study the specificity of the histone-DNA complex by virtue of its activity as a template for RNA synthesis. The main line of reasoning is as follows: A biological system is selected that manufactures protein X, but not protein Y, at period X in the life cycle, and manufactures protein Y, but not protein X at period Y of the life cycle. The chromatins, comprising nucleohistones X and Y will be isolated from cells at the respective periods X and Y of the life cycle. A DNA-dependent RNA synthesis system will be set up and coupled to an RNA-dependent protein synthesis system. The function of DNA will be filled by the native chromatins, X and Y. It is hoped to show that protein X, but not protein Y, is synthesized by the system when chromatin X is used as template in the system, and conversely, that protein Y, but not protein X, is synthesized when chromatin Y is used as template. The virtue of this experiment lies not in biochemistry, but in the fact that it is a step toward the development of a direct link between differentiation and biochemistry. How is this experiment to be related to the function of histone? It is hoped that removal of histones from the two kinds of nucleohistones of chromatins X and Y will result in

DNA capable of acting as templates for the support of the synthesis of both proteins X and Y, and this irrespective of the parent chromatin. Thus, the nucleohistone X does not have the capacity to support the synthesis of protein Y until the histones with which it is complexed are removed, and similarly for nucleohistone Y, which does not support the synthesis of protein X until the histone on it is removed.

The experiment outlined above will almost certainly work as described. (This has since been done.) The principal challenge to, and question concerning, its interpretation involves the nature of the process adopted for the removal of histone. Is the removal of histone the only consequence of the process used? Is the alteration in the nucleohistone which confers upon it the ability to support synthesis of a larger variety of proteins related directly to removal of histone? Two types of experiments may be seen as essential if these questions are to be rewarded with a direct answer: (1) Treatment of nucleohistone to increase the number of kinds of proteins it can cause to be synthesized must be correlated with the amount of histone removed from the nucleohistone; (2) Treatments that reduce the number of kinds of proteins synthesized must be related to the addition of histone to the DNA and to the formation of nucleohistone complex. Obviously these experiments are difficult, but they are not impossible.

The success of this experiment will also provide strong indication that the structure and properties of at least some of the isolated chromatin must closely resemble that of the chromatin inside the living cell in order to maintain the biochemical specificity. If so, physical-chemical studies of isolated chromatin will give us meaningful information about the properties of chromatin inside the cell. This answer is, therefore, directly related to the question raised in I B.

The rationale behind the proposed experiments, a rationale which makes them attractive in spite of their possible technical difficulty, resides in their bearing on a general concept of genetic control, namely that at a region X of nucleohistone X a specific dissociation of histone from DNA has taken place, a dissociation which allows the DNA at region X to be functional. At other regions of nucleohistone X, including region Y, its DNA is covered with histone, and thus prevents the utilization of the information stored in the DNA of these regions. This concept and hypothesis leads obviously to the next subject for consideration--How can dissociation of DNA and histone at a specific locus in the genome, such as X or Y, be brought about in nature?

III. DISSOCIATION OF THE DNA-HISTONE COMPLEX

We note first that we are not going to discuss the biological or physiological programming of the dissociation of nucleohistone here. We simply ask what are the mechanics of the dissociation? The problem is, if dissociation of the nucleohistone is to take place at region X, how many processes can we imagine which nature might employ to achieve this purpose ?

A. By increasing the dielectric properties of the medium, as by increasing the local concentration of electrolytes

This is the only procedure that has been used experimentally to dissociate isolated nucleohistones. It is, however, highly unlikely that it is the procedure adopted by nature. In the first place, confinement, control, and maintenance of a high concentration of any small ion at a specifically localized but perhaps shifting area, is difficult. In the second place, the effectiveness or efficiency of small ions for the dissociation of polyelectrolytes is low. In the third place, high concentrations of electrolytes or high levels of dielectric properties would interfere with the functioning of DNA, prevent the binding of polymerase to DNA, cause precipitation of proteins, and so forth.

B. By interaction with polyanions, for example, acidic proteins or nucleic acid

This presents interesting possibilities, although we have too few data and insufficient insight to assess the properties of such interaction. Two problems would appear to be of major concern: (1) The degree of irreversibility of the nucleohistone complex. It is of importance to be able to assess the effectiveness of the polyanions, such as other nucleic acids, as reagents for the dissociation of the nucleohistone. Technically, the experiment is not too difficult, and the result could be conclusive, particularly if labeled nucleic acids were used. Separation of free nucleic acids from the nucleohistone complex could be accomplished by electrophoresis or by sucrose zone centrifugation; (2) Possible interference of polyanions with the polymerase. It will be of importance to know how inhibitory RNA and other polyanions are to action of nucleic acid polymerases. This question can also be answered experimentally. One may, in addition, consider the possibility that nucleoside triphosphates serve to dissociate the nucleohistone. The effectiveness of these agents will be undoubtedly greater than that of monovalent ions such as NaCl, but here again, data must be obtained.

C. By interaction with other polycations, for example, polyamines and diamines

This possibility has three attractive features: (1) Experiments with the RNA polymerase system of Micrococcus lysodeikticus (see Weiss in this volume) clearly indicate that low concentrations of diamines or protamines at low equivalence ratios of DNA to diamine, not only do not reduce the synthetic capacity of the DNA-dependent RNA polymerase system, but actually enhance it. We also have experimental support for the idea that certain types of biological polycations are not inhibitory to the Escherichia coli or to the chromosomal RNA polymerase. Among such polycations, simple oligoamines, protamines, and arginine-rich histones are typical examples. Protamines, for example, are generally used in the purification of RNA polymerase; (2) Bacteriophage DNA, presumably in the state of action readiness, is combined with diamine inside the viral head [4, 5]. Diamines have similarly been found in plant virus [6]. The DNA of sperm is combined with a simple polyamine, protamine. These facts appear to be messages from nature stating that the negative charges of functional DNA should preferably be neutralized by an appropriate type of harmless diamine or polyamine; (3) Diamines and polyamines offer greater possibilities for specificity and certainly greater effectiveness in dissociation of the nucleohistone complex than do the common salts. The length of the hydrocarbon chain (varying $n(CH_2)_n$) is related to the effectiveness of such diamines in the stabilization of DNA against melting [7, 8]. In addition, the effect of diamines on the melting temperature of DNA is dependent on the base ratio of the DNA used. The hydrocarbon portion of the diamine could, in principle, interact with the hydrophobic portions of proteins, lipids, steroids, and even nucleic acid (see Ts'o in this volume and Tabor, Tabor, and Rosenthal [8]). These possibilities are, of course, yet untested. It is known, however, that treatment with diamines can lead to chromosomal abnormalities [9, 10]. The effects of diamines and polyamines on DNA and on RNA polymerase, the effectiveness of diamines in dissociation of nucleohistones, the concentration, location, and biochemistry of diamines and polyamines within the cell, all are still to be investigated. Nevertheless, we like this idea. The data presently available, and the deductions above, suggest to us that a procedure in which a noninhibitory polycation replaces the inhibitory histone is the most logical way of transferring DNA from a nonfunctional to a functional state.

D. By enzymatic hydrolysis of the histone

This procedure has two immediately apparent disadvantages: (1) the energy loss incurred; (2) the hazard that the polymerases, also doubtless basic proteins, may be hydrolyzed. It would appear most unlikely that the cell would adopt this procedure. Nevertheless, more extensive data on the turnover of histones in relation to the expression of genetic control will provide insight concerning the matter.

E. By changing the conformation of DNA and histone in a manner appropriate to reduction of their affinity in the nucleohistone complex

Electrostatic interactions of polyelectrolytes are, in general, dependent on the conformation of the macromolecules involved. It is sensible to suppose that changes in such conformation will substantially alter the interaction between the two polyelectrolytes DNA and histone. This notion is a corollary to that discussed above in II, concerning the irreversibility of complex formation. It is known that native DNA has higher affinity constants for monovalent and divalent ions than does denatured DNA [11-13]. Since the T_m of DNA is elevated by histones, as by mono- and divalent ions, it is reasonable to suppose that denatured DNA may also have lower binding constants for histones than does native DNA. Experimental verification of this supposition is urgent. We have recently shown that binding of bases, aromatic compounds, carcinogens, mutagens, and steroids, tends to uncoil DNA, to produce the denatured form (see Ts'o in this volume). Thus, in general, the binding of physiologically active substances by DNA may be expected to alter the vigor of the DNA-histone interaction.

IV. EVIDENCE OF THE CONTROL BY HISTONE OF DNA FUNCTION

The only DNA function thus far biochemically demonstrable is that of template in the synthesis of DNA and RNA. Questions concerning the control of DNA function by histone are hence principally concerned with the effect of histones on DNA-dependent nucleic acid synthesis.

A. Effect of histones in cell-free systems

It is known with certainty that the effect of certain histones on the DNA-dependent RNA-synthesizing system is one of marked inhibition. Nucleohistones exhibit little capacity to replace DNA in the support of RNA synthesis. Removal of histone from the complex by various means, such as phenol, detergent, organic solvents, or cesium chloride density flotation, greatly increases the ability of DNA to serve as template. Re-addition of histone to DNA significantly and stoichiometrically inhibits the capacity of the DNA to support DNA-dependent RNA synthesis. Although the results are clearly and repeatedly observable, their interpretation is not so obvious.

Considerable attention and care have been given in our laboratories to make certain that the nucleohistone complexes used, either native or reconstituted from DNA and histone, remain in solution. Appropriate physical and chemical measurements assure us that the inhibitory action of histone on RNA synthesis is not due to the precipitation of DNA by the histone—is not due to removal of DNA from solution in the reaction mixture. The experimental data also indicate that there is no undesirable effect of histone on the polymerase. Thus RNA polymerase is capable of utilizing free (histone non-complexed) DNA to support RNA synthesis in the presence of nucleohistone complex [14].

The mechanism of histone inhibition of the template role of DNA merits closer examination. The inhibition is so absolute and so independent of length of incubation that the mechanism does not appear to reside in difficulties concerning release of product. There is simply no product, no synthesis of RNA. The data imply that DNA and enzyme, or the catalytic sites of the enzyme, just do not get together. Three types of experiments are here suggested, as relevant to the study of the mechanism of inhibition: (1) The effect of the order in which polymerase and histone are introduced to the DNA. In the past, histone and DNA have first been complexed and polymerase then added to the system. What will happen if polymerase is first added or complexed to DNA in the absence of substrate, and histone subsequently complexed to this complex? (2) The effect of ionic strength and of divalent ions on the polymerase and on the inhibitory action of the histones. Such experiments may provide information concerning the electrostatic interactions between the polymerase, DNA, and histone; (3) Search for types of polycations capable of releasing the histone inhibition. If the notion is correct that certain polycations can be found which are effective in replacing histone in the nucleohistone complex, and which do so without inhibiting the polymerase, then information concerning the structure, properties, and mechanism of such replacement might even provide new insight into the mechanism of the action of the polymerase. This field of study will assuredly be a fascinating one, both in its biophysical and in its enzymological aspects.

It is perhaps appropriate to mention that our knowledge of the effects of histone on DNA polymerase is in its infancy (see Hnilica in this volume). Most of the arguments considered above, although directed to DNA-dependent RNA synthesis, are presented with the tacit assumption that the effect of histones on DNA-dependent RNA synthesis will prove to be basically similar, if not identical.

B. Role of histones in the in vivo system

Though there are many interesting questions concerning the role of histones in the intact cell, unfortunately, there are few answers. If histones must be removed from chromatin before DNA or RNA can be synthesized in vivo, where do the histones go, when do they come back, are they destroyed? If not, in what state are they when they leave the DNA?

The following general statements may serve as a summary of the present status of our knowledge of these questions: (1) The ratio of DNA to histone varies from cell type to cell type in the same organism, and varies from period to period during the life cycle. (2) The types of histones present in cells at various stages in the life cycle, and in different cell types can, and do differ. (3) Net histone synthesis and histone turnover can take place in the absence of DNA synthesis (see Flamm and Birnstiel in this volume). (4) Histones do not segregate semi-conservatively, as does DNA, and may migrate from one chromosome to another during cell division (see Prescott in this volume). (5) Studies of polytene chromosomes show that genetic activity is associated with characteristic morphological changes in the chromosome at the active locus. These changes in structure, known collectively as "puffing," must involve changes in histone or in DNA-histone interaction, but the nature of the involvement is as yet unknown (see Clever in this volume). (6) The general belief is that during the synthesis of DNA, the DNA-histone ratio changes temporarily in favor of DNA (see Dounce in this volume).

One of the major obstacles to progress in the study of histones is that thus far there is no sensitive and reliable cytochemical procedure for determination of histones in the cell (see Swift in this volume). A most serious problem is posed by the fact that the commonly used acid fixation step may extract histone. In addition, the dyes, such as fast green, used for histone staining, also stain, although less intensely, other basic proteins such as ribosomal protein. Better cytochemical procedures for histones are essential.

It is quite apparent that there is virtue in the use for histone studies of tissue cultured cells, particularly such cultures as can be grown as single cells, and most especially if they can be synchronized. Availability of synchronized cell suspensions grown in defined medium is essential, if meaningful answers are to be provided to many critical questions concerning the in vivo role of histones.

V. POSSIBLE DIFFERENCES BETWEEN REGULATION OF DNA SYNTHESIS AND OF RNA SYNTHESIS BY HISTONES INSIDE THE CELL

It is again tacitly assumed that histones are inhibitory to DNA synthesis, just as they are to RNA synthesis. Certain matters here are worthy of our consideration.

(A) It will be a difficult task to study the molecular state of histone in relation to regulation of RNA synthesis inside a normal cell. Changes in amounts and kinds of RNA synthesis during the life cycle of a normal cell are probably gradual and not glaringly demonstrable. The biological material of choice for such a study should be one in which the activity of the cell goes through a drastic change, a dramatic awakening from a dormant to an ultra-active state. Possible examples are fertilization of the egg, hormonal stimulation of the growth of the uterus, germination of the seed, breaking of bud dormancy, and transformation of vegetative tissues to sexual organs. It should be possible to determine and compare the molecular states of histone and of DNA in the resting cell before and after the change from inactivity to activity. As for the study of histones in DNA synthesis, synchronized cell cultures or single cells must be used. The states or changes of state of histone during the period of DNA duplication will be of greatest interest. We note in this connection, however, that the in vitro studies of DNA polymerase from higher organisms are as yet few.

(B) From the biological point of view, the regulation of DNA replication and RNA synthesis by histones should differ from one another in at least two aspects. (The arguments here presented are based on the assumption that separation of histone from DNA is a prerequisite to DNA replication.) (1) The synthesis of RNA is presumably jointly controlled by the genetic program of the cell, and by responses to feedback from environment. One may imagine a hypothetical case concerning the molecular history of the genomal DNA of a creature during development. At region A, say, DNA is always free, and at region Z, DNA is covered at all times. At time B, DNA in region B is free, while the DNA in region C is covered. At time C, DNA in region B is now covered, and in region C is free. This sequence is repeated in each developing individual. It is not at present certain that there is any geometrical or spatial relationship between regions B and C, or regions C and D, even though there are definite relationships in time and in sequence of events between period B and period C, period C and period D. These are required by the program. In the case of DNA replication, however, most probably a definite spatial or structural relationship relates sequence of events, at least over a sizeable region [15]. Replication of DNA at regions B, C, D, etc., of the chromatin probably does have a spatial continuity corresponding to the event continuity at regions B, C, D, etc. This difference in coupling between space and time for synthesis of DNA as compared to that for RNA may indicate and require different types of processes for dissociation of the nucleohistone complex.

(2) The fate of template and product after synthesis is presumably also different in RNA synthesis from that in DNA synthesis. The newly synthesized RNA must be immediately transported away from the chromosome without being complexed by histone. Many molecules of RNA of identical sequence will be copied from a small region of DNA. Thus this region of DNA must be kept free of histone for a specified time. Conversely, the newly synthesized DNA must presumably be immediately covered with histone to prevent excessive DNA replication. (Is this the means of control of polyploidy?) The region of DNA which has been already copied must be immediately covered to prevent repetition of replication. Again, these different requirements as to immediate fate of template and product require different procedures for dissociation and recombination of DNA with nucleohistone.

VI. FINAL REMARKS

A very considerable amount of effort has been given in the past to studies of several of the physical and chemical aspects of histones. This has been made clear in the present volume. The achievements have been great, and the results have been useful. Further progress along the lines of these previous studies is undoubtedly essential to a fuller understanding of histones. It is now evident, however, that other lines of inquiry are needed to provide fundamental insight into the problem of the biological role of histones. These presently essential lines of inquiry are physical and chemical in nature, and they do not necessarily depend on the progress of the previous main lines of histone study. The approaches now needed are quite different. Thanks to previous effort, we already have enough knowledge and technology to start many of the presently required lines of research without undue delay. By now posing our new questions in a new manner, our new lines of research require for their study new kinds of biological material—for example, synchronized, exponentially growing clones of cells of higher organisms. The development of these new lines of histone study arise, however, as we should explicitly realize, from the marriage of modern molecular biology to classical histone chemistry.

REFERENCES

1. Bayley, P. M., Preston, B. N., and Peacocke, A. R., Biochim. Biophys. Acta, 55, 943, 1962.

2. Murray, K., and Peacocke, A. R., Biochim. Biophys. Acta, 55, 935, 1962.

3. Glisin, V. R., and Doty, P., Biochim. Biophys. Acta, 61, 460, 1962.

4. Ames, B. N., Dubin, D. T., and Rosenthal, S. M., Science, 127, 814, 1958.

5. Ames, B. N., and Dubin, D. T., J. Biol. Chem., 30, 579, 1961.

6. Johnson, M. W., and Markham, R., Virology, 17, 276, 1962.

7. Mahler, H. R., and Mehotra, B. D., Biochim. Biophys. Acta, 68, 211, 1963.

8. Tabor, H., Tabor, C. W., and Rosenthal, S. M., Ann. Rev. Biochem., 30, 579, 1961.

9. Davidson, D., and Anderson, N. G., Exptl. Cell Res., 20, 610, 1960.

10. Marquardt, H., Experientia, 5, 401, 1949.

11. Dove, W. F., and Davidson, N., J. Mol. Biol., 5, 467, 1962.

12. Shack, J., and Bynum, B. S., Nature, 184, 635, 1959.

13. Ascoli, F., Botré, C., and Liquori, A. M., J. Mol. Biol., 3, 202, 1961.

14. Huang, R. C. C., Bonner, J., and Murray, K., J. Mol. Biol., in press.

15. Taylor, J. H., Molecular Genetics (New York: Academic Press, 1963), pt. 1, chap. 2.

AUTHOR INDEX

A

Abbot, M. T., 107
Afinson, C. B., 35
Alexander, H. E., 148
Alexander, M., 333
Alfert, M., 182, 183, 192, 240, 314,
  318, 332, 334, 342
Allfrey, V. G., 35, 215, 228-230, 239,
  240, 245, 267, 282, 287, 289, 297,
  341, 342, 360
Amano, M., 173, 183
Ambler, R. C., 29, 35
Ambrose, E. J., 131
Ames, B. N., 379
Anastasi, A., 34
Anders, M., 306
Anderson, D. C., 245
Anderson, N. G., 379
Ando, T., 65
Ansley, H. R., 228
Arndt, U. W., 133
Aronson, J. F., 186, 191
Ascoli, F., 148, 379
Autoniades, H. N., 162

B

Bahr, G. F., 183, 318, 332
Baine, P., 148
Bakay, B., 314
Baker, C. M. A., 333
Bamford, C. H., 131
Bang, I. C., 9, 10, 12
Barclay, R. K., 51, 131
Barner, H. D., 241
Barnett, L. B., 287
Baumann, E., 12
Bauer, H. Z., 318, 332
Bayley, P. M., 379
Becker, H. J., 171, 182, 333

Beer, M., 132, 147
Beermann, W., 182, 183, 185, 187,
  191, 192, 318, 319, 332, 334
Bender, M. A., 199, 335, 342
Benoit, H., 148
Benzer, S., 223, 229
Berg, P., 104, 107, 229, 266, 299, 306
Bessman, M. J., 229
Billen, D., 289, 297
Birnstiel, M. L., 57, 166, 231, 237-
  240, 361
Biserte, G., 202, 227
Bloch, D. P., 33, 35, 50, 51, 183, 228,
  240, 334, 335, 338, 340, 342
Blout, E. R., 121, 132
Bollum, F. J., 228
Bonner, J., 35, 107, 224, 229, 239,
  240, 251, 253-256, 261, 262, 266,
  280, 282, 288, 289, 297, 306, 314,
  329, 334, 341, 342, 347, 357-360,
  365-367, 370, 379
Botré, C., 148, 379
Boveri, T., 335, 341
Brachet, J., 182
Bradbury, E. M., 106, 117, 123-135,
  127-129, 131-133, 370
Breitman, T., 287
Breslar, A., 306
Breuer, M. E., 182, 185, 191, 332
Bridges, C. B., 185, 186, 191, 318, 332
Bridges, P. N., 191
Briggs, R., 331, 334, 335, 342
Brink, R. A., 337, 339, 342
Brock, Th. D., 333
Brown, L., 132
Bucher, N. L. R., 229
Bueche, A. M., 148
Burger, M., 334
Burgi, E., 147
Burma, O. P., 306
Burton, K., 240
Busch, H., 79, 80, 83, 84, 91, 242, 245,
  289, 297

SUBJECT INDEX

A

Acetyl groups, fractions, histones, (Butler), 40
Acrylamide
  electrophoresis of histone in gel, 72
  preparations of gel, 73
Actinomycin C, effects on puffing, 327, 328
Actinomycin D
  effect on amino acid incorporation in nuclei, 273
  effect on RNA synthesis in nuclei, 273
Actinomycins, effect on loops, 284
Activity coefficients, molal
  cytidine, 151
  purine, 151
  uridine, 151
Adenine, solubility in bases and nucleosides, 153
Amino acid composition
  chorella histones, 63
  histone fraction, (Butler), 41
  lysine-rich histone, 53, 55, 56
  nucleoprotein fractions according to Rochester's group, 205
  products of enzymatic degradation of nucleohistones, 313
  rat liver ribosome, 43
  rice embryo histones, 63
  thymus histone, 70
  thymus histone fractions, (Butler), 39
  thymus histones, (Iwai), 63
  Walker tumor, histone fraction, 242-245
Amino acid incorporation
  amoeba, 195, 196
  chromosome protein, 193-198
  effects of Actinomycin D, 273
  effects of ecdysone, 320

histone and other proteins after hepatectomy, 225
histone, rat liver, 242-245
histone synthesis in tobacco cells, 234
isolated chromatin, 237
isolated nucleoli, 237
Leucine-C^{14} into histone, rat liver, 216-222
Leucine-C^{14} into nucleoprotein of regenerating liver, 220
L-lysine incorporation in nucleoprotein, 243
in nucleoprotein of tobacco cells, 233
sub-nuclear fractions of tobacco cells, 234, 235, 237
in vitro system, supported by messenger: RNA and ribosomes, 264, 265
Amino acids
  distribution in histone, 31
  distribution and spacing, histones, 46, 47
Amino acids, N-terminal
  fraction 2B histone from thymus, 89
  lysine-rich histone, 55
  thymus histone fractions, (Butler), 39
Amoeba proteus, chromosome protein turnover, 194
Amoeba, cutting of cytoplasm, 195
Arginase, papilloma, 366
Arginine, distribution and spacing, in histone, 48
Arginine-lysine ratio, histone fractionation, 17, 18
Arginine-lysine, ratio to DNA phosphate, 42
ATP synthesis, effect of histone, 275
Autoradiographs, electron microscope, nuclei, 269

389